*Lunar Science:*
*A Post-Apollo View*

**Frontispiece:** Astronaut Harrison H. (Jack) Schmitt collecting samples from a boulder at Station 6 (base of the North Massif) on the north side of the Taurus-Littrow Valley, during the Apollo 17 mission. The front portion of the Lunar Roving Vehicle is visible at the left. The directional antenna (umbrella shape) is pointed toward Earth. (NASA Photo.)

# Lunar Science:
# A Post-Apollo View

## Scientific Results and Insights
## from the Lunar Samples

STUART ROSS TAYLOR

*Lunar Science Institute*
*Houston, Texas, U.S.A.*

*and*

*Research School of Earth Sciences*
*Australian National University*
*Canberra, Australia*

**PERGAMON PRESS INC.**

New York · Toronto · Oxford · Sydney · Braunschweig

PERGAMON PRESS INC.
Maxwell House, Fairview Park, Elmsford, N.Y. 10523

PERGAMON OF CANADA LTD.
207 Queen's Quay West, Toronto 117, Ontario

PERGAMON PRESS LTD.
Headington Hill Hall, Oxford

PERGAMON PRESS (AUST.) PTY. LTD.
Rushcutters Bay, Sydney, N.S.W.

PERGAMON GmbH
Burgplatz 1, Braunschweig

Library of Congress Cataloging in Publication Data

Taylor, Stuart Ross, 1925–
    Lunar science: a post-Apollo view.

    Includes bibliographical references.
    1. Moon.  I.  Title.
    QB592.T38  1975          559.9′1          74-17227
    ISBN 0-08-018274-7
    ISBN 0-08-018273-9  (pbk.)

*Cover picture:* Fine detail visible on the lunar surface in this near terminator photo taken during the Apollo 16 mission. View looking south. East is to the left. The large crater with a central peak is Arzachel (97 km diameter) and the larger one in front of it is Alphonsus (116 km diameter). The smooth area to the right (west) is part of Mare Nubium. (NASA.)

*Back cover:* Lick Observatory photo of 4 day old moon.

Printed in the United States of America

*To*
*Noël*
*Susanna, Judith and Helen*

# Contents

x    Contents

# Preface

The Apollo lunar landings represent one of the great triumphs of human imagination and ingenuity. Throughout recorded history the moon has been an object of admiration, longing, and interest. Man long ago realized the connection of the moon with the tides, and in many mystical and religious connotations the moon has had a profound effect on human affairs[1]. The cycle of the lunar month, the disappearance and rebirth of the moon, and the changing phases have been intimately associated with folklore and human intellectual development since our primitive beginnings[2]. We are children of the earth, with a beautiful silver ball, tantalizingly remote, to gaze at and wish for[3].

Now suddenly we have set our feet on the lunar surface and collected the samples; hurriedly at first, in awe of the harsh environment and unknown terrors[4], and then with growing confidence in our ability to survive the vacuum and the high temperatures, in extended missions, complete with vehicles. We have nearly 400 kilograms of rocks, a veritable feast of samples considering that much significant information may be gained from a few milligrams.

Scientists have examined and analyzed the rocks and soils with every modern and sophisticated technique and have published the results in more than 30,000 pages of scientific literature. New and often unexpected data have appeared to confound old hypotheses. The resulting clarification of ideas and problems from the limited number of missions provides fresh support for old adages about the value of small amounts of data in constraining speculation. We now have a reasonably coherent picture of the history of events and processes occurring on the moon for more than four billion years, a monument indeed to the ability of *Homo sapiens* to reconstruct the history of past events. Even in the more dimly understood events surrounding the formation of the moon and the earth, we have many more constraints to apply to the theories and a growing confidence that we have opened a new window to the early history of the solar system.

Much of this knowledge, less than four years old, is not widely known or available to those outside the lunar investigation teams. A mass of data and the formidable jargon of science, often as impenetrable and baffling as a jungle thicket, surround the precious samples. Yet the observations tell an elegant story.

The purpose of this book is to attempt to recount this story and to explain the scientific results and discoveries of the manned lunar missions as they are understood at present. Discussions with many colleagues have emphasized the need for such a work, although the formidable nature of the task is apparent. In an earlier book[5], a summary was given of the advances in knowledge resulting from the first manned landing of Apollo 11 in the Sea of Tranquillity. Now the landing of Apollo 17 (December, 1972) in the Taurus-Littrow valley has marked the close of the first phase of manned lunar landings. Much is known about the lunar samples, and it is appropriate to review and summarize the scientific findings of the Apollo Project. To those readers who may judge this attempt to be premature, I offer the opinions of Poincaré, quoted at the beginning of chapter 7.

The previous work gave detailed descriptions of the mineralogy and chemistry of the Apollo 11 samples. It was possible to provide a general interpretation of the data, which in broad outline has changed surprisingly little with subsequent missions. In this book there is less emphasis on sample description and data. The vast amounts of data now available need an independent synthesis. Rather I have stressed the interpretative aspects of the study, with the aim of providing a coherent story of the evolution of the moon and its origin so far as we can judge it at present. The present work is thus a sequel to *Moon Rocks and Minerals*, not a revised edition.

Such a task calls for much selection and evaluation. A vast body of data is already available, but a mere catalogue or data dump must be avoided. At the same time, a condensation of the literature without evaluation is not of much use. It is no service to the reader merely to record the existence of a controversy on a particular topic. The intent is to provide an understanding of the current state of knowledge about the moon as revealed by the lunar samples and the Apollo missions. Such a framework and guide will hopefully enable and encourage interested people to proceed to the more detailed lunar literature.

With such a broad canvas, the selection and evaluation of the data necessarily reflect the knowledge, interest, and bias of the author. The approach recalls that of the historian as much as the scientist. As Bertrand Russell has remarked, "a book should be held together by its point of view,"[6] and I make no apology for the selection or the interpretations made. These appear to me to be the most reasonable at this date and are offered in the spirit of scientific progress as elucidated by Karl Popper[7]. Many specialists may be chagrined to find that their work is dealt with only briefly or even perhaps omitted from this account. The effort to reduce 30,000 pages of published literature into a book involves a reduction by two orders of magnitude. Thus, each page here represents 100 in the original literature, so that many observations have had to be fitted into less space than that occupied by the typical abstract of a paper.

Many questions are posed and discussed throughout the book. The moon (and Mars, as well) has provided many scientific surprises, salutary in reminding us both of the dangers of extrapolating from terrestrial experience and of the empirical and observational basis for science. The broad scope of the work has led me to many unfamiliar fields. I have been sustained in this endeavor both by the many workers[8] who have enlightened me about their specialities and by the observation that those previous writers who took a broad overview of lunar problems seem to have been more often correct than those who took a more circumscribed view[9].

The question of literature citation has proved difficult owing to the bulk of published material. It is impractical in this work to produce a full-scale bibliography, which would amount, in conventional referencing style, to well over 100 printed pages. Fortunately the information is contained at present in a relatively few major sources.

Throughout the text, I have attempted to list references to all sources of information, statements of fact, opinion, and interpretation other than my own, so that the interested reader can pursue questions in the original literature. Rather than break up the text with names and dates, I have adopted the method commonly used by historians and some scientific journals of referencing by number. The numbered references are grouped at the end of each chapter. To conserve space, an abbreviated but adequate referencing style is employed[10].

Because of the predilection of the investigators to produce multi-author papers[11], it is not feasible to cite full bibliographic details. Except for two-author papers, first authors only are listed. I have tried in general to reference the latest relevant and informative paper in the field. This procedure has the advantage of reducing much repetitive referencing since citations of earlier works will be found in the later papers. It is a peculiarity of the lunar literature that references to ideas or data by an author may appear in several places, due to the widespread use of extended abstracts. Thus, much vital information about Apollo 17 first appeared in this form in the *Transactions of the American Geophysical Union* (*EOS*, Vol. 54, 580–622). Selection of references therefore becomes an important consideration.

Nearly all the work is of high quality, and citations to many excellent papers have had to be omitted because of space. Most of these can be found by consulting reference lists in the cited papers or the *Proceedings of the Lunar Science Conferences.* I have tried to avoid references to internal agency reports and other "gray" literature, not always successfully. Publication deadlines have prevented formal referencing to the *Fifth Lunar Science Conference Proceedings* (1974), although the data and ideas discussed at that meeting (March, 1974) have been incorporated. References to the volume of extended abstracts (*Lunar Science V,* 1974) for that meeting are included. The literature coverage extends to April, 1974.

Stuart Ross Taylor

*Houston, Texas*
*April, 1974*

## REFERENCES AND NOTES

1. Among many curious correlations of lunar phases with biological rhythms, it may be noted that the average duration of human pregnancy is 266 days, close to the length of nine lunar synodical months* (265.8 days) and that the average duration of the human menstrual cycle is 29.5 days, compared with the average lunar synodical month of 29.53 days. Menaker, W., and Menaker, A. (1959) Lunar periodicity in human reproduction, *Amer. Jour. Obstetrics Gynecology.* 77: 905, and Osley, M., et al. (1973) Ibid., 117: 413.

   More sinister correlations, indicating a connection between lunar cycles and psychiatric disturbances (recalling the ancient association of the moon and lunacy) are described by Lieber, A. L., and Sherin, C. R. (1972) *Amer. Jour. Psychiatry.* 129: 69.

2. See, for example, Bedini, S. A., et al. (1973) *Moon,* Abrams, N.Y.

*A *lunar synodical month,* or lunation, is the time between successive new moons and is 29 days, 12 hours, and 44 minutes. This contrasts with the *sidereal month,* which is the average period of revolution of the moon around the earth, as determined by using a fixed star as reference point. The length of a sidereal month is 27 days, 7 hours, and 43 minutes.

3. For a discussion on the political aspects of the manned landings, see Logsdon, J. M. (1970) *The Decision to go to the Moon: Project Apollo and the National Interest*, MIT Press, Cambridge.
4. For example, an often discussed possibility was that the highly reduced samples might ignite in the pure oxygen atmosphere of the landing module.
5. Levinson, A. A., and Taylor, S. R. (1971) *Moon Rocks and Minerals*, Pergamon Press, Elmsford, N.Y.
6. Russell, Bertrand (1967) *Autobiography 1914–1944*, Atlantic Monthly Press, pp. 340–341.
7. Popper, K. (1968) *Conjectures and Refutations: The Growth of Scientific Knowledge*, Harper & Row, N.Y.
8. See Acknowledgments.
9. The rationale for this statement will become apparent later in the book. The classic example is the correct interpretation of many lunar surface features by R. B. Baldwin (1949) in *The Face of the Moon*, University of Chicago Press.
10. See Appendix I.
11. One paper has 30 authors (NASA SP 315, p. 6-1, 1973), and there are many with ten or more. Authors should recall the adage that no committee ever wrote a symphony.

# The Author

**Stuart Ross Taylor** Ph.D. (Indiana University) is a Professorial Fellow at the Research School of Earth Sciences, the Australian National University, Canberra. His research interests have been in trace element geochemistry, analytical chemistry, tektites, continental composition and evolution, island arc volcanic rocks, and lunar studies.

Dr. Taylor was a member of the Lunar Sample Preliminary Examination Team (LSPET) for Apollo 11 and 12 missions and carried out the first chemical analysis of a returned lunar sample. He is a Principal Investigator for the lunar sample program. His research publications total over 100 papers and books. He has held visiting posts at the University of California, San Diego, at the Max Planck Institut für Chemie, Mainz and at The Lunar Science Institute, Houston, Texas. He is an Associate Editor of the journal *Geochimica et Cosmochimica Acta*.

# Acknowledgments

This book was written during a period of nine months spent at the Lunar Science Institute, Houston, as a Visiting Scientist. I am grateful to the Institute for generous support during this period and to Dr. J. W. Chamberlain, formerly Director of the Lunar Science Institute, who invited me to work at Houston. I express my thanks to Dr. D. W. Strangway, Dr. J. W. Head, and Dr. R. O. Pepin, subsequent directors of the Lunar Science Institute, for their help and assistance in this project.

A very large number of lunar scientists have helped me in the preparation of this work, and I have benefited greatly from discussions with them, particularly on matters outside my own specialty. Thanks are due to Dr. F. Hörz, Dr. Petr Jakeš, and Dr. Robin Brett for much assistance. It would be impossible to list all the other workers from whom I have drawn ideas, insight, and inspiration. A partial list includes D. D. Bogard, D. R. Criswell, E. K. Gibson, W. Gose, L. A. Haskin, D. S. McKay, R. Merrill, L. Nyquist, H. Palme, J. A. Philpotts, M. Prinz, A. M. Reid, W. I. Ridley, E. Schonfeld, C. H. Simonds, J. Warner, and R. J. Williams.

To these and to my colleagues on the Preliminary Examination Teams for the Apollo 11 and 12 missions, I express my thanks. No lunar religion ever had a more devoted band of adherents. A number of my colleagues have kindly read various portions of the book. Dr. F. Hörz has read chapters 2, 3, and 5. Dr. Robin Brett has read chapters 4 and 5. Dr. N. Bhandari and Professor R. M. Walker have read chapter 3. Chapter 6 has been read by Dr. D. Criswell and Dr. D. W. Strangway. The sections in chapter 7 on the geological evolution of the moon are derived from much collaborative work with Dr. Petr Jakeš. The comments and suggestions that I have received have been invaluable and have resulted in much improvement in the text. The responsibility for the interpretations, errors, and shortcomings remains my own.

The preparation of the book was greatly aided by the superb facilities and the efficient staff of the Lunar Science Institute. Particular thanks are due to Mrs. Lila Mager, who typed the manuscript with speed and precision. Following my return to Canberra, she was responsible for the final preparation of the manuscript. It would have been very difficult to accomplish the work in such a short time without her able assistance. The excellent library facilities of the Institute were made freely available by the librarian, Mrs. Fran Waranius, who raised no objection to the transfer for extended periods of much of her collection to my office. Other members of the staff who made special contributions include Mrs. Carolyn Watkins, Mrs. Jody Heiken, who helped in supplying illustrations, and Mr. D. Kinsler, who carried out much drafting work.

Some preparatory work was carried out at the Max Planck Institut für Chemie, Mainz, and I am grateful to Dr. H. Wänke for his hospitality. I am grateful to the Australian National University, Canberra, for granting the leave period to enable me to work at Houston unimpeded by other cares.

The following colleagues supplied photographs or prints of diagrams, and I am grateful for their ready assistance and cooperation: E. Anders, P. Dyal, Farouk El-Baz, K. Fredriksson, E. K. Gibson, D. H. Green, J. F. Hays, W. K. Hartmann, J. W. Head, K. A. Howard, E. A. King, D. S. McKay, G. D. O'Kelley, A. M. Reid, E. Roedder, M. Sato, R. Schmitt, H. Wänke, G. J. Wasserburg, and D. E. Wilhelms.

Acknowledgment is made to the following publishers for permission to use previously published illustrations either directly, or in a modified form: Academic Press, Figs. 2.5, 2.6; American Geophysical Union, Fig. 2.13; Lick Observatory, Figs. 2.1, 2.2, 2.4, 2.7, 4.1; Mt. Palomar Observatory, Fig. 2.8; MIT Press, Figs. 4.37, 4.39, 5.7; North Holland, Figs. 3.3, 3.4; D. Reidel, Figs. 3.13, 4.28, 4.29, 5.21, 5.24, 6.1; Sky Publications, Fig. 2.15.

I am grateful to Mr. G. Deegan and Mrs. S. Halpern, Pergamon Press, for much assistance, and to Pergamon Press for permission to use a number of figures from the Proceedings of the Fourth Lunar Science Conference. A final appreciation is due to the National Aeronautics and Space Administration, whose policy decisions resulted in the successful landings, and to the astronauts, whose field work in an alien terrain was so expertly carried out. In the following list, the order is: Mission Commander, Lunar Module Pilot, and Command Module Pilot.

Apollo 11:   Neil A. Armstrong, Edwin E. Aldrin, and Michael Collins.

Apollo 12:   Charles Conrad, Alan L. Bean, and Richard F. Gordon.

Apollo 14:   Alan B. Shepard, Edgar D. Mitchell, and Stuart A. Roosa.

Apollo 15:   David R. Scott, James B. Irwin, and Alfred J. Worden.

Apollo 16:   John W. Young, Charles M. Duke, and T. K. Mattingly.

Apollo 17:   Eugene A. Cernan, Harrison H. (Jack) Schmitt, and Ronald E. Evans.

CHAPTER 1

# Introduction

## 1.1 THE PRE-APOLLO SETTING

The scientific study of the moon by the Apollo missions was the culmination of many years of thought and planning. Seen against the background of historical perspective, the origins go back to the dawn of human understanding. One writer has remarked that it followed inevitably from the shaping of the first flint tool. Although the moon was the object of intense thought and interest from the earliest times[1], its nature remained unguessed at, except for occasional insights by philosophers such as Anaxagoras (ca. 500–428 B.C.), who thought it to be a stone, and Democritus (ca. 460–370 B.C.), who proposed that the surface was mountainous.

Most were content with the concept of a perfect sphere, until Galileo in 1610 saw through his telescope valleys, mountains, plains, and large bowl-shaped depressions on the lunar surface. By the end of the seventeenth century more than 25 maps had been made, those of Helvelius (1647) and Giovanni Domenico Cassini (1680) being notably accurate. On these maps, most of the familiar features are readily identified[2]. The philosophy of lunar nomenclature proposed by Riccioli (1651), who used the names of scientists and thinkers, has survived. Following the analogy drawn by Galileo between terrestrial seas and the dark areas on the moon, he named the various maria.

The concept that the great craters were volcanic in origin seems to have arisen intuitively in the seventeenth century, since a plausible analogy could be drawn with the Italian volcanoes. Monte Nuovo, an ash cone 140 meters high had formed in the Phlegrean Fields just north of Naples only

1

100 years earlier, in 1538, thus providing a small-scale example of crater-producing processes to the Renaissance scientists.

The first lunar photograph appeared in 1840, and during the next 100 years a remarkable set of lunar photographs[3] was accumulated, although it was not until 1960 that a fully comprehensive lunar photographic atlas appeared[4]. The acceptance of the volcanic origin of craters, clearly stated by Dana[5] in 1846, was not fully challenged until Gilbert's classic paper[6] in 1893, and the debate continued until very recently[7]. The first modern statement of the nature of the lunar surface, which has proved essentially correct, was made by Baldwin[8] in 1949 in which he discussed both the evidence for an impact origin of the large craters, and the probable basaltic nature of the maria surfaces. Urey's book[9] in 1952 stimulated much interest in the chemistry of the moon, meteorites, and planets. These two books set the intellectual stage for the scientific exploration of the moon at last becoming a technological possibility. Table 1.1 gives some basic lunar data, compared to Earth and Mars.

Several efforts to make geological interpretations of the lunar landscape, dating back to Gilbert[6], have been proposed, but the systematic stratigraphic interpretation begins with Shoemaker and Hackman[10]. They realized that the succession of events on the moon could be unraveled, using the classical geological principle of superposition. A *relative* time scale could be constructed, and geological maps of the moon prepared. Attempts to relate lunar time scales to absolute chronology were attempted using crater counting. Some workers[8, 11] proposed ages of 3 to 4 billion years for the maria surfaces, although other efforts were less successful—with ages ranging from tens to hundreds of millions of years[12].

Parallel with the lunar photogeologic mapping came direct exploration of the moon by spacecraft. Indistinct photographs of the back of the moon were obtained in October, 1959, by Luna 3. Good, but restricted, coverage was obtained from the later Ranger spacecraft, as they crash-landed on the surface (Table 1.2). The pace accelerated. The first direct measurements[13] of the chemical composition of the lunar surface were made by the orbiting Luna 10 spacecraft. These gamma-ray values, later substantiated, indicated basaltlike compositions. Theories that the lunar surface was composed of granites, ultrabasic rocks, chondritic meteorites, or tektites received a setback. Meanwhile a successful program of orbital photography provided complete photographic coverage of the moon, with a total of 1,950 photographs of high quality. Our understanding of the surface features of the moon, if not of their absolute ages, increased dramatically. The nature of the far side of the moon, the

**Table 1.1**  Basic Data.*

|                              | Moon    | Earth   | Mars  |
|------------------------------|---------|---------|-------|
| Mean radius (km)             | 1,738   | 6,371   | 3,388 |
| Mass ($\times 10^{25}$ g)    | 7.353   | 599     | 64.4  |
| Mass                         | 0.0123  | 1.0     | 0.11  |
| Density (g/cm$^3$)           | 3.34    | 5.517   | 3.94  |
| Surface area ($\times 10^6$ km$^2$) | 37.9 | 510.1 | 144.2 |
| Surface gravity (cm/sec$^2$) | 162     | 980.7   | 373   |
| Surface gravity              | 0.165   | 1.0     | 0.38  |
| Velocity of escape (km/sec)  | 2.37    | 11.2    | 5.0   |
| Mean moon-earth distance (km)| 384,402 | —       | —     |

*Extremely accurate measurements of earth-moon dis-
tances are being conducted by the lunar laser ranging
experiment. This consists of measuring the time for a laser
beam to be reflected from any of the reflectors at the sites
of Apollo 11, 14, and 15 (Bender, P. L., et al. [1973] *Science.*
182; 229). Two additional reflectors are carried on the
Lunokhod vehicles. By 1973, the earth-moon distance was
being measured to within 15 cm. Further improvements
(1974) have enabled the distance to be measured to within 2
to 3 cm. These measurements open a new dimension in the
dynamics of the earth-moon system and permit such
intriguing possibilities as direct measurement of relative
motions of the differing plates composing the earth's crust.

existence of a nearly perfect example of a ringed basin (Mare Orientale)
(Fig. 2.3), and many fine details on the surface were clearly revealed.
Geologists could now study the surface in comfort, rather than by
spending cold nights at telescopes. Possible landing sites could be studied
closely, and soft-landing Surveyors settled on the surface, testing the
possibility of manned landing. The last Surveyors (V, VI, and VII) carried
out preliminary chemical analyses[14]. These indicated basaltic compositions in Mare Tranquillitatis, later to be the site of the first landing, and in
Sinus Medii near the center of the visible face. The last Surveyor landing
was on the ejecta blanket of the greatest of the young craters, Tycho,
whose rays dominate pictures of the full moon (Fig. 2.1). The composition
of this highland site was curiously high in aluminum and low in iron,
compared with the earlier analyses. The accumulating photographic,
chemical, magnetic, and gravitational evidence produced many specula-

**Table 1.2**  Successful Pre-Apollo Lunar Landings.

| Spacecraft | Date | Landing site | Data returned |
|---|---|---|---|
| Ranger 7* | August, 1964 | Mare Cognitum | Photographs |
| Ranger 8* | February, 1965 | Mare Tranquillitatis | Photographs |
| Ranger 9* | March, 1965 | Crater Alphonsus | Photographs |
| Luna 9 | February, 1966 | Western Oceanus Procellarum | Photographs |
| Surveyor I | June, 1966 | Oceanus Procellarum, north of Flamsteed | Photographs |
| Luna 13 | December, 1966 | Western Oceanus Procellarum | Photographs; soil physics |
| Surveyor III | April, 1967 | Oceanus Procellarum (Apollo 12 site) | Photographs; soil physics |
| Surveyor V | September, 1967 | Mare Tranquillitatis (25 km from Apollo 11 site) | Photographs; soil physics; chemical analyses |
| Surveyor VI | November, 1967 | Sinus Medii | Photographs; soil physics; chemical analyses |
| Surveyor VII | January, 1968 | Ejecta blanket of Crater Tycho (North Rim) | Photographs; soil physics; chemical analyses |

*The Ranger spacecraft were crash-landed. All others were soft landers.

tions about the geological, geochemical, and geophysical state of the moon[15]. The geographical era was ending. As scientists pondered the many mysteries, the National Aeronautics and Space Administration (NASA) perfected the technology for a manned landing.

## 1.2  THE APOLLO LANDINGS AND THE LUNAR SAMPLES

Six Apollo missions were successfully completed, with only one abortive attempt[16] (Fig. 1.1, Table 1.3). Planning for the return of samples was difficult. How does one deal with material from another planet? Popular cautionary tales from the early exploration of the earth were heeded. Extensive quarantine procedures to isolate the samples for an initial period of 50 days were developed, while the astronauts were to be isolated for 21 days. Facilities for inspection and analysis of the samples behind biological barriers were constructed[17].

The Apollo 11 landing on the moon took place on July 20, 1969, at 3:17:40 P.M., Eastern Standard Time, near the southern edge of Mare

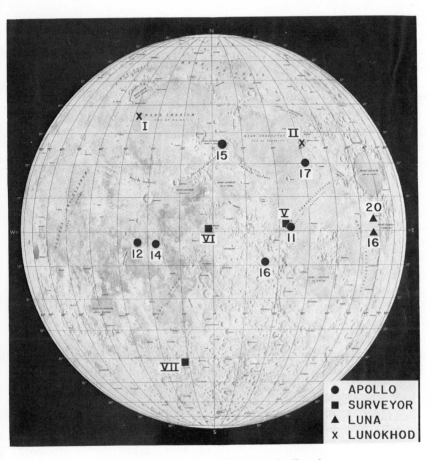

**Fig. 1.1**   Apollo, Luna, and Surveyor landing sites.

**Table 1.3**   The Apollo Lunar Landings.

| Mission | Landing site | Latitude | Longitude | EVA duration (hours) | Traverse distance (km) | Date |
|---|---|---|---|---|---|---|
| 11 | Mare Tranquillitatis | 0°67′N | 23°49′E | 2.24 | — | July 20, 1969 |
| 12 | Oceanus Procellarum | 3°12′S | 23°23′W | 7.59 | 1.35 | Nov. 19, 1969 |
| 14 | Fra Mauro | 3°40′S | 17°28′E W | 9.23 | 3.45 | Jan. 31, 1971 |
| 15 | Hadley-Apennines | 26°06′N | 3°39′E | 18.33 | 27.9 | July 30, 1971 |
| 16 | Descartes | 8°60′S | 15°31′E | 20.12 | 27 | April 21, 1972 |
| 17 | Taurus-Littrow | 20°10′N | 30°46′E | 22 | 30 | Dec. 11, 1972 |

Tranquillitatis. The site was named Tranquillity Base. Astronauts Neil Armstrong and Edwin Aldrin collected 21.7 kg of samples in 20 minutes of hurried collecting toward the end of their 2-hour sojourn (EVA, or extra-vehicular activity) on the lunar surface. These samples were received in the quarantine facilities of the Lunar Receiving Laboratory in Houston on July 25; 4 weeks of intensive examination began. A team of scientific workers (the Lunar Sample Preliminary Examination Team, or LSPET, comprising 11 NASA scientists and 15 other scientists from universities and government agencies) carried out preliminary geologic, geochemical, and biological examination of the samples, providing basic data for the Lunar Sample Analysis Planning Team (LSAPT). The scientific report "Preliminary examination of lunar samples from Apollo 11" appeared in *Science* on September 19 (Vol. 165, p. 1211). Many of the first-order conclusions about the samples (such as their chemical uniqueness, their great age, and the absence of water, organic matter, and life) were established in this period[18].

After this work, LSAPT allocated rocks and soils to about 140 scientists, known as principal investigators, for detailed studies[19]. These had been selected in the following manner. NASA issued a general worldwide invitation to scientists to submit proposals for work on the lunar samples. Reviewing committees selected groups of investigators, initially from nine countries (the United States, Great Britain, Canada, Germany, Switzerland, Finland, Belgium, Australia, and Japan), each of which was headed by a leader known as the principal investigator (PI)[20]. A few of the groups consisted of only the PI, but most had several co-investigators (known as Co-Is); on one project there were 18 co-investigators. The total number of principal and co-investigators (plus some associates not officially classified) who worked on the Apollo 11 rocks is about 550, and this figure does not include the multitude in various technician and support categories.

These groups changed during the Apollo missions, as a result of

**Table 1.4**  Number of Principal Investigators Engaged in Lunar Sample Program.

|  | 1968–69 | 1969–70 | 1970–71 | 1971–72 | 1972–73 | 1973–74 |
|---|---|---|---|---|---|---|
| Number of PIs |  |  |  |  |  |  |
| U.S. | 84 | 105 | 115 | 143 | 132 | 110 |
| Foreign | 29 | 49 | 75 | 65 | 51 | 40 |
| Total | 113 | 154 | 190 | 208 | 183 | 150 |
| Number of institutions | 33 | 61 | 88 | 118 | 110 | 80 |

**Table 1.5**    Summary of Lunar Sample Program for Apollo 14–17.

Total Number of Principal Investigators
189

Foreign ----------------------------------------------- United States
55                                                                    134

| Appointment period | | Appointment period | |
|---|---|---|---|
| 1 year | 3 year | 1 year | 3 year |
| 34 | 21 | 99 | 35 |

40 Different institutions             64 Different institutions
15 Countries*                            28 States and the Virgin Islands

The greatest number of Principal          The greatest number of Principal
Investigators were located:                 Investigators were located:

| By country in: | | By states in: | |
|---|---|---|---|
| United Kingdom | 12 | California | 27 |
| France | 8 | Texas | 17 |
| West Germany | 7 | District of Columbia | 13 |
| Canada | 7 | Massachusetts | 10 |
| Australia | 5 | New York | 9 |
| Japan | 4 | Pennsylvania | 7 |
| | | Illinois | 6 |
| By institution at: | | Colorado | 4 |
| Australian National University | 3 | Minnesota | 3 |
| University of Tokyo | 3 | Ohio | 3 |
| University of Cambridge, England | 3 | | |
| Geological Survey of Canada | 3 | | |

*Belgium, Finland, Holland, India, Norway, South Africa, Switzerland; in addition to those listed above.

interest, finance, and competence as the work and proposals were reviewed on an annual basis. Table 1.4 gives the numbers by year—the peak period was 1971–72, when a total of 208 PIs were working on various aspects of the lunar samples. A summary of the PI program is given in Table 1.5 for the Apollo 14–17 missions, covering the years 1971–73, indicating the widespread nature of the scientific effort [21].

The quarantine procedures were continued for the Apollo 12 and 14 missions, but then dropped as the harmless nature of the lunar samples was demonstrated beyond any doubt [22]. The preliminary examination of the samples could proceed at a more relaxed pace once the quarantine constraints were removed and the basic nature of the lunar material understood. Emphasis shifted to the more detailed and sophisticated laboratory techniques available in the PI's laboratories.

A total of 2,196 samples, weighing a total of 381.69 kg (841.6 pounds), was collected on the moon (Table 1.6). This represents a cost per sample of $11,000, or $28,500 per pound, assuming a cost of $24 billion for the total Apollo program[23]. Samples totaling 19.3 kg (5.1 percent) have been allocated to date for analytical work involving some degradation of the material[24]. The amount of sample actually consumed in analytical operations is 1.64 kg (3.62 pounds). (The amount of sample used does not include 2.1 kg used for biomedical testing.) In addition to the United States samples, the Russian Luna 16 mission (Table 1.7) returned 100 g (0.22 pound) from Mare Fecunditatis and the Luna 20 mission returned 30 g (0.07 pounds).

The scientific return from this amount of material, in terms of our understanding of the early solar system, must be judged good value. The bookkeeping problems associated with the sample distribution are considerable. A total of 35,600 individual sample numbers now exists, each representing a piece of the moon, split from the original samples. About 5 kg are incorporated in sample displays available for public viewing[24].

**Table 1.6**    Sample Return Per Mission[24].

| | Total weight (kg) | Percent allocated for study (%) | Sample no. prefix* |
|---|---|---|---|
| Apollo 11 | 21.7 | 19 | 10- |
| Apollo 12 | 34.4 | 7.8 | 12- |
| Apollo 14 | 42.9 | 6.6 | 14- |
| Apollo 15 | 76.8 | 3.9 | 15- |
| Apollo 16 | 94.7 | 3.1 | 6- |
| Apollo 17 | 110.5 | 3.1 | 7- |

*A basic five-digit numbering system is used. For the Apollo 11, 12, 14, and 15 samples, the final three digits identify the sample. Thus, 10084 is sample number 84 collected on the Apollo 11 mission, and 15455 is number 455 from the Apollo 15 site at the Apennine Front.

For the Apollo 16 and 17 missions, the initial digit 1 is dropped, and the second number becomes that of the station on the traverse. Thus, 66095 is sample 095 from station 6 of the Apollo 16 sample traverse at the Descartes site. Splits from samples are listed by additional digits, separated by a comma from the sample number. Thus, 15455,20 is split number 20 from rock 15455.

**Table 1.7**    (A) Russian Lunar Sample Missions.

| Mission | Landing site | Latitude | Longitude | Date |
|---------|-------------|----------|-----------|------|
| Luna 16 | Mare Fecunditatis | 0°41'S | 56°18'E | Sept., 1970 |
| Luna 20 | Apollonius highlands | 3°32'N | 56°33'E | Feb., 1972 |

(B) Russian Lunar Traverse Vehicles.

| Vehicle | Landing site | Date | Traverse length |
|---------|-------------|------|-----------------|
| Lunokhod 1 | Western Mare Imbrium | Nov., 1970 | 20 km |
| Lunokhod 2 | Le Monnier Crater, Eastern Mare Serenitatis, 180 km north of Apollo 17 site | Jan., 1973 | 30 km |

The numbering system, which identifies the rock or soil sample by mission and, in the later missions, by locality, is explained in Table 1.6. To the community of lunar investigators, many of the rock numbers are as familiar as household words. Thus, 15415 (Genesis rock), 15455 (the black and white breccia), 14321 (Big Bertha), 66095 (rusty rock), 12013 (rock 13), 15555 (Great Scott), and 10084 (the first Apollo 11 sample analyzed) have all achieved some measure of immortality.

Each mission produced its surprises. Apollo 11 provided unusual chemistry and ancient rocks: Apollo 12 revealed the existence of an extremely fractionated rock type, labeled KREEP; Apollo 14 yielded a plethora of breccias; a peculiar green glass of primitive composition appeared at Apollo 15; Apollo 16, expected by some to sample volcanic rocks found none; while Apollo 17, looking for young cinder cones, found old orange glasses. The moral, reinforced by our observations on Mars, is that geological processes are different on other planets and that the value of terrestrial analogies and experience is limited.

## REFERENCES AND NOTES

1. For a fascinating account of the influence of the moon on primitive art, illustrated with many beautiful photographs, see Bedini, S. A., et al. (1973) *Moon*, Abrams, N.Y.
2. See Mutch, T. A. (1972) *Geology of the Moon, A Stratigraphic View* (second edition), Princeton University Press, for reproductions and discussion of the early maps and for a summary of classical observations.
3. See Mutch (1972) for a list of the more important observatories engaged in lunar photography.
4. Kuiper, G. P. (1960) *Photographic Lunar Atlas*, University of Chicago Press.

5. Dana, T. D. (1846) *AJS.* 2: 335.

6. Gilbert, G. K. (1893) *Bull. Phil. Soc. Washington.* 12: 241.

7. Fielder, G. (1967) *Lunar Geology*, Dufour, p. 162; Green, J. (1965) *Ann. N.Y. Acad. Sci.* 123: 385; Moore, P., and Cattermole, P. J. (1967) *The Craters of the Moon*, Norton, N.Y., 19.

8. Baldwin, R. B. (1949) *The Face of the Moon*, University of Chicago Press; (1963) *The Measure of the Moon*, University of Chicago Press.

9. Urey, H. C. (1952) *The Planets*, Yale University Press.

10. Shoemaker E. M., and Hackman, R. J. (1962) in *The Moon* (Z. Kopal and Z. K. Mikhailov, editors) Academic Press, N.Y., p. 289.

11. Hartmann, W. K. (1965) *Icarus.* 4: 164.

12. Gault, D. E. (1970) *Radio Sci.* 5: 289; Baldwin, R. B. (1969) *Icarus.* 11: 320.

13. Vinogradov, A. P., et al. (1966) *Geokhim.* 3: 707.

14. Turkevich, A. L., et al. (1971) *PLC 2*: 1209; (1973) *PLC 4*: 1159.

15. As one skeptic remarked, many saw in the photographs the proofs of their own theories.

16. See Cooper, H. (1973) *Thirteen, the Flight that Failed*, Dial Press, N.Y., for an engrossing account of Apollo 13 and much information on NASA operational methods and procedures.

17. McLane, J. C., et al. (1967) *Science.* 155: 525; (1969) NASA SP 214, 123, 142.

18. An account of this unique period is given by Cooper, H. S. F. (1970) *Moon Rocks*, Dial Press, N.Y.

19. The number participating in work on Apollo 11 samples during the period September–December 1969.

20. A selected suite of lunar workers were, in their turn, studied from sociological and psychological viewpoints. The results indicate that scientific objectivity seems to be less common than was supposed. See Mitroff, I. (1974) *The Subjective Side of Science: A Philosophical Enquiry into the Psychology of the Apollo Moon Scientists*, Elsevier.

21. J. Harris, Johnson Space Center, personal communication.

22. See section on organic geochemistry.

23. This fictitious costing of priceless material does not take into account the value of the scientific return from other aspects (e.g., geophysical and geological) of the missions. It also assumes that the total rationale for the expenditure was scientific, a wishful thought.

24. R. Laughon, Johnson Space Center, personal communication.

# CHAPTER 2

# Lunar Geology

The surface of the Moon is neither smooth nor uniform. It is uneven, rough, replete with cavities and packed with protruding eminences.

Galileo, 1610 (Trans. Z. Kopal)

## 2.1 THE FACE OF THE MOON

Many advances in our understanding of the lunar surface features occurred in the immediate pre-Apollo period, during the manned missions, and in the postmission analyses of the photographs and astronauts accounts. In this chapter, the broad framework of the lunar landscape, to which reference is made throughout the text, is outlined, and the stratigraphic relations are discussed.

After Galileo's observation in 1610 that the moon had a rough rather than a smooth surface, three and a half centuries of speculation followed about the nature and origin of the lunar landforms. Many of the features can be discerned in Figs. 2.1 and 2.2. The first figure is a full-moon photograph, dominated by the young ray craters, such as Tycho, Copernicus, and Kepler. These rayed craters are among the results of the most recent events on the moon, and the debris from the great collisions [1] that formed them overlies the older formations. A better idea of the details of the surface morphology is seen in Fig. 2.2, a composite photograph. The twofold division into light-colored, cratered highlands and smooth, dark maria is clearly visible.

From the overlapping relationships on these two photographs, the

**Fig. 2.1** Full-moon photograph, showing dark maria, lighter highlands, and several young ray craters. The rays from Tycho (87 km diameter) dominate the southern portion of the photograph. Mare Imbrium is prominent in the northwest quadrant, immediately north of the bright ray crater Copernicus. The dark circular spot north of Mare Imbrium is the lava-filled crater, Plato (101 km diameter). Mare Serenitatis lies to the east of Imbrium. Kepler is west of Copernicus. (Lick Observatory photograph.)

beginnings of a lunar stratigraphy can be discerned. Many other features may be distinguished. The radial distribution of debris from the Imbrium basin, some straight rilles, wrinkle ridges, and color variations in the basalt filling the mare basins are all apparent.

The clearest evidence for the formation of the large ringed basins comes from the Orientale basin (Fig. 2.3). This nearly perfectly preserved far-side feature provides the best evidence for the impact of very large objects. Extrapolation to the near side enables the deduction that such

**Fig. 2.2** Composite full-moon photograph, showing much surface detail. Note the contrast between the heavily cratered light highlands and the smooth dark maria. Several rilles appear near the center of the disk. Color differences are apparent on the maria surfaces. Note the radial structure, southeast from Apennine Mountains bordering Mare Imbrium. (Lick Observatory photograph.)

ruined and filled basins as Mare Imbrium were due to the same causes [2]. The lack of such clear features as the Orientale basin on the visible face handicapped interpretation. The notion that the widespread ridges radial to Mare Imbrium were ejecta from a giant collision first occurred to Gilbert [3] in 1893 and was later independently rediscovered several times [4].

The oldest regions are the lunar highlands, saturated with large (50–100 km diameter) craters, such as the area around Tycho [5] in the southern highlands (Fig. 2.4). Coincident with the later stages of the

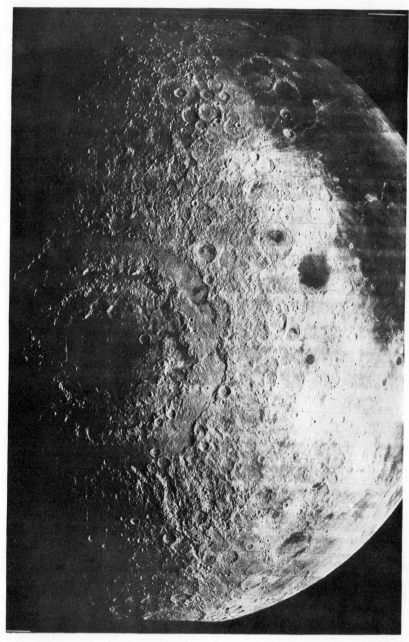

**Fig. 2.3** The great ringed basin of Mare Orientale. The diameter of the outer mountain ring (Montes Cordillera) is 900 km. Note the small amount of mare basalt flooding the central area and the small patches of basalt at the foot of the second scarp. The structures radial to the basin are well developed. The small mare basalt area to the northeast is Grimaldi. The western edge of Oceanus Procellarum fills the northeast horizon. (NASA Orbiter photo IV-M-187.)

**Fig. 2.4**  The southern highlands, showing typical terrain saturated with large craters. Tycho, with a central peak, is left of center. Clavius (232 km diameter) is the prominent crater near the southern limb, with a partially destroyed rim, and four large fresh craters on its floor. (Lick Observatory photograph.)

cratering was the excavation of the giant ringed basins. The youngest of these, Imbrium and Orientale, dominate wide areas of the lunar surface, but many more are apparent (Fig. 2.2), and both near- and far-side mapping[6] of these has revealed at least 43 with an even distribution on both faces. The apparent anisotropy of the moon is caused by the lack of mare basalt flooding on the far side, not by a different cratering history[7]. The face of the moon at 3.9 aeons[8] (billion or $10^9$ years) is shown in the reconstruction in Fig. 2.5.

Following closely, and perhaps overlapping the terminal or earlier stages of the intense cratering, came the great floods of fluid basalt, spreading widely over the visible face. These are the first events of which we have direct terrestrial analogies, in the flood basalts of the Columbia River Plateau, the Deccan Traps, and others[9]. The lava floods continued

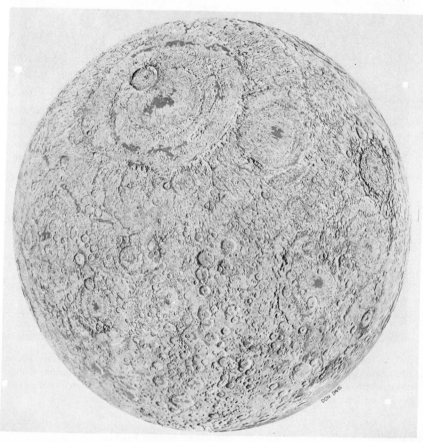

**Fig. 2.5** The face of the moon at 3.9 aeons, just after the Imbrium basin collision, showing the highland surface, just prior to the onset of the maria basalt flooding. Note that Sinus Iridum is post-Imbrium basin formation. Archimedes and Plato have not yet formed. (Diagram courtesy of D. E. Wilhelms, reproduced from *Icarus*. 15: 368, Academic Press.)

for 800 million years and then ceased as the heat engine shut off [10]. The surface was nearly in its present form. A reconstruction, much resembling Fig. 2.2 but with the younger craters removed, is shown in Fig. 2.6.

Although the nature and origin of the lavas will be discussed later [11], an immediate stratigraphic conclusion of some importance was drawn from the photographs. It is that the lava flooding of the basins occurred well after the ringed basins were formed. A close-up telescopic view of the southeast edge of Mare Imbrium (Fig. 2.7) (including the Apollo 15 landing site) is revealing. The Apennine ridge, second ring of the Imbrium

**Fig. 2.6**    The face of the moon at about 3.2 aeons at the end of the period of mare basalt flooding. Note that craters such as Archimedes, Plato, and Sinus Iridum, are post-Imbrium basin formation, but predate the mare basalt fill. (Courtesy D. E. Wilhelms.)

**Fig. 2.7** The southeast sector of Mare Imbrium. The Apennine Mountains form the prominent northeast-trending ridge. The large lava-filled crater is Archimedes, postbasin formation but prelava fill. The two fresh craters northeast of Archimedes are Autolycus and, to the north, Aristillus. These postdate the lava fill. The large crater in the southwest corner is Eratosthenes. Archimedes is 80 km in diameter. (Lick Observatory.)

basin, runs diagonally from the southwest corner (near the crater Eratosthenes). Archimedes, the large prominent north central crater, was formed after the excavation of the basin but before the lava that flooded both it and the Imbrium basin. Other craters (Eratosthenes, Autolycus, and Aristillus, in the northeast quadrant), as well as many small craters, formed later than the lava floods. An inspection of Fig. 2.2 reveals other postbasin prefill craters (e.g., Plato, Sinus Iridum). In all, eight craters with diameters in the range 11–266 km were formed within the Imbrium basin before the flooding of the maria basalts occurred.

A further stratigraphic truth is available on the photographs. There are no debris from the giant ringed basins lying on the lava plains. This observation, emphasized by Urey[12], also means that the smooth mare fill came later than the excavation of the basins. These are clearly of differing ages, as shown, for example, by the various degrees of destruction of their rims. Accordingly, the processes that dug out the basins did not produce the floods of lava that fill them. That is, impact melting caused by the collisions forming the ringed basins was not a major process.

Superimposed on lava plains and highlands alike are a series of craters, some older and subdued such as Eratosthenes, and others younger with bright rays (e.g., Kepler, Copernicus, and Tycho) (Table 2.1). A telescopic view of Copernicus, surrounded by many secondary impact craters is seen in Fig. 2.8. The best estimate for the age of formation of the crater is 900 million years[13], although this conclusion depends on the interpretation that the light gray layer in the regolith at the Apollo 12 site is a ray from Copernicus. Tycho is estimated to be about 100 million years old; it is the

**Table 2.1**  Sizes of Selected Large Lunar Craters.

| Crater | Diameter (km) | Apparent depth (km) |
|---|---|---|
| Bailly | 295 | 3.96 |
| Clavius | 232 | 4.91 |
| Ptolemaeus | 150 | 1.22 |
| Langrenus | 132 | 4.05 |
| Hommel | 120 | 3.35 |
| Alphonsus | 117 | 1.95 |
| Plato | 101 | 2.41 |
| Copernicus | 91 | 3.35 |
| Tycho | 87 | 4.27 |
| Kepler | 32.5 | 2.29 |

**Fig. 2.8** Earth-based telescopic view of Copernicus (91 km diameter) showing ray pattern and secondary impact craters. (Mt. Palomar photo.)

youngest major cratering event, occurring while the Cretaceous dinosaurs roamed heedless of the tiny flash of light from the impact and the production of the beautiful ray pattern (Fig. 2.1).

## 2.2  STRATIGRAPHY OF THE LUNAR SURFACE

The early proposals by Shoemaker and Hackman[14] were based on the stratigraphy revealed around the Imbrium basin. They divided the lunar sequence into five recognizable systems (Table 2.2). This sequence formed the basis for further mapping, but immediate and typical complexities arose. The most important modifications were the subdivision of the Imbrium system. An early, or Apenninian series, referred to the excavation of the basin itself. Included in this was the ejecta blanket, named the Fra Mauro formation. A later, Archimedian series included the period of formation of the postbasin prefill craters (Archimedes, Plato, Sinus Iridum). After this came the Procellarum group, which suffered many shifts in status in the stratigraphic hierarchy[15].

Further complexities arose as the mapping was extended into regions of the moon remote from the Imbrium basin. The rugged Fra Mauro ejecta blanket or structure (Figs. 2.8, 2.9) graded insensibly into smoother deposits. These smooth plains were widespread over the lunar highlands (Fig. 2.10). Age relationships became confusing since these deposits appeared to be of differing ages in different regions. Furthermore in many areas they were the latest premare fill material. This dilemma was partially resolved by assigning them to a new formation, the Cayley formation[16], of which we shall hear more.

The growing recognition of the importance of the great ringed basins led to the realization that much of the highlands contains a complex overlap of ejecta blankets. This view has been somewhat modified by the

Table 2.2  Original Stratigraphic Subdivision of the Imbrium Basin.

| System | Events |
| --- | --- |
| Copernican | Young craters, rays, bright albedo |
| Eratosthenian | Older craters, no rays, low albedo |
| Procellarum | Mare lava flooding |
| Imbrian | Basin excavation |
| Pre-Imbrian | Highland crust cratering |

From Shoemaker and Hackman, 1962[14].

**Fig. 2.9**   Oblique view of the Fra Mauro ejecta blanket. The spacecraft boom points to the center of the crater Fra Mauro. Note the fine detail visible on this near terminator photograph taken during the Apollo 16 mission. (NASA 16-1420.)

recognition that the secondary cratering due to the great collisions extends well beyond the deposition of primary crater ejecta[17]. Many other workers, perplexed by the complexity of highlands stratigraphy, appealed to younger volcanic ash flows, of nueé ardente type, to account for the smooth highland plains.

As the other basins were studied, the familiar terrestrial problem of correlation arose to bedevil the lunar stratigraphers attempting to extend the Imbrium basin formations to the younger (Orientale) and older (Humorum, Serenitatis, and Nectaris) basins. It was soon realized that the Imbrium event was only one of many such.

Separate formations were established. The Orientale basin ejecta was subdivided into Helvelius formation (smooth facies) and Cordilleran formation (hummocky facies). For other basins the ejecta were mapped as Vitello formation (Humorum basin) and Janssen formation (Nectaris basin). Thus, the basic stratigraphy of the lunar surface was established (Tables 2.3, 2.4). The culmination of this phase is marked by the publication of the Geological Map of the Moon by the Astrogeology Branch of the U.S. Geological Survey[18].

Detailed accounts of lunar stratigraphy have been provided both by Mutch and Wilhelms[15, 18, 19]. Wilhelms provides a table of the stratigraphic formations by basin eastwards from Orientale, through Humorum, Imbrium, Serenitatis, Nectaris, and Fecunditatis to Crisium. Mapping of the polar regions is in progress[20]. A division into geographical pro-

**Fig. 2.10**   The Apollo 16 site showing the smooth plains of the Cayley formation to the left of the landing site and the hilly Descartes formation to the right (east). The bright white dot is South Ray Crater just south of the landing site. The diameter of Dollond B, the large crater floored with Cayley formation, in the northwest quadrant, is 36 km in diameter. (NASA.)

**Table 2.3**  Final Stratigraphic System Adopted for Lunar Mapping.

| System | Units |
| --- | --- |
| Copernican | Deposits of Copernicus and other fresh-appearing rayed craters |
| Eratosthenian | Deposits of Eratosthenes and similar slightly subdued craters whose rays are no longer visible or are very faint at high sun illuminations |
| Imbrian | Dark mare materials in the Imbrium basin and Oceanus Procellarum |
| | Deposits of Archimedes and other mare-flooded craters superposed on circum-Imbrium deposits and structures |
| | Circum-Imbrium deposits and structures |
| Pre-Imbrian | Deposits of Julius Caesar and other similar degraded craters covered by Imbrium basin deposits and cut by its structures. |

From Wilhelms and McCauley[18].

vinces has been made on the near side [21, 22]. The visible face of the moon has changed little throughout the complex geological events occurring on the surface of the earth during the past 3 billion years. A space traveler visiting the primitive lifeless earth three and a half aeons ago would have seen the moon (Fig. 2.6) much as it is today. A well-timed visitor would have seen the dull red glow of a mare basalt flood. Meanwhile, the earth began the slow and complex synthesis of organic compounds that resulted ultimately in the recollection of lunar and terrestrial history.

## 2.3  STRATIGRAPHIC AND ABSOLUTE AGE SCALES

Although many attempts had been made to establish chronologies on the basis of crater-counting studies, the first age determinations that linked the relative stratigraphic scales to absolute time were made on the Apollo 11 samples by the Preliminary Examination Team[23] using potassium-argon (K-Ar) techniques. They found ages ranging from 2.7 to 3.7 billion years, or aeons, and commented that

> Perhaps the most exciting and profound observation made in the preliminary examination is the great age of the igneous rocks from this lunar region—it is clear that the crystallization of some Apollo 11 rocks may date back to times earlier than the oldest rocks found on Earth[23].

Subsequent scientific investigations applied most of the techniques of modern radiometric age dating to the lunar rocks. Their great age was

**Table 2.4** Simplified and Modified Lunar Stratigraphy.

| System | Maria | Circumbasin materials | Highlands | Craters |
|---|---|---|---|---|
| Copernican | | | | Young ray craters    Tycho Copernicus |
| Eratosthenian | Marius Hills domes. Younger basalt flows in Imbrium, etc. Dark mantle material. | | | Eratosthenes |
| | Older basalts | | | |
| Imbrian | | Helvelius formation (Orientale) | | Plato, Archimedes |
| | | Fra Mauro formation Montes Apennius Alpes formation | Cayley formation Descartes formation | |
| | | | | Alphonsus |
| Pre-Imbrian | | Janssen formation (Nectaris) | | Clavius |
| | | | Old cratered highlands | Ptolemaeus Hommel |

Based on Wilhelms and McCauley [18].

confirmed. Now it is possible to place dates alongside many of the events unraveled by the stratigraphic studies. The full significance of the dating studies is discussed later, but it is useful and convenient to provide a summary at this stage as a framework for further discussion. Table 2.5 ties together the stratigraphic and the absolute time scales.

## 2.4  LUNAR TOPOGRAPHY

Detailed measurements of the elevation of the lunar surface beneath the track of the Command Module were carried out on Apollo 15, 16, and 17 missions [24]. The precision of the measurements was ±2 m, and they were carried out at about 33-km intervals. The interpretation of the maria basins as structural lows was confirmed. The mean altitude of the highlands is 3 km above the maria for the Apollo 15 orbits and 4 km higher than the maria along the Apollo 16 orbital track.

**Table 2.5**  Absolute Chronology of the Stratigraphic Time Scale.

| System (period) | Location | Event | Age (aeons) |
|---|---|---|---|
| Copernican | Copernicus | Crater formation | 0.90* |
| Eratosthenian | Oceanus Procellarum (Apollo 12 site) | Basalt crystallization | 3.16–3.26 |
| | Hadley Rille (Apollo 15) | Basalt flows | 3.28–3.44 |
| | Mare Fecunditatis (Luna 16) | | 3.42 |
| Imbrian | Mare Tranquillitatis (Apollo 11) | Basalt crystallization | 3.59–3.71† |
| | Taurus-Littrow (Apollo 17) | Basalt crystallization | 3.82 |
| | Fra Mauro (Apollo 14) | Imbrium basin excavation | 3.9 |
| | Cayley formation (Apollo 16) | Late ringed basin ejecta | ~4.0‡ |
| Pre-Imbrian | Taurus-Littrow (Apollo 17) | Serenitatis basin excavation | 4.1§ |
| | | Old highland cratering | >4.0 |

*Eberhardt, P., et al. (1973) *Moon*. 8: 104. The assigned age depends on the identification of KREEP material at Apollo 12 site as ejecta from Copernicus.

†The age of the oldest terrestrial rocks is about 3.7 aeons. Pankhurst, R. J., et al. (1973) *EPSL*. 20: 157.

‡See section 2.8 for full discussion of significance of Cayley ages.

§Kirsten, T., et al. (1973) *EPSL*. 20: 125.

The highlands, particularly on the far side, were extremely rough on a fine scale, but the maria surfaces were exceedingly smooth. Over distances of up to 500 km, slopes of 1:500 to 1:2000 are common, and the differences in elevation are within 150 m over such distances. The different basins are filled to different levels with maria basalts. Both Mare Crisium and Mare Smythii are low (about 4 km below the highlands), while the surface of Oceanus Procellarum lies a little less than 1 km below the neighboring highlands (Fig. 2.11).

The smoothness of the maria is in accord with the extreme fluidity of the lavas that filled them, rather than with postmare leveling (e.g., by dust) since the Al/Si orbital data reveal little lateral movement of material. Correlation of the laser altimetry, the orbital Surveyor photography, and the Apollo photographic coverage revealed the existence, on the far side, of ancient ringed basins[25].

The laser altimetry experiment also revealed that the center of mass was displaced 2–3 km from the geometric center, toward the earth. This offset cannot be accounted for by the mascons, which shift the center of mass only about 40 m[24]. The displacement is compatible with a thicker far-side crust of highland material.

## 2.5  THE LARGER LUNAR CRATERS

A typical view of the heavily cratered highland terrain is shown in Fig. 2.4. The dimensions of some of the great craters are given in Table 2.1. Although these structures have been overshadowed by the more recent recognition of the importance and ubiquity of the larger ringed basins (to be discussed next), they are not minor or unimportant features. Rather, they are among the greatest landscape structures known. In area, Copernicus is slightly smaller and Plato a little larger than Belgium.

The nature and origin of these great craters was the subject of intense interest and speculation for more than three centuries. The debate eventually became polarized between the volcanic and the impact hypotheses. The volcanic hypothesis was championed especially by Dana (1846), Spurr (1944–68), and Green (1965)[26]. Impact origins were defended chiefly by Gilbert[3], Baldwin[27], and Urey[4].

In his discussion Gilbert[3] expended much effort on the problem of the circularity of the lunar craters, an apparently obvious difficulty for the impact hypothesis as it was understood at the time. The question was not resolved until increasing familiarity with terrestrial explosion craters and the mechanics of impact made it apparent that circular craters result from

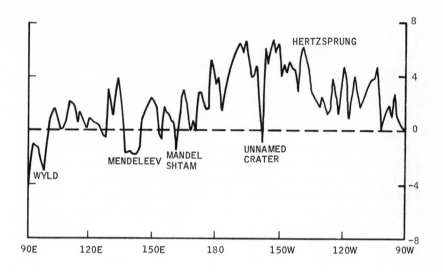

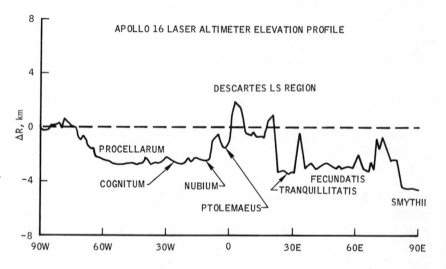

**Fig. 2.11**   Laser altimeter profile from Apollo 16 lunar revolutions 17 and 18. The data are shown as deviations from a sphere of 1,738 km radius. Note the high elevations on the far-side highlands[24].

the explosive nature of impacts at high velocities, regardless of direction[28].

Various minor categories of lunar craters show asymmetry. These are either (a) elongate craters produced by the impact of secondary ejecta at low impact velocities, or (b) craters whose ejecta blankets are not radially symmetrical but have missing sections (e.g., Proclus, on the western edge of Mare Crisium). This ejecta pattern has been duplicated experimentally by impacts at oblique angles[29]. An alternative explanation[30] favors the shielding effect of fault scarps.

Notwithstanding these exceptions, the overall evidence of an impact origin was clear to Gilbert. The argument is an interesting example of apparent constraints due to difficulties in extrapolation. Most scientists will have little difficulty in recognizing similar situations in their own specialties. Later studies by Shoemaker[31] and experimental studies by Gault[32], together with excellent lunar photography and our increasing familiarity with the characteristics of terrestrial explosion craters enabled Baldwin[33] to comment in 1965 that the "136-year-old battle is over," and this view has become the consensus.

Decisive features favoring impact rather than volcanic origins include:

(a) Ejecta blankets. Simple collapse, as in terrestrial calderas, does not produce thick, widespread deposits of ejecta.

(b) The rayed ejecta pattern resembles that of terrestrial explosion craters.

(c) The depth-diameter ratios likewise fit those of terrestrial explosion and meteoritic impact craters.

(d) The energy required to dig the crater and throw out the ejecta far exceeds that available from lunar seismic or volcanic processes.

(e) The widespread production of breccias, shock-metamorphosed material and impact-melted glasses.

There is not space in a book devoted primarily to the scientific achievements of the Apollo missions to record the details of the long-fought controversy, which was resolved before the first return of samples. Vestiges of the volcanic hypothesis continued to haunt the lunar scene and influenced Apollo landing site selections in the lunar highlands[34], although by now the proponents of widespread highland lunar volcanism had diverted their attention from the craters themselves to the nature of the material covering their floors.

Distinctions may be drawn between the apparent density of cratering in the highlands. A twofold division has been proposed between "cratered" terrain (mainly the near side highlands) and "heavily cratered" terrain (parts of the far side) [21], and detailed age studies may eventually unravel the history of the highland crust (see chapter 5).

## 2.6   CENTRAL PEAKS AND PEAK RINGS

Central peaks have long been recognized as typical of the larger lunar craters. Although long ascribed to volcanic activity, they are now accepted as due to elastic rebound during the impact event.

Peak rings have been recognized more recently as a widespread phenomenon. An isolated ring of peaks, with a diameter of 670 km protrudes through the lavas of Mare Imbrium, like nunataks through the Greenland ice sheet (Fig. 2.2). The Orbiter photography revealed many more examples (e.g., Schrödinger, Fig. 2.12). There appears to be a transition from central peaks to peak rings with increasing size. The basins Antoniadi (140 km diameter) (Fig. 2.12) and Compton (175 km diameter) are unique in exhibiting both central peaks and outer peak rings.

Larger basins (e.g., Schrödinger) exhibit only peak rings. Smaller craters (e.g., Lansberg, 40 km diameter) show a central peak. Hartmann and Wood [35] consider the peak rings to be due to the extrusion of viscous lava along concentric faults. Baldwin [36] and Dence [43] argue that they are formed during the impact itself, perhaps during collapse of the central peak, and this origin is thought more probable. Central peaks, peak rings, and ringed basins occur at smaller diameters on larger planets [35] (the sequence is Moon-Mars-Earth) presumably related to the effect of gravity on impact structures.

## 2.7   THE LARGE RINGED BASINS

These are the most spectacular structures on the moon and far exceed the dimensions of impact features observed on the earth. Their origin by impact of large meteorites, asteroids, or comets is now accepted [35–39]. Major questions remain. What is the precise mode of origin? Do the ringed structures originate at the same time as the basins, or are they due to later subsidence along ring faults? What are the relative ages of the basins? What is their distribution on the far side? What effect did the excavation of the basins have on lunar stratigraphy? Are they responsible for the widespread smooth-plains-forming units in the highlands?

It can be seen that the questions raised by the ringed basins are fundamental to much of lunar stratigraphy. Further questions are the effect of the impacts on the thermal regime of the moon and the amount of impact melting. The latter is small. The impacts excavate the large basins.

**Fig. 2.12**   Peak rings and central peaks. Schrödinger basin, lower right center, 300 km in diameter, has an inner ring of peaks. Antoniadi, 140 km diameter, at "2 o'clock" from Schrödinger has both a peak ring and an inner peak. North is to the left. (NASA-IV-8M.)

They are filled with lava from the lunar interior very much later, sometimes several hundred million years later, sometimes never. This later filling of the basins by lava has been recognized for a long time by lunar stratigraphers [27].

In this context, we refer to the impact-produced basins as "ringed basins" and to the material filling them as "mare." Thus the Imbrium basin is the hole and Mare Imbrium is the lava sea flooding the basin. How many basins are there, and what is the relative distribution of front and far-side impacts? Fig. 2.13 shows the presently known basins greater than 220 km in diameter[39].

The front and rear surfaces are about equally covered with large basins[6]. The back of the moon contains much evidence of partially destroyed basins. As noted, the main difference between the back and the front is a result of the much greater flooding of the front side with lava, rather than the impact history. One of the largest basins, 2,000 km in diameter centered at lat. 10°S, long. 170°W on the far side, was revealed by the Apollo 15 and 16 laser altimeter traverses, which showed an 8-km-deep depression of this magnitude. Another example is the ringed basin Al-Khwarizmi[41] (Fig. 2.14), almost battered out of recognition.

These old, ringed basins are almost obliterated by large craters and are the oldest discernible structure of this kind yet found on the moon. Thus, objects capable of producing basins larger than Imbrium or Orientale were impacting the moon earlier than 3.9 aeons ago. How much earlier? The oldest events we see on the moon's surface, appearing dimly through the more recent craters, are almost totally destroyed ringed basins. How many more of these lost basins are there? These are questions to which we shall return later, in discussions of the highlands ages. Geomorphic arguments based on crater counting and crater morphology suggest ages older than 4.0 aeons for the excavation of the oldest basins. A grouping of 17 of the basins by age is shown in Table 2.6.

Returning to the origin of the basins, Hartmann and co-workers[35, 42] propose that the great circular structures arise by subsidence along ring faults very much later than the impact (Fig. 2.15). The subsidence is triggered by subsurface melting, and some liquid is extruded. Evidence for this may be seen in the Orientale basin, the youngest and best-preserved of these great structures.

Dence[43], Van Dorn[37], and Baldwin[36] disagree with this interpretation and consider that the ring structures originate at the same time as the formation of the basin, although they differ in the proposed mechanism. Dence[47] assumes the concentric ridges and central uplifts were formed in smaller craters, by forming a deep transient crater. Immediate slumping along ring faults produces the concentric fault scarps. This is an attractive model, except that the depth of the transient crater becomes very great for the large ringed basins. A value of 230 km is quoted for Imbrium[43]. This would excavate material from deep beneath the highland crust (~60 km thick). Compositional evidence for this deeply excavated material appears to be lacking, although Dence[43] ascribes the

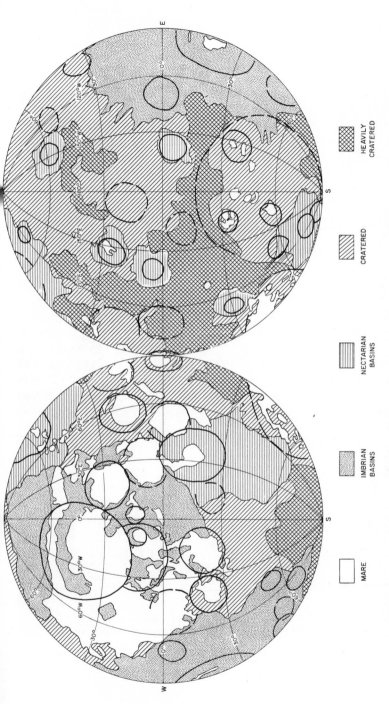

**Fig. 2.13** Province map of the lunar highlands, showing the distribution of 43 large basins with diameters greater than 220 kilometers. Mare lava fill is shown in white. The terrain affected by the young "Imbrium" basin collisions (e.g., Imbrium, Orientale) is distinguished from that due to the older Nectarian basins. The other parts of the highlands are divided into *cratered* and *heavily cratered* terrain. Those highland regions with low numbers of craters have been covered by basin ejecta. Note that the distribution of basins is random. Some old basins have been nearly obliterated. Presumably older basins have been totally destroyed. The highland surface appears to be saturated with basins as well as impact craters, so that we see only the final stages of the bombardment history.

This interpretation favors a continued impact history extending back in time toward the origin of the highland crust, rather than a sudden spike of great collisions at about 4.0 aeons. (Map courtesy Keith A. Howard; Howard, K. A. et al., *Rev. Geophys. Space Phys.*; in press.)

33

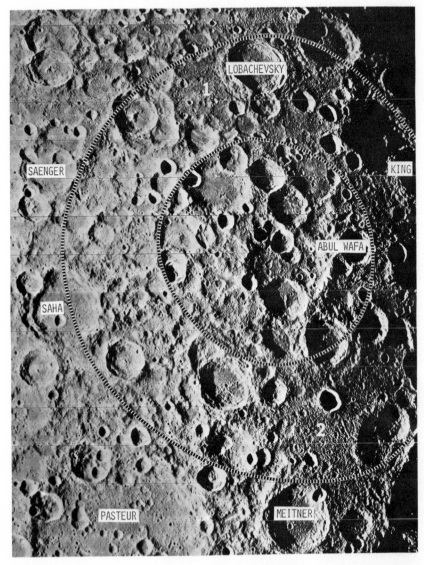

**Fig. 2.14**  The very old ringed basin Al-Khwarizmi centered at 1°N, 112°E [41].

**Table 2.6** Relative Ages of Ringed Lunar Basins.*

| Basin | Relative age |
|---|---|
| Orientale | Youngest |
| Imbrium ⎤ Compton ⎦ | Young |
| Crisium Moscoviense Humboltianum Apollo Grimaldi Bailly Nectaris Crisium* | Medium |
| Humorum Serenitatis Smythii | Old |
| Tranquillitatis Nubium Fecunditatis | Very old |

Ringed lunar basins are craterlike structures with concentric rings. Data adapted from Hartmann and Wood[35] and Stuart-Alexander and Howard[39].

Within each group, the order is that of increasing age.

*See reference 35.

emerald green glass from Apollo 15 to this event. It appears in fact to be related much more closely, in both age and chemistry, to the much later basaltic lava flooding[44].

Van Dorn[37] and Baldwin[36] offer an alternative viewpoint. They consider that the rings represent a frozen shock wave. Evidence for this view is found in the following observations: (*a*) The ages of the rings and basins appear to be the same from crater-counting studies. There is some dispute about this, however, and crater counting, like statistics, seems able to prove any point of view. (*b*) In the inner areas of ringed basins, the preexisting crust appears to have been totally destroyed, and no traces of old crust remain. Possibly it was buried under fall-back or base surge deposits, or collapse of a central uplift. However, no trace of the old crust appears inside the inner ring of the Orientale basin (Fig. 2.3), whereas the

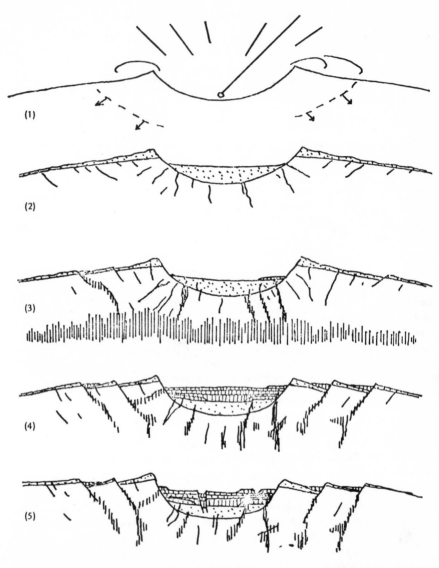

**Fig. 2.15**  Origin of the Orientale basin according to Hartmann and Yale[42]. In this model, the concentric ridges are due to later subsurface melting and extrusion. The sequence of events is (1) impact and expanding shock wave; (2) impact crater and ejecta immediately after formation; (3) intrusion of subsurface magma, faulting; (4) extrusion of lava flows and major faulting, producing concentric cliffs; (5) present state of basin after additional lava extrusion and faulting. Difficulties with this model are discussed in the text, and an instantaneous production of the concentric ridges is favored.

old cratered surface appears dimly through the debris cover outside the ring.

Baldwin proposes the following model[36]:

(a) a shock wave fluidizes the area;

(b) a Tsuanami-type wave moves outward and wipes out the previous surface;

(c) collapse of the central uplift may cause secondary rings to appear.

The variety of explanations offered is due to our lack of experience of events of this magnitude. Mare Imbrium is about the size of Texas, and extrapolation from smaller impact events is difficult. It appears to this reviewer that the instantaneous origin of the concentric ringed structures provides a better explanation than theories of later subsidence.

The original depth of the ringed basins is yet another problem[40]. Dence[43], as noted, argues for a deep initial transient crater for Mare Imbrium, 700 km in diameter and 230 km deep. Baldwin estimates for Orientale, with a primary basin diameter of 620 km, a depth of about 45 km. Owing to the curvature of the moon, the bottom of the basin is nearly flat. There is a factor of five between these estimates. Criteria for distinguishing between these alternatives are difficult to find. The effective absence of debris apparently derived from deeper than the lunar crust is the best indicator that shallow, rather than deep, excavation is the rule for the ringed basins.

## 2.8   RELATION OF RINGED BASINS AND SMOOTH-PLAINS-FORMING DEPOSITS

The smooth plains, which are widespread in the highlands, and which appear to be only marginally older than the mare basin fill[45], have been the cause of much speculation. They were equated with terrestrial ash flows by many workers, and this interpretation excited hopes of rhyolitic or granitic crustal compositions, with consequent profound implications for topics as diverse as lunar thermal regimes and the origin of tektites. A primary reason for the selection of the Apollo 16 Descartes site was to seek these volcanic rocks.

The Cayley Plains are well shown in Fig. 2.10, as are the Descartes hills, once thought to be lava domes but now known to be more prosaic debris from basin impacts. The Apollo 16 sample return found mainly breccias and no primary igneous rocks. Late highland vulcanism could not be appealed to.

The stratigraphic problem was acute. These extensive flat-lying deposits clearly postdated much of the highlands cratering. The deposits were widespread. They were just older than the maria basalts. They appeared, in places, to postdate the Fra Mauro formation ejected from the Imbrium basin[46].

Attention was directed to the latest ringed basin, Orientale. It was now considered that the light plains material, after the Apollo 16 mission known to be impact-derived rubble, was derived by deposition from base surge deposits or by ballistic trajectories, mainly from Orientale[47]. It seems clear that the ringed basins are responsible in some way for the smooth highland plains. The precise mechanism is still elusive. Thus calculations of the thickness of ejecta blankets often disagree by large factors [48], but it is clear that the direct contribution from the Orientale collision at the Apollo 16 site is very small, on the order of a meter or so[48].

Others[38] propose that secondary cratering has been much overlooked as a landscape-modifying process. The well-known landslide at the Apollo 17 site was probably triggered by impacts of ejecta from Tycho striking the top of the South Massif. It is suggested that this process is responsible for much of the valley filling in the highlands. That is, small impacts have transported highlands materials into the depressions[38]. Thus the similarity in chemistry between the Cayley Plains and the adjacent hilly Descartes formation at Apollo 16 is explained. Certainly there is little difference in chemistry, age, or petrology.

A significant point in favor of the secondary cratering hypothesis is the volumetric relationship. Not enough ejecta can be derived from the Orientale basin to provide for the widespread Cayley formation. But the secondary craters excavate many times their own volume. Oberbeck[38] calculates that about twice the original crater mass is deposited by the secondary craters out beyond the thick ejecta blankets.

This general explanation tying in the smooth plains to the great ringed basins aids some of the stratigraphic problems. Many lithologically similar units will be of different ages (Fig. 2.16). Much overlapping will occur. The process will occur during the Orientale basin formation. Some of the large postmare craters may also contribute, producing stratigraphic reversals, as for example, at the Apollo 17 landslide where the old highlands material now overlies the younger maria lavas.

The Helvelius formation is of particular interest since it is the youngest of the ringed basin ejecta blankets (Fig. 2.17). Conclusions drawn from its study are relevant to the interpretation of the Fra Mauro ejecta from Imbrium and the older Janssen formation blankets from the Nectaris collision, which are still preserved in the southern portions of the visible face as the youngest basin ejecta in that area.

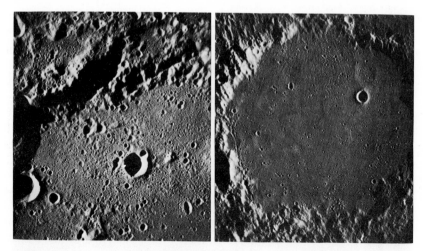

**Fig. 2.16** Two examples of light plains fill at the same scale: left, northwest quadrant of Mendeleev Crater on the lunar far side (Apollo 16 metric frame 2078); right, the 150-km diameter crater Ptolemaeus in the western part of the central nearside highlands (Apollo 16 metric frame 990). The two different crater densities suggest different ages of the two plains units, the fill of Mendeleev being older. (Mattingly, T. K., and El-Baz, F., *PLC 4*: 52.)

The mode of origin of the Helvelius formation is in dispute. It is popularly supposed to represent a base surge deposit. It appears, from the Orbiter photographs, to have flowed across the landscape much like a terrestrial landslide[49] acting like a flexible sheet. Where it crosses obstructions, traverse ridges develop. There appears to be little textural evidence for turbulent flow, as might be expected in a base surge deposit. However, terrestrial landslides travel on an air cushion, and the lunar mode must be different, unless the vapor from the impacts acts in this manner in the lunar vacuum.

A significant observation in favor of the local derivation of much of the highlands plains-forming units is that the geological mapping shows little or no correlation with the orbital chemistry[50]. Thus there is no correlation between either the Al/Si values (as measured by the orbital XRF experiment) or with the orbital gamma ray thorium values and the mapped distribution of Cayley formation. For example, in areas showing high gamma ray values, the amount of Cayley plains-type material may range from 0 to 85 percent[50]. This lack of correlation between chemistry and geology indicates that the plains-forming units do not originate as one uniform sheet of ejecta but instead reflect the local geology, an argument for their local derivation.

**Fig. 2.17**  Helvelius formation, 700 km southeast of the center of the Orientale basin. Note the strong flow pattern toward the southeast (bottom right). (NASA Orbiter IV 167-H.)

## 2.9   LAYERING IN THE HIGHLANDS

Astronaut observations and photographs at the Apollo 15 Hadley-Apennines site revealed a layered structure, particularly well exposed at Silver Spur[58], dipping away from the Imbrium basin. The survival of well-developed primary crustal layering is unlikely because of the intense pre-Imbrium cratering. A preferred explanation is that the layering was formed relatively late in the evolution of the highlands, as ejecta from mare-basin-forming impacts. The Apennine front is close to the Serenitatis basin outer rim. The layering observed is thought to have formed during the Serenitatis impact, being uplifted and exposed in the Apennines by the Imbrium impact. The survival of the layering is due to the decline in frequency of large-crater-forming impacts, after the Imbrium collision (witness the survival of the Apennine ridge).

Fine-scale lineaments or striations, similar to those seen on Mt. Hadley at the Apollo 15 site, were observed by the Apollo 16 crew[59]. These patterns were seen at all sun angles, and changes in the relative positions of the sun, moon, and the astronaut observer did not change their appearance. Thus they are probably real lineations in the highlands[59] rather than artifacts of the lighting[58].

## 2.10   MARIA LAVA FLOWS

The petrological, geochemical, and age significance of the maria basin basalts is given in chapter 4. In this section, the geological observations are discussed.

Among other observers, Baldwin[51] noted individual lava flows, and some are apparent on the Orbiter photographs[52]. The low-sun-angle photographs taken during Apollo 15 and 17 missions showed lava flows in great detail in southwestern Mare Imbrium and cast much light on the nature of the mare filling processes. The low lighting illuminated many features (see Fig. 2.9).

As in terrestrial examples, but much larger, there were channels with levee banks along the centers of some flows (Fig. 2.18). These were typically 20–50 m high. Three stages of very late flows can be distinguished across Mare Imbrium. Since these are the latest flows they are of considerable interest. Fig. 2.19 shows their distribution. They are reported[53] to be of Eratosthenian age, and based on crater counting, ages as young as 2.5 aeons have been suggested. Before such suggestions can be confirmed, the crater-counting age techniques need further validation in view of the many discrepancies in the past between radiometric dates and crater-count ages.

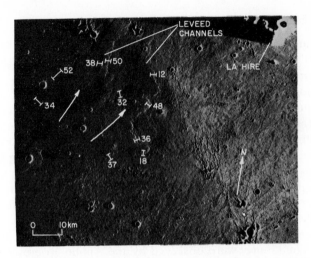

**Fig. 2.18**  Young lava flows on Mare Imbrium, with leveed channels about 2 km wide running down the center of the flow. The numbers (e.g., 32, 18) are scarp heights in meters. Sun angle is 2°. (From Schaber, G. G., 1973, *PLC 4*, Fig. 12.)

Of great interest is the direct evidence of the mechanism of eruption. These youngest series of flows appear to come from a fissure about 20 km long near the crater Euler in southwestern Mare Imbrium (Fig. 2.19). This site appears to be at the intersection of two concentric ring systems, one due to the partly buried second Imbrium ring and the other to the now buried outer ring of a very old "south Imbrium" basin, 900 km in diameter, centered near Copernicus. The intersection of these deep circum-basin fractures may well be significant in channeling the lava toward the surface. Less easy to evaluate, and probably coincidental, is the location of the site above one of the currently active seismic regions [54].

The extent and volume of the flows is remarkable. The three phases of lava extrusion reached distances of 1,200, 600, and 400 km. The area covered was $2 \times 10^5$ km², an area equal to that of the Columbia River basalts. The flows ran down slopes as gentle as 1:1000. Again there are analogies with the Columbia River basalts [9, 55], which flowed over similar slopes. However, the lunar flow fronts were 1.5–1.8 times as high as the Columbia lavas [54] (Fig. 2.18).

The differences in flow lengths and heights of flow fronts appear to be a simple function of lunar versus terrestrial gravity. The effect of viscosity is harder to evaluate. Schaber [53] suggests that differences in viscosity are less important than rates of extrusion, citing the lower viscosity of the shield-building Hawaiian basalts compared with the Columbia River flood basalts. It is significant that doubling the flow thickness will extend the flow length by a factor of six! The extreme extent of the lunar lavas is thus due to a combination of rapid rate of extrusion coupled with low viscosity. The apparent absence of evidence for deep lava lakes and the absence of evidence of strong fractional crystallization in deep or shallow reservoirs indicates that extrusion took place as a widely spaced series of rapid effusions.

From the correlation with the earth-based radar reflectivity profiles, these late flows appear to be Ti-rich, possibly close in composition to the Apollo 11 and 17 titanium-rich basalts[56]. If so, a young province of this composition occurs in an area on the west side of the moon remote from the older Ti-rich basalts on the eastern limb.

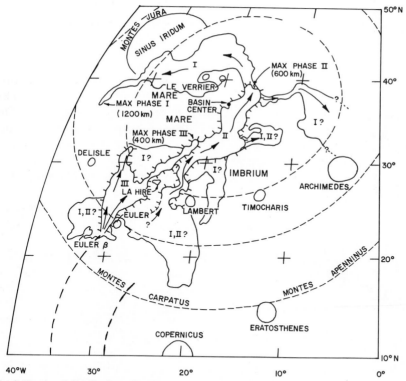

**Fig. 2.19**   Areal distribution of younger flows in Mare Imbrium, showing three successive phases (I, II, and III) and the source region near the Crater Euler. (From Schaber, G. G., 1973, *PLC 4*, Fig. 4.)

**High Tide Marks**

Clear evidence of lowering of mare basalt levels has been observed in most of the western maria where highland surfaces protrude through the basalt flows [57]. Benches interpreted as due to former higher levels of the maria basalts are a ubiquitous feature in these areas. Such subsidence will cause compression (see section on wrinkle ridges), thus providing one mechanism for producing the wrinkle ridges.

## 2.11  RILLES

Three major varieties, straight, curved, and sinuous, have long been recognized. The straight rilles are commonly more than 5 km wide, hundreds of kilometers long, and cut across craters and maria alike, indifferent to the surficial topography (Fig. 2.20). Curved, or arcuate, rilles are a variant of this type. Particularly fine examples of these, concentric to Mare Humorum, are shown in Fig. 2.21. These two classes appear to be

**Fig. 2.20**  Straight rilles, 1–2 km wide, crossing old degraded crater rims near Fra Mauro. (NASA Orbiter V-138M.)

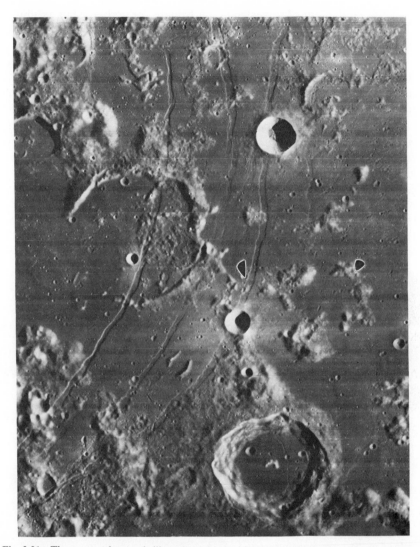

**Fig. 2.21**  Three sets of curved rilles, about 2 km wide, concentric to Mare Humorum. The large crater, bottom right, is Campanus, 48 km diameter, flooded with mare basalt and containing a sinuous rille. The distance from the curved rilles to the center of Mare Humorum is about 250 km. The ruined crater intersected by the inner rille is Hippalus. (NASA Orbiter IV-132-H.)

the lunar equivalent of terrestrial fault troughs, or grabens, but exhibit no seismic activity at present[60]. Lunar rilles of all species cluster around the edges of the maria, a fact noted by many observers[61].

The sinuous rilles, together with the related tightly meandering rilles (Fig. 2.22), have been the object of intense study. The resemblance of these two kinds of rilles to the familiar meander patterns of terrestrial river channels long encouraged speculation that liquid water had existed, at least briefly, on the lunar surface. The view that the maria were filled with dust or other incoherent material[62] encouraged the possibility of erosion by water. It was not until the initial sample return[63] that these ideas evaporated. As the basaltic nature of the mare basin fill was established, detailed examinations and comparisons with terrestrial lava channels, tubes, and tunnels proved instructive[64].

Although rille systems were highly favored as landing sites, only one, Hadley Rille, was investigated during the Apollo program. Hadley Rille,

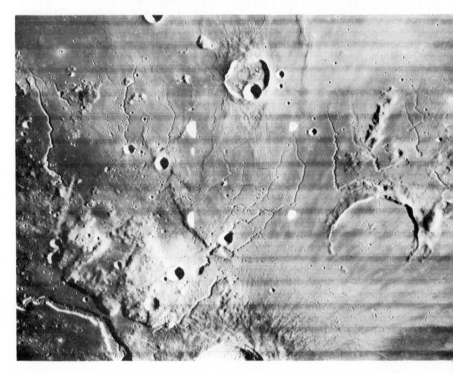

**Fig. 2.22**  Sinuous rilles on the north edge of the Aristarchus plateau. The crater Aristarchus (northern half shown) is 39 km in diameter. (NASA Orbiter IV-151-H1.)

**Fig. 2.23** The Apollo 15 landing site, showing Hadley Rille (about 1 km wide). The prominent craters are Autolycus (nearest) (39 km diameter) and Aristillus (56 km diameter) showing central uplift.

135 km long and sinuous, averages 1.2 km in width and 370 m in depth, and greatly resembles a collapsed terrestrial lava tube[65]. An overview, including the Apollo 15 site, is given in Fig. 2.23. The sinuous bends are not structurally controlled by simple fracturing, for the two sides do not match up.

The rille originates in a cleft adjacent to the highland scarp. Many others originate in similar fissures or craters, and the association with the edges of the maria basins recalls, on a much larger scale, the tendency of basaltic lava lakes to fill from the sides as well as from beneath[66].

The rille is deepest where it is widest, in contrast to river channels, a feature consistent with the collapsed lava tube hypothesis. Where it is shallow and flat bottomed it may have been an open channel. The physical problems of roofing across kilometer-wide channels of very fluid lavas in an environment of 1/6 terrestrial gravity are not well understood. The very fluid nature of the lava[67] encourages turbulent rather than laminar flow, increasing the erosive power of the fluid. Elevation profiles[68] shows that the floors of the rilles do indeed slope downstream.

The general absence of deltas where the rilles fade out onto the broad maria surfaces has often been noted. Explanations include (a) the fluid nature of the lavas, as shown by the low flow fronts, and (b) the covering of rille ends by later maria flows. There is occasional evidence of ponding at the downstream end.

The consensus from the Apollo studies is that Hadley Rille is a lava channel that was partly roofed. The meteorite bombardment will collapse most roofs after the emptying of the channel. There is clear evidence at the Hadley site[65] that the surface of the mare (Palus putredinis, or the Swamp of Decay) has subsided differentially by about 100 m, after partial solidification. Hadley Rille provides a suitable drainage channel[69].

Much insight into the subsurface nature of maria basins was gained from the examination of the wall of Hadley Rille. The regolith is about 5 m thick, underlain by exposed massive bedrock for about 55 m (Fig. 2.24). The remaining 300 m, to the bottom of the rille, is blanketed with talus, including many massive blocks (Fig. 2.25) up to 15 m across. The rock units in the walls are 10–20 m thick, massive, and little jointed. The implication is that the mare filling consists of individual, thick massive flow units, not strongly jointed.

## 2.12  WRINKLE RIDGES

Wrinkle ridges tend to form concentric rings in the maria fill in the ringed basins (Table 2.7). Other good examples of concentric patterns of wrinkle ridges occur in maria Serenitatis, Nubium, Fecunditatis, and Tranquillitatis. Many origins have been proposed. These divide into three classes (a) internal origin; (b) draping over buried highland or other structural ridges following subsidence; (c) produced by compressional forces during cooling of lava flows.

Hartmann and Wood[35] consider that those features are due to extrusion along concentric ring fractures extending to depth, forming channels for the extrusion of maria lavas. Some of the flows in Imbrium appear to originate in or near the wrinkle ridges. If mare flooding occurs mainly along these concentric fractures, the origin of the wrinkle ridges can be understood as constructional due to upwelling of lava or due to uplifting of a frozen lava surface by intrusion of further magma from beneath.

**Fig. 2.24**   Outcrops in the wall of Hadley Rille. (NASA AS 15-89-12116.)

The morphology of the ridges, however, supports the view that they are compressional features. They consist, not of squeezed-out lava, but are deformed, folded, preexisting mare surface[70], as is apparent from many photographs (Fig. 2.26). The intense crumpling that occurs along their crests, with some local examples of overthrusting, attests to their compressional origin. The absence of tension cracks seems to rule out intrusion of lava from beneath, which would stretch the crust. They greatly resemble the wrinkles produced in a rug pushed against a wall or furniture. They do not resemble terrestrial lava domes[70] despite assertions to the contrary[71], and are thus most probably related to compression attendant on mare subsidence, which results in crustal shortening.

**Table 2.7**   Ratios of Diameters of Wrinkle Ridge Systems to those of Ringed Basins[35].

| Basin | Wrinkle ridge diameter (km) | Rim diameter (km) | Ratio |
|---|---|---|---|
| Imbrium | 640 | 1340 | 0.48 |
| Crisium | 330 | 450 | 0.73 |
| Humorum | 195 | 425 | 0.44 |
| Moscoviense | 90 | 205 | 0.44 |

**Fig. 2.25**   The bottom of Hadley Rille. (NASA AS15-84-11287.)

**Fig. 2.26**  Wrinkle ridges in Mare Serenitatis near the southern margin of light central fill are arranged both radial to, and concentric with, the center of the basin. Note grabenlike rilles in dark fill and zig-zag pattern in ridge near left margin produced by offsets along angular joint blocks. The dark fill slopes toward the center of the mare. (Apollo metric photo AS17-0449.) (From Bryan, W. B., 1973, *PLC 4*, Fig. 4.)

## 2.13  LOW ALBEDO AREAS

A number of very dark regions occur in the maria. The best-documented examples occur around the southeastern edge of Serenitatis (Fig. 2.26), notably in the Sulpicius Gallus area and in the Taurus-Littrow Valley at the Apollo 17 site. The Taurus-Littrow dark mantle is bluish dark gray [72] compared to "very dark tan" at Sulpicius Gallus, the "blue gray" outer ring or annulus of mare lava fill in Serenitatis and the "tan gray" younger lavas filling the center of the mare.

The dark mantle material was a prime objective of the last lunar mission, but despite the abundant photogeologic evidence, it was not so obvious on the ground, or in the returned samples. The photographic effect is probably due to the many small, opaque black spheres [73]. There was no field evidence of the expected blanket of young pyroclastic material from cinder cones, identified with the "dark halo" craters [74].

On closer inspection, these appear to be impact craters, with the dark halo due to the ejecta of the dark Ti-rich glass. The origin of the dark mantle thus remains a mystery, but arguably it is due to the concentration of dark glass in the soil. The origin of the black glass and of the closely related orange glass is still debated, but a fire fountain origin seems most reasonable, particularly so if the rates of eruption were as rapid as those of the last flow in Mare Imbrium [75]. Thus, the dark mantle areas may be a clue to the last centers of eruption of the maria basalts [76].

The low albedo area forming the outer ring of lava fill in Serenitatis has the same color and albedo as most of the lava filling Mare Tranquillitatis, which accordingly is older than the basalt fill in the center of Serenitatis [77] (Fig. 2.26).

## 2.14  SWIRLS

Enigmatic light colored surface markings, named "swirls," have been observed [78] mainly on the far-side highlands. They appear to have no topographic relief and cross the landscape independent of elevation. They are well developed near the crater King, the basin Al Khwarizmi, and east of Mare Marginis and Mare Smythii. The swarms of light colored markings extend over a triangular area of $25 \times 10^4 \, km^2$. They are thus not minor, but form a widespread, if enigmatic, phenomenon.

## REFERENCES AND NOTES

1. The origin of these large craters and basins by impact processes is regarded as established beyond reasonable doubt. See section 2.5.
2. See section on ringed basins.
3. Gilbert, G. K. (1893) *Bull. Phil. Soc. Wash.* 12: 241.
4. Urey, H. C. (1952) *The Planets*, Yale University Press; and (1962) *Phys. Astron. Moon*, Academic Press, N.Y., p. 484.
5. See Table 2.1 for sizes of large lunar craters.
6. Howard, K. A., USGS, personal communication.
7. See section 3.9 on cratering history.
8. The engaging term aeon, to denote 1 billion, or $10^9$, years was proposed by Urey. The word is appropriate to designate the passage of a thousand million years, and conjures a vision of the vast abyss of time into which we look.
9. Waters, A. C. (1961) *AJS.* 259: 583; Wheeler, H. C., and Coombs, H. A. (1967) *Bull. Volc.* 31: 21; Bingham, J. W., and Grolier, M. S. (1966) *USGS Prof. Paper.* 1224-G; Cotton, C. A. (1952) *Volcanoes as Landscape Forms*, Whitcombe and Toombs, chapters 8 and 17; Shaw, H. R., and Swanson, D. A. (1970) *Proc. 2nd Columbia River Basàlt Symposium*, East Washington State College Press.
10. The age range of the maria basalts is from 3.96 to 3.16 aeons, overlapping at the high end with the terminal stages of the great bombardment.
11. No apology is offered for anticipating the identification of the mare fill as basaltic lava. This conclusion was reached by, among others, Baldwin [27] and by Kuiper, G. (1966), and Whitaker, E. A. (1966), in *The Nature of the Lunar Surface*, W. N. Hess et al., editors, Johns Hopkins Press, Baltimore.
12. Urey, H. C., ibid.

13. Eberhardt P., et al. (1973) *Moon.* 8: 104.
14. Shoemaker, E. M., and Hackman, R. J. (1962) in *The Moon,* Academic Press, N.Y. 289.
15. Wilhelms, D. E. (1970) USGS Prof. Paper 599-F, p. 29; Mutch, T. (1972) *Geology of the Moon,* Princeton University Press, p. 136.
16. Wilhelms, D. E., ibid., p. 23.
17. Oberbeck, V. R., et al. (1973) NASA Tech. Mem. TM-X. 62: 302.
18. Wilhelms, D. E., and McCauley, J. F. (1971) *Geologic Map of the Nearside of the Moon,* USGS I-703. A full list of current geological maps of the moon is available from U.S. Geological Survey, Washington, D.C.
19. Wilhelms, D. E., USGS Prof. Paper 599-F, p. 16.
20. Lucchitta, Baerbel K. In press.
21. Wilhelms, D. E. (1971) *Icarus.* 15: 363.
22. Ibid., 371.
23. LSPET (1969) *Science.* 165: 1211.
24. Kaula, W. M. (1972) *PLC 3*: 2189, NASA SP 215, 30-1; (1973) *PLC 4*: 2811; (1974) *LS V*: 399, 675.
25. El Baz, F. (1973) *Science.* 180: 1173, NASA SP 315, 29–33.
26. See References 5, 6, 7, chapter 1; also Spurr, J. E. (1944–49) *Geology Applied to Selenology,* Science Press, Lancaster, Pa.; Rittmann, A. (1962) *Volcanoes and Their Activity,* Interscience, p. 286.
27. Baldwin, R. B. (1949) *The Face of the Moon,* University of Chicago Press.
28. A meteorite traveling at 25 km/sec has kinetic energy equivalent to 6 times the equivalent mass of a high explosive such as TNT. See Baldwin, R. B.[51] chapter 6, and Shoemaker, E. M. (1962) *Physics and Astronomy of the Moon,* Academic Press, N.Y. p. 283.
29. Hörz, F., NASA-JSC, personal communication; Whitaker, E. A. (1974) NASA SP 330.
30. El Baz, F., and Worden, A. M. (1972) NASA SP-289, p. 25-1.
31. Shoemaker, E. M. (1962) in *Physics and Astronomy of the Moon,* Academic Press, N.Y., p. 283. Discussions of terrestrial meteorite impact craters, which contributed greatly to our understanding of the lunar craters, are given by the following references in *The Solar System* Vol. IV (University of Chicago Press) (1963): Beals, C. S., et al., p. 235; Dietz, R. S., p. 285; Krinov, E. L., p. 183; and Shoemaker, E. M., p. 301. Much detailed information is given in French, B. M., and Short, N. M. (1968) *Shock Metamorphism of Natural Materials,* Mono Book Corp., Baltimore, and in Dence, M. R. (1973) *Meteoritics.* In press.
32. Gault, D. E. (1966) in *Nature of the Lunar Surface,* Johns Hopkins Press, Baltimore, p. 135; and (1964) in *The Lunar Surface Layer,* Academic Press, N.Y., p. 151.
33. Baldwin, R. B. (1965) *A Fundamental Survey of the Moon,* McGraw-Hill, N.Y., p. 137. The first mention of the impact theory appears to have been by M. von Bieberstein in 1802 (Green, J., *Ann. N.Y. Acad. Sci.* 123: 385) making the debate 163 years old, although most authors cite Gruithuisen, F. von P. (1829) *Analekten-Erd und Himmels-Kunde* (München) as the original source.
34. Hinners, N. W. (1972) NASA SP-315, 2-1.
35. Hartmann, W. K., and C. A. Wood (1971) *Moon.* 3: 3; Hartmann, W. K. (1972) *Icarus.* 17: 707.
36. Baldwin, R. B. (1972) *Phys. Earth Planet. Interiors.* 6: 327.
37. Van Dorn, W. G. (1968) *Nature.* 220: 1102.
38. Oberbeck, V. R., et al. (1973) NASA Tech. Memo. TMX 62, 302.
39. Stuart-Alexander, D., and Howard, K. A. (1970) *Icarus.* 12: 440.

40. Opik, E. J. (1969) *Ann. Rev. Astron. Astrophys.* 7: 473.

41. El-Baz, F. (1973) *Science.* 180: 1173.

42. Hartmann, W. K., and Yale, F. G. (1969) *Sky and Telescope.* 37: 1.

43. Dence, M. R. (1974) *LS V*: 165.

44. See section 4.3 on emerald green glass.

45. Mutch, T. A. (1972) *Geology of the Moon*, Princeton University Press, p. 136.

46. Boyce, J. M., et al. (1974) *LS V*: 82.

47. Chao, E. C. T., et al. (1973) *LS IV*: 127.

48. McGetchin, T., et al. (1973) *EPSL.* 20: 226.

49. Head, J. (1973) *GSA Abstracts.* 5: 661.

50. Hörz, F., et al. (1974) *LS V*: 357.

51. Baldwin, R. B. (1963) *The Measure of the Moon*, University of Chicago Press, p. 333.

52. Mutch, T. (1972) *Geology of the Moon*, Princeton University Press, p. 201.

53. Schaber, G. G. (1973), *PLC 4*: 73.

54. Schaber, G. G. (1973) NASA SP-330.

55. Mutch, T. (1972) *Geology of the Moon*, Princeton University Press, p. 178.

56. Schaber, G. G., et al. (1974) *LS V*: 660.

57. Mattingly, T. K., and El-Baz, F. (1973) *PLC 4*: 55.

58. Wolfe, E. W., and Bailey, N. G. (1972) *PLC 3*: 15.

59. Mattingly, T. K., and El-Baz, F. (1973) *PLC 4*: 53.

60. Latham, G., et al. (1973) *PLC 4*: 2515.

61. For example, Baldwin, R. B. (1963), chapter 21. See especially Figs. 47 and 48, which show the association of rilles with edges of maria.

62. Gold, T. (1966), in *The Nature of the Lunar Surface*, Johns Hopkins Press, Baltimore, p. 105. See especially Fig. 5-18, p. 120, which shows a crater cross-section filled successively with water, ice, and sediment.

63. LSPET (1969) *Science.* 165: 1211.

64. Greely, R. (1971) *Moon.* 3: 289; Greely, R. (1971) *Science.* 172: 722.

65. Howard, K. A., et al. (1972) *PLC 3*: 1.

66. The classic example is the filling of the Halemaumau pit crater following the 1924 Kilauea eruption. Stearns, H. T. (1966) *Geology of the State of Hawaii*, Pacific Books, Calif., p. 127, 142.

67. Murase, T., and McBirney, A. R. (1970) *Science.* 168: 364; Weill, D. F., et al. (1971) *PLC 2*: 413.

68. Schubert, G., et al. (1974) *LS V*: 675.

69. See section 2.10 on high water marks.

70. Bryan, W. B. (1973) *PLC 4*: 93.

71. O'Keefe, J. A., et al. (1967) *Science.* 155: 77.

72. NASA SP-330, (1974).

73. See section on orange glass from Apollo 17.

74. El-Baz, F. (1972) NASA SP-289, 25-66; El-Baz, F., and Worden, A. M. (1972) Ibid., 25-1.

75. Heiken, G., et al. (1974) *GCA.* 38: 1703.

76. Head, J. W. (1974) *LS V*: 316.

77. El-Baz, F., and Evans, R. E. (1973) *PLC 4*: 139.

78. El-Baz, F. (1972) NASA SP-315, 29-93; Evans, R. E., and El-Baz, F. (1973) *LS IV*: 231; Schmitt, H. H. (1974) NASA SP-330.

# CHAPTER 3

# The Surface of the Moon

a soil strange enough in its chemical character to bewilder the savants at a museum.

Jules Verne (1865)

The nature of the lunar surface material long fascinated investigators. At full moon, the surface is bright from limb to limb, with only marginal darkening toward the edges[1]. Thus the surface was early judged to be rough rather than smooth. The pre-Apollo workers concluded that the top surface layer was porous on a centimeter scale and had the thermal properties of dust[2]. The thickness of the dust layer was a nice question. Workers realized that the impacts of meteorites would pulverize the surface, and most concluded that a layer of rubble and finely divided debris a few meters thick covered the immediate surface[3]. Other views called for kilometer thicknesses of fine dust[4].

These basic questions were resolved by the unmanned missions (Table 1.2), but many detailed questions remained to be posed and solved by the Apollo landings. The surface material turned out to be as distinctive and full of scientific puzzles as any imagined by the writers of science fiction.

## 3.1 THE EXTREME UPPER SURFACE

The nature of the "very surface" (the upper few centimeters) has been investigated mainly in the later Apollo missions. Drill cores were returned from all missions, but although the techniques and recovery improved markedly as experience was gained, this method of sampling is of marginal value for studying the very top layer. The top layer is best studied *in situ*, since the degree of compaction of the grains and their configuration will not readily survive transport to a terrestrial laboratory.

The importance of the very top layer in cosmic ray, solar flare, and track studies has led to the development of new sampling techniques. One such device consists of a free-floating cloth-covered plate designed to sample the top 100-$\mu$m layer. Another, a spring-loaded cloth-covered plate, sampled the top 0.5 mm[5]. Other samples in this category, from the Apollo 16 highlands site at Descartes, include top and bottom samples from a boulder and soil samples from shadowed areas. Work on this material is still in progress.

Measurements of conductivity indicate that the top layer is strongly insulating[6]. There is an increase of about 47°K in the top 83 cm. The top surface (2–3 cm) is a loosely packed porous layer. Surface temperatures are extreme. At the Apollo 17 site, the surface reaches a maximum of 384°K (111°C) and cools to 102°K (− 171°C) at the end of the lunar night[6]. The near-surface temperature is 216°K (− 57°C). These temperatures are about 10°K higher than those observed at the Apollo 15 site. The agreement with previous estimates based on terrestrial observations was very close[7].

The question of the lateral movement of the surface layer or of underlying layers has been extensively discussed, and extensive surface transport of dust has been proposed[8]. Although much material has been redistributed by impact processes (Fig. 2.1), the underlying bedrock is the dominant influence on the composition of the regolith. With some exceptions[9] the truth of this statement is apparent from the chemistry of the soils at the various sites. The chemical data from the orbital experiments (Al/Si, Mg/Si, and the gamma ray Th values) show breaks generally coincident with the maria-highland boundaries[10]. Thus movement of a surficial layer occurs only on a local scale, and the chemistry and nature of the regolith is dominated by local bedrock components.

Evidence for local stirring of the very top dust layer has been deduced from the light scattering observed at the terminator by the Apollo 17 astronauts[11]. These observations are consistent with effects observed by Surveyor 6 and Lunokhod 2 and are perhaps due to dust levitation caused by temperature changes at the terminator[11]. The effect does not produce any widespread migration of dust, which would blur the sharp mare-highland boundaries observed by the orbital chemical analyses[10]. Processes occurring in the upper layer of the regolith are discussed further throughout this chapter.

## 3.2  THE REGOLITH

This term was revived by Shoemaker to describe the continuous layer, usually several meters thick, of debris draped over the entire lunar bedrock surface. It is a debris blanket in every sense of the term, ranging from very fine dust to blocks meters across (Fig. 3.1). Although the finer components (<1 mm) are often referred to as soil, the distinction from terrestrial soils, formed by the complex interaction of the atmosphere and biosphere on rocks, is complete. The active processes on the moon at present are cosmic, not planetary. Bombardment of the surface

**Fig. 3.1**  Rake samples being collected from the lunar upper surface near the Apollo 16 landing site. Rock sample 60018 was taken from the top of the boulder. (NASA AS 16-116-18690.)

occurs at all scales from 50 to 100-km diameter cratering events to erosion by particles producing micrometer-size pits, while cosmic ray and solar flare particles produce damage on an atomic scale. The surficial material is saturated with solar wind gases.

The thickness of the regolith has been established mainly by observations of those craters that are seen to excavate bedrock, and by direct observations along the edge of Hadley Rille [12] (Fig. 2.24). Here, the base is seen to be irregular. The average thickness of the regolith on the maria is 4–5 m, while the highland regolith is about twice as thick, averaging about 10 m, implying a more rapid rate of regolith development, particularly in the period between 3.8 and 4.0 aeons.

The seismic properties are uniform on highlands and maria alike, and the "compacted dust" hypothesis does not receive much support from the nature of the seismic signals [13]. Rather, they indicate that the regolith consists of discrete layers, of which more will be discussed later.

There are many local variations in thickness. Perhaps the best example is in the Taurus-Littrow Valley, where, near the landing site, thickness ranged from 6.2 to 36.9 m. Such changes are arguably due to the local concentration of medium-sized craters (such as Camelot, 700 m diameter) producing uneven thicknesses due to local throwout, burying smaller craters. Regolith development on the rims of young craters is very limited. The thickness on top of the North Ray crater rim (Apollo 16 site) is only a few centimeters. North Ray crater is 50 million years old [14] (Fig. 3.2). A total of 26 core samples of varying depths up to 3 m [15] were taken during the missions, along with the many scoop samples of soil. The cores provided valuable data after some initial confusion due to the early sampling techniques, which did not return undisturbed cores [16].

The bulk density of the soils ranges from 0.9 to 1.1 g/cm$^3$ at the top surface, but increases with depth to values up to 1.9 g/cm$^3$. The density increases markedly in the upper 10–20 cm [16, 17]. The porosity of the upper surface is 45 percent, with higher values around crater rims, as judged from soil mechanics study of the astronauts footprints. Thus the top surface is very loose, due to stirring by micrometeorites, but the lower depths, below about 20 cm are strongly compacted, arguably by shaking during impacts. The compressibility of the soil is similar to that of ground-up terrestrial basalt.

All these mechanical properties, vital for manned landings and astronaut surface activities have been extensively studied [18]. Notwithstanding the differences in composition, particle size and shape, and grain size distribution, from a soil mechanics or engineering point of view the lunar soil does not differ significantly in its behavior from what would be

**Fig. 3.2**  View across North Ray crater from Station 11 at the Apollo 16 site, Descartes Highlands. The crater is 900 m across. The regolith at this site is only a few centimeters thick. (NASA AS16-116-18599.)

expected on earth of granular, slightly cohesive terrestrial soil with the same particle size distribution and packing characteristics. The one major difference that might be singled out is the intraparticle adhesion, which is demonstrated, for example, by the vertical walls produced by the indentations of the footprints.

The similarity of lunar soil in mechanical properties to those of terrestrial examples is due to the fact that the mechanical properties depend on size, density, and shape of the particles rather than on their chemical composition. The consensus from the soil mechanics studies[18] and from the seismic data[13] is that the mechanical properties of the lunar soils are about the same at all sites.

## 3.3  STRUCTURE OF THE REGOLITH

The Apollo 11 core samples indicated that the regolith might be extremely homogeneous and well mixed in accord with the pre-Apollo thinking. The term "gardening" was much employed. Samples from subsequent missions demonstrated that the lunar "gardener" was less than thorough. The first strong evidence of distinct layering in the regolith was found at the Apollo 12 site in the Ocean of Storms.

Here the astronauts encountered a layer of "light gray fines," sometimes on the surface, as at Sharp Crater, or a few centimeters beneath, as revealed by a trench dug at Head Crater. This material was distinctly different from the other soil, which was derived mainly from the local mare basalt. Together with rock 12013, the celebrated KREEP sample, it revealed the presence of high concentrations of uranium, thorium, and the rare earth elements on the lunar surface in amounts reminiscent of terrestrial pegmatites. The light gray fines are arguably a ray from Copernicus. If so, they date that crater at 900 million years[14]. In any event, the material is foreign to the local bedrock and closely resembles the older Fra Mauro material.

The complex layered nature of the regolith has now been fully revealed by many core samples. The greatest insight came from the study of the Apollo 15 deep core, which clearly revealed that the regolith was not a homogeneous pile of rubble. Rather, it is a layered succession of ejecta blankets. An apparent paradox is that the regolith is both well mixed on a small scale and also displays a layered structure. For example, the Apollo 15 deep core tube, 242 cm long, contained 42 major textural units ranging from a few mm to 13 cm in thickness. There is no correlation between layers in adjacent core tubes. The individual layers are well mixed.

The paradox is resolved in the following manner. The regolith is continuously gardened by large and small meteorites and micrometeorites. Each impact inverts much of the microstratigraphy and produces layers of ejecta, some new and some remnants of older layers. The new surface layers are stirred by micrometeorites, but deeper stirring is rarer.

The result is that a complex layered regolith is built up, but is in a continual state of flux. Particles now at the surface may be buried deeply by future impacts. In this way, the regolith is turned over, not in the manner of a terrestrial gardener digging with a spade, but more like a heavily bombarded battlefield. The layering in an individual core tube has no wider stratigraphic significance. It is local, temporary, and accidental. Thus we have the well-stirred and homogeneous regolith, with one portion very like another, uniform moon-wide, as shown by the seismic data, yet layered locally.

These processes have been placed on a quantitative basis by Gault and co-workers[19], who studied the effect of the meteorite flux on the regolith. Their important conclusions deserve direct quotation: "The most significant result is the large number of turnovers which occur in the upper 1 mm of the surface as compared to deeper layers. It is 99% probable that the upper 0.5 mm is turned over almost 100 times in $10^6$ years while even at the 50% probability level the 1 cm depth has yet to be disturbed; it requires $10^7$ years to assure (99%) that the surface has been turned over to a depth of 1 cm at least once. Time scales for one turnover at 10 cm to 1 m depths are measured in $10^9$ year units, and it is not surprising that the A-15 drill core material returned from more than 2 meter depth had lain undisturbed for about 500 million years. It is only the upper 0.5–1 mm of the lunar surface that is subjected to intense churning and mixing by the meteoritic complex at the present time. This thin veneer of regolith should be considered a primary mixing layer of lunar materials from all points on the Moon and a major source for impact melts, agglutinates, and vapor products"[19].

### Rate of Accumulation

The accretion rate for the past three aeons averages about 1.5 m per aeon[20], 1.5 mm per million years, or about 15 angstrom units per year (corresponding to a layer of about 6 oxygen anions). However, such averages are misleading. The accumulation of the regolith occurs as a result of the addition of discrete layers and is not continuous. The local accretion rate is extremely variable. In comparison with terrestrial erosion and deposition, lunar processes are slow indeed[21].

The accumulation rate, which is directly related to the meteoritic cratering flux, discussed later, steepens appreciably in the period between 3.5 and 4 aeons, so that the highland surfaces have about double the regolith thickness. The present regolith in the highlands dates from about 3.9 to 4.0 aeons, which marked the close of the intense bombardment, culminating in the impacts that formed the Imbrium and Orientale ringed basins. The accumulation rate for the period 3.5–4.0 aeons is about an order of magnitude greater than in later epochs.

### Local and Foreign Components

Exotic components may be present. About 5 percent of the regolith at any site may be derived from distances greater than 100 km, while 0.5

percent come from distances greater than 1,000 km. Fifty percent comes from distances less than 3 km [22–24]. Thus, most of the regolith is of local origin. In accordance with the predictions, components of the Apollo 11 soil sample were derived from highlands sources, leading to the identification of the highlands as "anorthositic" [25].

The Apollo 11 site was the simplest regolith visited. The Apollo 12 site yielded the KREEP component, already noted, so that two distinctive compositions were present. The Apollo 14 regolith is dominated by Fra Mauro material, interpreted here as Imbrium ejecta but subject to other interpretations [26]. Copernicus is within range and may have contributed ejecta to the locality. The Apollo 15 regolith is also complex, both on account of the proximity of mare and highlands and the presence of rays (and probable associated craters, such as Dune), from Aristillus or Autolycus, crossing the site. At the Apollo 16 site at Descartes, deep within the rugged cratered highlands, a ray from Tycho, 1,300 km to the southwest, crosses the site. There is also the vexing question of the contribution from the Imbrium and Orientale collisions, and the origin of the Cayley plains-forming unit.

The view is adopted here that the material is mainly of local derivation, that the rays are mainly local material, ploughed up by secondary crater-forming ejecta, and that the Imbrium and Orientale ejecta blankets did not cover the surface of the moon with homogeneous blankets of ejecta. The local variations in the chemistry, shown by the orbital XRF and gamma-ray data [10] and their lack of correlation with Cayley plains-forming units, seems sufficient evidence for local derivation of these materials and

**Table 3.1**   Average Composition of Soil Samples (< 1 mm fraction).

|  | Apollo 11 (%) | Apollo 12 (%) | Apollo 14 (%) | Apollo 15 (%) | Luna 16 (%) | Luna 20 (%) | Apollo 16 (%) |
|---|---|---|---|---|---|---|---|
| $SiO_2$ | 42.04 | 46.40 | 47.93 | 46.61 | 41.70 | 45.40 | 44.94 |
| $TiO_2$ | 7.48 | 2.66 | 1.74 | 1.36 | 3.38 | 0.47 | 0.58 |
| $Al_2O_3$ | 13.92 | 13.50 | 17.60 | 17.18 | 15.33 | 23.44 | 26.71 |
| FeO | 15.74 | 15.50 | 10.37 | 11.62 | 16.64 | 7.37 | 5.49 |
| MgO | 7.90 | 9.73 | 9.24 | 10.46 | 8.78 | 9.19 | 5.96 |
| CaO | 12.01 | 10.50 | 11.19 | 11.64 | 12.50 | 13.38 | 15.57 |
| $Na_2O$ | 0.44 | 0.59 | 0.68 | 0.46 | 0.34 | 0.29 | 0.48 |
| $K_2O$ | 0.14 | 0.32 | 0.55 | 0.20 | 0.10 | 0.07 | 0.13 |
| $P_2O_5$ | 0.12 | 0.40 | 0.53 | 0.19 | — | 0.06 | 0.12 |
| MnO | 0.21 | 0.21 | 0.14 | 0.16 | 0.21 | 0.10 | 0.07 |
| $Cr_2O_3$ | 0.30 | 0.40 | 0.25 | 0.25 | 0.28 | 0.14 | 0.12 |
| Total | 100.30 | 100.21 | 100.22 | 100.13 | 99.26 | 99.91 | 100.17 |

the regolith derived from them. Some of these questions belong to the realm of the megaregolith, discussed next, but it is difficult to discuss any lunar question in isolation.

The Apollo 17 regolith yields more complexities [27]. The landslide from the South Massif has spread highlands material across the basaltic mare surface. If caused by secondaries from Tycho, the age of the landslide is of the order of 100 million years. The astronauts' observation indicate an upper surface layer, 5–10 cm thick of medium gray soil, which may be newly developed regolith. At depth there is some evidence of sorting, with larger fragments deeper, consistent with a fluid flow process such as an avalanche [28]. The other unique feature at the Taurus-Littrow site is the dark mantle, due to the preponderance of dark, titanium-rich glass in the soil [28, 29]. This is attributed to fire fountaining during the eruption of the mare basalts [30], although alternate views can be found [29]. What is certain is that the dark mantling material is not a young volcanic deposit but was formed about the same time as the maria basalts, 3.8 aeons ago [31], and that it is derived from local sources.

## 3.4    CHEMISTRY OF THE REGOLITH

A full discussion of this topic must await the description of the maria and highland rock types, but it is convenient at this stage to introduce the subject. The average chemical composition of fine grain size (< 1 mm) regolith at the various sites is given in Table 3.1. There are considerable variations in chemistry, which reflect the nature of the underlying bedrock. Thus the Apollo 11 soils have high Ti and other characteristics of the Apollo 11 maria basalts. In contrast, the Apollo 16 site, deep within the highlands, is dominated by the high Al and Ca, and low Fe and Mg contents of the highland rocks.

The chemical compositions of the soils have been interpreted by many workers in terms of mixing models, which have reached increasing levels of sophistication [32]. Basic to the problem is the identification of the "end-members" involved in the mixing models. This problem will return in the study of the highland compositions, but it is complex in detail at all sites.

During the formation of the regolith, a very wide sampling of the lunar surface occurs. The sampling of rocks is necessarily restricted and, to a degree, accidental. The aluminous maria basalts, for example, are almost certainly underrepresented in the collections [33]. Rock 12013 was picked up during an unscheduled extension of the first EVA on Apollo 12. Thus, it is somewhat surprising that we get such a good match between the regolith and the whole rock compositions at the maria sites. The more pulverized highlands present less of that particular problem, but put the problem back into a megaregolith stage. Average chemical compositions for the lunar regolith in the maria and the highlands are given in Table 3.2. These reflect the bedrock differences to be discussed in later chapters and indicate the truth of the comment that there is no large-scale lateral transfer of surface material between highlands and maria. This observation is in accord with naked-eye or telescope observation.

## 3.5 "AGE" OF THE SOILS

Scientists realized early that the exceedingly complex mixture represented by the soil would contain components of varying ages. This was dramatically emphasized by the apparent paradox that the maria soils had *model* Rb-Sr ages around 4.6 aeons, although they were lying on and principally derived from rocks whose crystallization ages, from mineral isochron studies and $^{40}Ar/^{39}Ar$ data, were 3.6–3.8 aeons [34–36].

This effect is shown in Figs. 3.3 and 3.4, where soil age data are shown

**Table 3.2** Average Chemical Compositions of Lunar Surface Regolith.

|  | Maria (wt %) | Highlands (wt %) |
|---|---|---|
| $SiO_2$ | 45.4 | 45.5 |
| $TiO_2$ | 3.9 | 0.6 |
| $Al_2O_3$ | 14.9 | 24.0 |
| FeO | 14.1 | 5.9 |
| MgO | 9.2 | 7.5 |
| CaO | 11.8 | 15.9 |
| $Na_2O$ | 0.6 | 0.6 |
| $K_2O$ | — | — |
|  | atomic % | |
| O | 60.3 | 61.1 |
| Si | 16.9 | 16.3 |
| Ti | 1.1 | 0.15 |
| Al | 6.5 | 10.1 |
| Fe | 4.4 | 1.8 |
| Mg | 5.1 | 4.0 |
| Ca | 4.7 | 6.1 |
| Na | 0.4 | 0.4 |

From Turkevich, A. L. (1973) *PLC* 4: 1159; *Moon.* 8: 365.

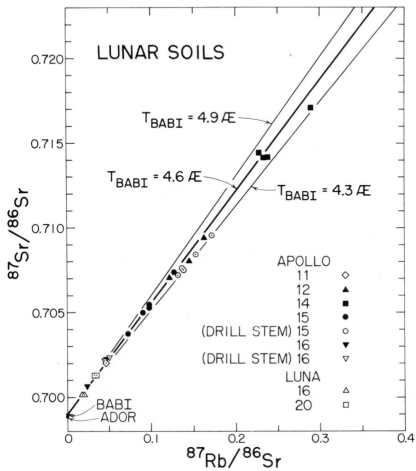

**Fig. 3.3** Rubidium-strontium evolution diagram for lunar soils. The data are without direct age significance since the soils are complex mixtures. The lines T BABI = 4.3 AE, 4.6 AE, and 4.9 AE show the growth of radiogenic strontium as a function of $^{87}$Rb from an initial ratio of 0.69898. This is the Basaltic Achondrite Best Initial ratio or BABI. ADOR is the initial ratio for the meteorite Angros dos Reis and is one of the most primitive ratios known. The initial isotopic ratio $^{87}$Sr/$^{86}$Sr for the moon appears to be close to BABI. Note that using this ratio, the lunar soil data cluster about the 4.6 aeon line (from *EPSL*, 17: 54, Fig. 1)[34]. (Courtesy G. J. Wasserburg.)

on a conventional Rb-Sr age diagram. There is a strong tendency for the soil data to scatter about a line indicating an age of 4.6 aeons, since the material had an initial ratio of 0.69898, equivalent to that observed in basaltic achondrites[37].

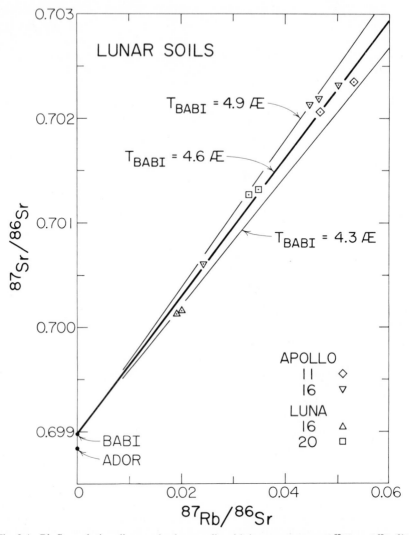

**Fig. 3.4**  Rb-Sr evolution diagram for lunar soils with lower amounts of $^{87}$Rb and $^{87}$Sr/$^{86}$Sr ratios. Note that there is some scatter about the 4.6-aeon line (from *EPSL*, 17: 54, Fig. 2)[34]. (Courtesy G. J. Wasserburg.)

Two explanations were immediately forthcoming[34–36]. Firstly, the rocks themselves had *model* ages of 4.5–4.6 aeons, indicating that most of the Rb-Sr fractionation occurred at that time and not during the partial melting forming the basalt magma. Secondly, it was postulated that the soils contained an exotic or "magic" component, high in radiogenic $^{87}$Sr (and Rb, K, REE, Th, U, etc.) later identified with the Fra Mauro or KREEP components[34]. The soil "model ages" of 4.6 aeons were thus postulated to be a consequence both of the presence of an exotic component and because the rocks themselves also show similar model ages.

The presence of a possible candidate for the "magic" or exotic component in the shape of the Fra Mauro samples has not proved to be the panacea expected. Further difficulties arose when it was found that the soils at the Apollo 14 site showed an increase in apparent age compared to the crystalline rocks[38]. These gave model ages of 4.3 aeons, while the soils clustered around 4.5–4.6 aeons.

Experience from later missions showed that some soils had model ages greater than 4.6 aeons (Fig. 3.5). Since there is much evidence indicating formation of the moon and the rest of the solar system at about 4.6 aeons ago[39], apparent ages older than this indicate that alternative explanations for the data are required. It should be emphasized that there are "no known rock types which can be added to the soils to produce high model ages > 4.6 AE"[38]. This fact militates against explanations that the exotic component is merely a finely divided KREEP component disseminated over the moon[40].

Since the soils have arisen by meteorite impact processes repeated many times, it is perhaps not surprising that the delicate interrelationships between radiogenic $^{87}$Rb and its daughter product $^{87}$Sr might be disturbed occasionally. Thus small losses of volatile Rb relative to Sr during melting and glass formation at elevated temperatures would provide an easy way to produce old apparent ages[38].

There is some evidence for the small-scale loss of elements such as lead[41]. What is perhaps surprising is that these effects have not been fully investigated earlier. However, the processes, such as microcratering, responsible for the reworking of the soil, have only recently become understood.

Further discussion of the age problem will be reserved until the maria and highland rocks have been treated in more detail. It should be noted here that these data provide evidence that a primitive and widespread geochemical fractionation occurred at 4.3–4.6 aeons[36].

## 3.6  GLASSES

The glasses found in abundance in the lunar soils are among the most spectacular of the materials returned from the moon. Their importance

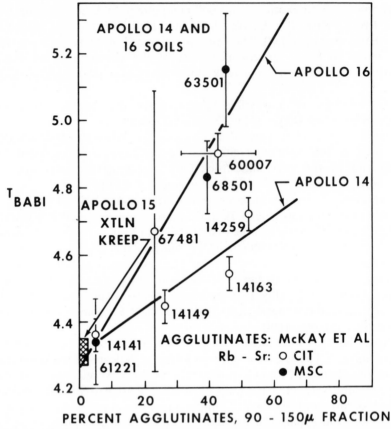

**Fig. 3.5** Model ages for soils as a function of agglutinate content of the soils. As the agglutinate (fused glassy particles) content increases, so does the apparent age of the soils. T BABI is the age (in aeons) based on an initial $^{87}Sr/^{86}Sr$ of 0.69898. The amount of fused glassy particles in the soils is a direct index of the amount of micrometeorite bombardment and hence of soil maturity.

for lunar science can scarcely be overestimated, and references to the glasses occur throughout the sections on the maria and the highlands. The existence of the glasses is mostly due to melting during meteorite impact, but two important exceptions occur. The beautiful emerald green glass from Apollo 15 provides us with the most primitive basaltic composition on the moon. The famous orange glasses from Taurus-Littrow (Apollo 17) contribute to our understanding of the dark mantle and of the mechanism of mare basalt eruption. Both these glasses are discussed in chapter 4 with the maria basalts. The emphasis in this section is on the common and abundant impact-derived glasses.

Because the glasses are small, abundant, and generally homogeneous, they are particularly suited to chemical analysis by electron microprobe techniques. This enables estimates to be made of the frequency of various chemical compositions, which may then be related to the parental rocks. This approach is particularly important for the heavily cratered and brecciated highlands, where terrestrial petrographic techniques have been less readily adapted to lunar studies than was the case with the maria basalts. This application of the glass studies is dealt with in the section on highland chemistry in chapter 5.

The presence of a new class of aluminous maria basalts, represented sparingly in the returned samples (12038, 14053, 14072) has been inferred from the glass studies. This group predates in part the Imbrium collision and may be an important component of the early maria flows.

### Form

Many different forms were found. The spheres are commonly about 100 $\mu$m in diameter but range widely in size. Ellipsoidal shapes are common, as are dumbbells, teardrops, and rods (Figs. 3.6, 3.7). These are the typical rotational shapes assumed by splashed liquids. Some of the spheroidal forms are flattened, indicating that they were plastic when they landed. In addition to the regular forms, there is a great abundance of angular fragments. Many of these are broken pieces of the more regular forms. Others occur as irregular masses coating rocks or as linings in pits clearly produced by impact of small particles. The outer surfaces of the spherules occasionally have small craters.

### Agglutinates

An important constituent in the lunar soils are the so-called "agglutinates"–glass-bonded aggregates, which consist of glassy, rock and mineral fragments welded together by glass (Figs. 3.8, 3.9). These aggregates form during micrometeorite impact into soil[42]. They may in part be the remnants of small glassy craters produced during the impacts, since some are bowl or doughnut shaped. Their abundance in a particular soil is an index of exposure to the micrometeorite bombardment and hence to soil maturity. Soils that have low agglutinate contents contain evidence from fossil tracks of a shorter exposure to cosmic radiation than do soils with a high agglutinate content[43]. The effect of increasing agglutinate content on the Rb-Sr soil ages has already been noted[38].

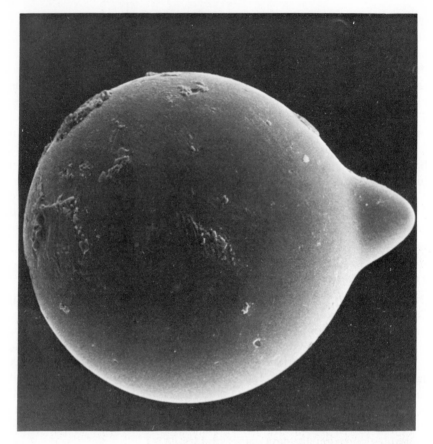

**Fig. 3.6** Scanning electron microscope (SEM) photograph of a green glass droplet with a tail. The surface has been fractured and spalled; splashes of material, identical in composition to the main body, adhere to the surface. Droplets with tails are rare. The diameter of the sphere is 175 $\mu$m. (NASA S72-52774, courtesy D. S. McKay.)

The formation of agglutinates offsets the grinding up of the soil particles by the micrometeorite bombardment. Eventually an equilibrium grain size in the soils of about 60 $\mu$m is reached by these two competing processes[44]. This tendency is illustrated in Fig. 3.11, which shows a gradation (A–D) from typically immature to mature soils. The grain size distribution from single impacts is shown in Fig. 3.11, E–G, while the calculated grain size distribution resulting from repeated impacts is given in Fig. 3.11, H. The comparison between D and H in this figure is instructive. It illustrates that the soils are not ground up finer and finer, but that the sticking together of glass is an important process in the evolution of the soil.

### Fe/Ni Spherules in Glasses

Tiny spherules of iron-nickel are present in many of the glasses. They are normally less than 30 $\mu$m in diameter and are usually present in the less homogeneous glasses. Commonly these spherules contain about 10 percent Ni as well as troilite and schreibersite, which are common minerals

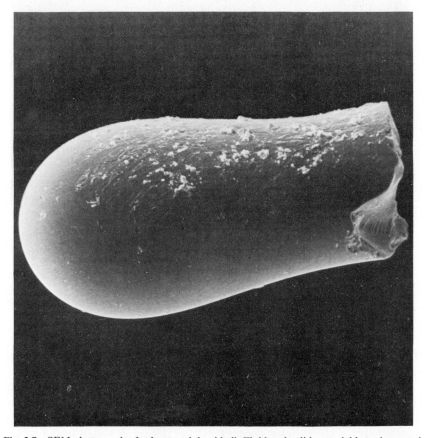

**Fig. 3.7**  SEM photograph of a fractured dumbbell. Fluid and solid material have impacted the original surface. The fluid material indicates a preferential impact orientation. Both projectiles and target have the same composition. (Dimensions 210 × 110 $\mu$m.) (NASA SP S72-52308, courtesy D. S. McKay.)

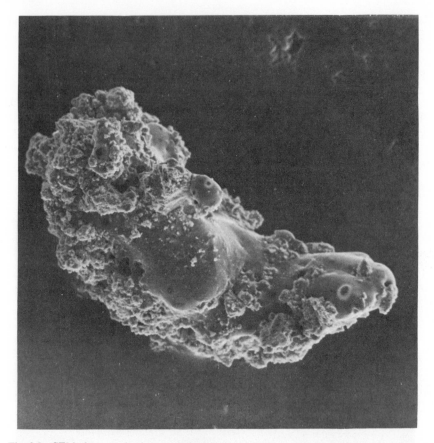

**Fig. 3.8** SEM photograph of an agglutinate, a particle that consists of lithic, mineral, and glassy debris bonded together by an inhomogeneous glass. Agglutinates are formed by hypervelocity micrometeorite impacts into the lunar soil. The longest dimension is 425 μm. (NASA SP-53160, courtesy D. S. McKay.)

of iron meteorites. They also occur on the surfaces of glass spheres (Fig. 3.10).

The glass also contains some nickel-free iron and troilite derived from the lunar rocks, which have formed immiscible droplets in the glass melt. The chief evidence for an external meteoritic origin for the nickel-rich iron spheres is their nickel content. Nickel is very depleted in the rocks. These nickel-iron spheres resemble those found in terrestrial glasses that have been formed at meteorite craters (e.g., at Henbury, Australia) by the fusion of country rock by the impacting iron-nickel meteorite. The presence of these globules indicates that most of the glasses bear a genetic relationship to meteorite impact.

### Color

A wide range in color is shown by the glasses from colorless through pale yellows, greens, brown, and orange to red and black. The colors show a clear relation to refractive index and to composition. Table 3.3 shows the interrelationship of color, refractive index, and density. (See also the sections on the emerald green and orange glasses.) The color of the glasses is clearly reflected in the chemistry. The lighter colored glasses

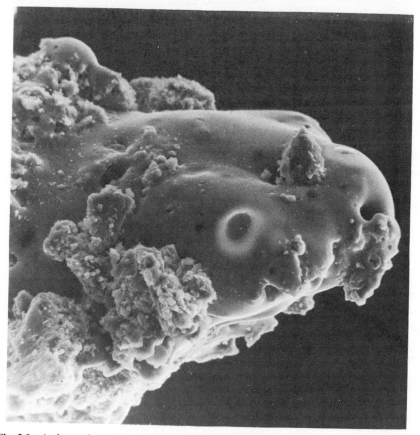

**Fig. 3.9**    A closer view of the agglutinate particle in Fig. 3.8; the vesicular schlieren glass is partially coated by debris. Thin sections reveal a vesicular interior with abundant glassy, lithic, and mineral inclusions. (Length 44 μm.) (NASA S72-53161, courtesy D. S. McKay.)

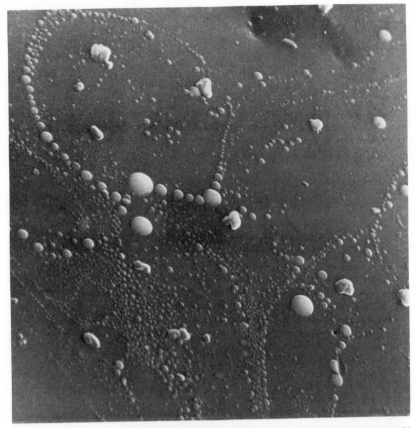

**Fig. 3.10** SEM photograph of a glassy agglutinate surface; the beaded pattern is formed by small iron droplets. Iron sources include both the impacting projectile and the reduction of target material. The photo is of an area 4.5 μm square. (NASA S72-53166, courtesy D. S. McKay.)

are similar in composition to the feldspathic or anorthositic fragments, whereas the more numerous red to yellow glasses resemble the bulk analyses of the rocks and the fine material.

**Chemical Composition**

There are no major differences in composition between the angular fragments and the spheroidal forms. Individual spherules are commonly homogeneous or only slightly heterogeneous.

The range in composition found among the glasses can be due to several causes:

(*a*) Melting of whole rocks and bulk samples of fine material, giving the range in composition found for the rocks.

(*b*) Melting of individual mineral phases by impact of small particles.

**Table 3.3**  Relationship between Color and Other Properties of Lunar Glasses.

| Color | Refractive index | TiO$_2$ % | FeO % | Density |
|---|---|---|---|---|
| Colorless, transparent | 1.50–1.60 | 0–0.1 | 0–1.6 | <2.7 |
| Light yellow, green to light green, transparent | 1.59–1.65 | 0.1–2 | 4–10 | 2.7–2.8 |
| Dark green, transparent | 1.65 | 0–1 | 7–16 | 2.8–2.9 |
| Yellow-brown, transparent | 1.65 | 1–2.5 | 8–14 | 2.7–2.8 |
| Light to dark brown and red-brown, transparent | 1.65–1.75 | 3–8 | 9–16 | 2.8–3.0 |
| Dark brown to opaque | 1.75 | 7–12 | 15–25 | 3.0–3.25 |

From Frondel, C. (1970) *PLC 1:* 450.

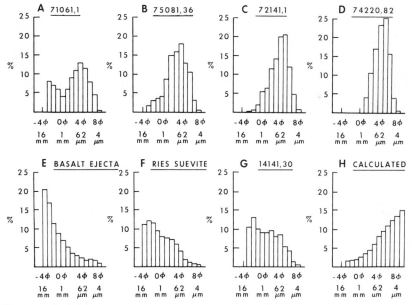

**Fig. 3.11** Grain size histogram. A. Typical immature soil; B. typical submature soil; C. typical mature soil; D. orange glass; E. single impact into basalt; F. suevite, Ries Crater, part of coarse tail not included; G. sample 14141; H. possible distribution from prolonged comminution of E[44].

(c) Selective vaporization or melting. The overall evidence seems to indicate that this process was not effective in altering the composition to any marked degree.

The chemistry of the glasses has provided much insight into the relative abundance of lunar rock types. Some of the large rocks sampled are not well represented in the glass compositions. This raises the thorny and perennial question of adequacy of sampling on the one hand, and on the other hand, the assumption that the glasses represent primary rock types rather than mixtures. Evidence bearing on this question from terrestrial meteorite impact glasses is equivocal. In small impacts (e.g., Henbury) the glasses can be matched to individual strata in the target area[45]. Larger craters (e.g., Manicouagan, 65 km diameter) show evidence of mixing of diverse rock types in the glass compositions[46]. How efficient is this process?

The evidence that the lunar highlands are laterally heterogeneous, from the orbital XRF Al/Si data, on the one hand, and the extreme heterogeneity of the hand specimen breccias on the other, suggests that the mixing and homogenization during the intense meteorite bombardment was not very thorough. This question will return in chapter 5, on the highlands. At this stage, it is concluded that although some mixing and homogenization occurs, it is not very efficient, and the glass compositional clusters represent primary rock types, *provided a large enough population is sampled.*

A typical example of the types of glasses present in lunar soils is given in Table 3.4. The table gives the various components found in the soils at the Apollo 15 site, a complex example because of the proximity of highlands and maria and the presence of the emerald green glass.

### Origin of the Glasses

The regular forms displayed by the glasses are characteristic of those assumed by splashed liquids, and there is general agreement that the glasses are produced by melting, during impact of the surface rock debris, by high velocity meteoritic collisions.

One suggestion[47] was that the glassy crusts observed were created by solar flash melting. This has not received much support from the detailed investigations. Fragments of the glassy crusts are present throughout the breccias, indicating a prolonged period of glass formation. Shock effects are observed under the crusts, and the glasses contain unmelted crystals at the surface of the crusts.

**Table 3.4**   Average Composition of Glass Types in Apollo 15 Fines.

| | Green glass (%) | Mare basalt | | | |
| | | Mare 1 (%) | Mare 2 (%) | Mare 3 (%) | Mare 4 (%) |
|---|---|---|---|---|---|
| $SiO_2$ | 45.43 | 45.70 | 44.55 | 43.95 | 37.64 |
| $TiO_2$ | 0.42 | 1.60 | 3.79 | 2.79 | 12.04 |
| $Al_2O_3$ | 7.72 | 13.29 | 11.77 | 8.96 | 8.46 |
| $Cr_2O_3$ | 0.43 | 0.33 | 0.26 | 0.46 | 0.48 |
| FeO | 19.61 | 15.83 | 18.83 | 21.10 | 19.93 |
| MgO | 17.49 | 11.72 | 8.84 | 12.30 | 10.49 |
| CaO | 8.34 | 10.41 | 10.46 | 9.02 | 8.81 |
| $Na_2O$ | 0.12 | 0.30 | 0.34 | 0.27 | 0.54 |
| $K_2O$ | 0.01 | 0.10 | 0.13 | 0.05 | 0.13 |
| Total | 99.57 | 99.28 | 98.97 | 98.90 | 98.52 |
| No. of analyses | 187 | 67 | 21 | 26 | 6 |
| Percentage of total analyses | 34.2 | 12.2 | 3.8 | 4.8 | 1.1 |

| | Highland basalt (%) | Fra Mauro basalt | | | "Granite" 1 (%) | "Granite" 2 (%) |
| | | Low K (%) | Moderate K (%) | High K (%) | | |
|---|---|---|---|---|---|---|
| $SiO_2$ | 44.35 | 46.56 | 49.58 | 53.35 | 73.13 | 62.54 |
| $TiO_2$ | 0.43 | 1.25 | 1.43 | 2.08 | 0.50 | 1.18 |
| $Al_2O_3$ | 27.96 | 18.83 | 17.60 | 15.57 | 12.37 | 15.73 |
| $Cr_2O_3$ | 0.08 | 0.20 | 0.17 | 0.12 | 0.35 | 0.03 |
| FeO | 5.05 | 9.67 | 9.52 | 10.25 | 3.49 | 6.67 |
| MgO | 6.86 | 11.04 | 8.94 | 5.77 | 0.13 | 2.51 |
| CaO | 15.64 | 11.60 | 10.79 | 9.57 | 1.27 | 6.86 |
| $Na_2O$ | 0.19 | 0.37 | 0.74 | 1.01 | 0.64 | 0.98 |
| $K_2O$ | 0.01 | 0.12 | 0.47 | 1.11 | 5.97 | 3.20 |
| Total | 100.92 | 99.66 | 99.24 | 98.83 | 97.85 | 99.70 |
| No. of analyses | 36 | 82 | 90 | 29 | 2 | 1 |
| Percentage of total analyses | 6.6 | 15.0 | 16.5 | 5.3 | 0.4 | 0.2 |

From Reid, A. M., et al. (1972) *Meteoritics.* 7: 406.

There are some similarities in form between the spherules and chondrules observed in chondritic meteorites, in addition to general textural similarities between the lunar breccias and the chondrites[48]. This may be considered supporting evidence for an origin of chondrules and chondritic textures by impact processes. Close analogies with chondrules have been noted, particularly in the Fra Mauro breccias.

The chondritic meteorites are, of course, different in composition from the lunar breccias, and there is ample evidence from the Apollo studies that the chondritic meteorites are not derived from the moon. These studies, however, as well as rare gas and track studies, indicate that the individual components of the gas-rich meteorites were probably in a regolith-type environment [49].

### Glasses and Lifelike Forms

Some of the glass forms resemble microfossils. "The abundant spheroids and ovoids are similar in shape to some algal and bacterial unicells, and the smaller ones are comparable in size. Indeed, if such particles were coated with carbon, they would make impressive pseudomicrofossils . . . . This is *not* to propose that there are or were solid glass Protozoa on the moon, but to add one more warning about a too-ready interpretation of exotic objects as of vital origin on the basis of gross morphology alone . . . . This warning deserves emphasis. Elsewhere on the lunar or Martian surface may be lifelike artifacts that will be harder to discriminate from the real thing" [50]. With the possibility of a sample return from Mars becoming more likely, this observation deserves wide circulation [51].

### 3.7 TEKTITES

It is appropriate to consider these impact-derived glasses following the discussion on lunar glasses. One of the achievements of the Apollo missions has been to solve the outstanding scientific question of a terrestrial versus lunar origin for tektites [52]. Before the receipt of the lunar samples, it was the scientific consensus that tektites were melted and splashed material formed during large cometary or meteorite impact events. Whether the impact took place on the earth or the moon was the topic of a long-standing scientific debate, which raged with particular intensity during the decade previous to the lunar landings. These impact events have been large-scale for the tektites have been sprayed over immense distances. In the youngest and best-preserved example, the Australian strewn field, tektites occur across the entire southern half of the continent. The numerous occurrences in Southeast Asia are probably related to the same event, and the recent discovery of microtektites in deep-sea cores (curiously within the zone marking the 700,000-year reversal of the earth's magnetic field; Bruhnes-Matuyama reversal), has extended the strewn field to about 4 percent of the earth's surface.

Four definite and separate tektite-strewn fields are known: bediasites (North America, 34 million years); moldavites (Czechoslovakia, 14 million years); Ivory Coast (1.3 million years); and Southeast Asian and Australian fields (0.7 million years). A fifth possible occurrence, of high-Na australites, possibly 3–4 million years old, remains to be substantiated. No observed normal geological processes (e.g., volcanic action) are capable of explaining this distribution, although many theories have been proposed. Neither do these small objects come from deep space, for they record no evidence of any exposure to cosmic radiation outside the earth's atmosphere. These considerations have restricted their origin to the earth or the moon. If they were formed from material excavated beneath the lunar surface by impact, they would lack the evidence of exposure to cosmic radiation, which is apparent in the lunar regolith.

Of immediate interest to the tektite problem was the large amount of glass present in the lunar soil. There is a great abundance of forms (e.g., spheres and dumbbells) (Figs. 3.6, 3.7) produced by splashing of silicate melts. Although generally small (less than 1 mm is typical), these forms resemble the primary tektite forms. The lunar glass, terrestrial volcanic glass, and protected tektite surfaces all show similar features, such as bubble pits, domal gas blisters, abraded and ablated surfaces, and spatter (Fig. 3.9). These features are good evidence for similar formational processes, but the consensus among workers on the lunar glasses is that they do not resemble tektites in refractive index, chemistry or infra-red spectral characteristics.

The chemistry of tektites appears to reflect that of the parent material, and losses during fusion appear to be restricted to elements and compounds more volatile than cesium. Terrestrial impact glasses provide small-scale analogues of tektite-forming events and indicate that only the most volatile components are lost during fusion. The present composition of tektites can then be used to infer that of the parent material.

Tektite chemistry is totally distinct from that observed in lunar maria basalts. These possess Cr contents that are two orders of magnitude higher than tektites, distinctive REE patterns with large Eu depletions, high Fe and low $SiO_2$ contents, low K/U ratios, and many other diagnostic features, none of which are observed in the chemistry of tektites. It would be difficult to produce tektite compositions from them by selective distillation or fusion of mineral components. Fig. 3.12 shows a comparison between lunar and tektite REE patterns and illustrates their decisive differences. The maria basalts are thus unsuitable parent material.

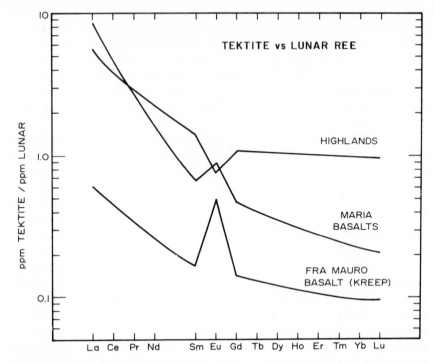

**Fig. 3.12** Rare earth element abundances in tektites ratioed to average lunar highlands and maria rocks. Note the wide discrepancies in composition particularly with respect to the abundance of europium.

Typical highland compositions characterized by high Al and Ca and low K are distinct from those of tektites (Table 3.5). Lunar samples with characteristic KREEP-type chemistry have contents of U and Th similar to tektites. However, they retain the lunar characteristics of high Cr and Eu depletion as well as many other distinctive differences. O'Keefe[53] specifically suggested that sample 12013 contained glass of tektitic composition. Glass is not present[54] and the REE contents are distinct[55] (Fig. 3.12). Likewise, Showalter et al.[56], after an extensive study, conclude that "although the abundances of major elements in tektite J2 (Javanite) are similar to those of rock 12013, comparison of the minor and trace elements shows that no fragment or sawdust of rock 12013 that has been analyzed to date is chemically similar to tektite glass," and they state that "rock 12013 is not related to tektites."

Three lunar occurrences analogous in composition to K-rich terrestrial granites are (*a*) late stage glassy K-rich mesostasis found in lunar basalts;

**Table 3.5**  Comparison of Lunar Highlands Chemistry with that of the Average Australite[52].

|  | Average highlands | Apollo 16 soil 68501 | Luna 20 soil | Surveyor VII Tycho | Average australite |
|---|---|---|---|---|---|
| $SiO_2$ | 44.9 | 44.9 | 42.3 | 46.1 | 73.3 |
| $TiO_2$ | 0.60 | 0.56 | 1.7 | — | 0.70 |
| $Al_2O_3$ | 24.6 | 26.9 | 22.7 | 22.3 | 11.7 |
| FeO | 6.6 | 5.3 | 8.0 | 5.5 | 4.55 |
| MgO | 8.6 | 6.3 | 8.4 | 7.0 | 2.02 |
| CaO | 14.2 | 15.1 | 17.0 | 18.3 | 3.50 |
| $Na_2O$ | 0.45 | 0.36 | 0.32 | 0.7 | 1.25 |
| $K_2O$ | 0.11 | 0.16 | 0.12 | — | 2.26 |
| $Cr_2O_3$ | 0.10 | 0.17 | 0.13 | — | 0.01 |
|  | 100.2 | 99.77 | 100.7 | 99.9 | 99.38 |
| Al/Si | 0.62 | 0.68 | 0.61 | 0.55 | 0.18 |
| Mg/Si | 0.24 | 0.18 | 0.26 | 0.20 | 0.035 |

(b) immiscible globules of granitic composition; and (c) minor amounts of granitic glasses in lunar soil. All these compositions are typified by high potassium values, typically 6–8 percent. The Mg contents are vanishingly low. Evidence for a lunar origin of tektites has been adduced from studies of lunar liquid immiscibility by Roedder and Weiblen[57], who concluded that "any such surface mass (of granitic composition derived from liquid immiscibility) would also remove one of the obstacles to a possible lunar origin for tektites." However, the data do not encourage this speculation. A comparison of K/Mg and K/Na ratios for australites, with the lunar granitic material, is given in Table 3.6. The potash granites have ratios an order of magnitude higher than tektites, while the high silica glasses[57] have ratios 30 to 50 times those of tektites.

One of the distinctive features of the lunar rocks is their great age. The lava floods forming the maria occurred between 3.8 and 3.2 aeons ago. No

**Table 3.6**  Comparison of $K_2O/MgO$ and $K_2O/Na_2O$ Ratios in Average Australites with Lunar Acidic Glasses Containing Greater Than 70 percent $SiO_2$[52].

|  | $K_2O/MgO$ | $K_2O/Na_2O$ |
|---|---|---|
| Australites | 0.90 | 0.55 |
| Lunar high-silica glasses | 31.5 | 30.5 |
| Lunar potash granites | 9.3 | 7.2 |

younger rocks are known at present, although some very minor activity may have occurred. The uplands were formed between 4.6 and 4.0 aeons ago. All these ages are much greater than those apparently observed for tektites. The Ivory Coast tektite data fall on a $2.0 \times 10^9$-year isochron defined by the Bosumtwi crater rocks. The moldavite Rb-Sr data indicate a <50-million-year isochron. The Southeast Asian and Australian tektite Rb-Sr data define isochrons within the range 100–300 million years. There thus appears to be an order of magnitude difference between the lunar ages and those indicated for the parent material of the Southeast Asian tektites.

The old ages for the lunar maria provide yet another difficulty for the lunar tektite hypothesis. The large young ray craters indicate a frequency of large-impact events on the moon at about one per hundred million years, about an order of magnitude less frequent than the tektite events. If Tycho were the source of tektites, it should be 0.7 million years old. The current estimate for the age of Tycho is 100 million years[58].

The most unequivocal and distinctive fingerprint of lunar material is the lead isotopic abundance, which is markedly radiogenic. The isotopic composition of lead in tektites is identical to that in modern terrestrial lead. An exception is the lead in Ivory Coast tektites, which resembles that of the impact glass and Precambrian country rocks at Bosumtwi crater, Ghana.

The $\delta^{18}O$ values for tektites range between +9 and +11.5 per mil. The lunar $\delta^{18}O$ values are low, ranging from +4 for ilmenite to +7 for cristobalite. There is a firm consensus that the oxygen isotope data are unfavorable to the lunar tektite hypothesis. Taylor and Epstein[59] conclude on this basis that "suitable parent materials are rare or non-existent on the lunar surface."

### Origin of Tektites

The cosmic-ray evidence precludes origins from outside the earth-moon system, either from elsewhere in the solar system, or outside. The overall evidence now supports the origin of tektites by cometary (or meteorite) impact on terrestrial sedimentary rocks. The chemical, isotopic, and age evidence (discussed above) from the lunar samples enable us to reject the lunar impact hypothesis. A fitting epitaph has been provided by Schnetzler[60]: "The lunar origin of tektites, a controversial and stimulating theory on the scientific scene for almost 75 years, died on July 20, 1969. The cause of death has been diagnosed as a massive overdose of lunar data."

O'Keefe[61] has revived the theory, originally proposed by Verbeek[62] that tektites come from lunar volcanoes. Several difficulties attend this hypothesis. Most of the objections to the lunar-impact theory, based on chemical, age, and isotope data still apply. Our sampling of lunar volcanic rocks in the maria does not encourage the view that lavas of tektite composition might be erupted. Such eruptions would need to be among the recent ($<$ 50 million years ago) lunar events, to account for the tektite ages. If they are powerful enough to accelerate tektite glass beyond the escape velocity (2.4 km/sec) of the lunar gravitational field, then tektite glass or other material of tektite composition should occur as well on the lunar surface in the upper portions of the regolith. Although many diverse compositions occur among the returned lunar samples, tektite compositions are not among them. We may safely conclude that tektites do not come from the moon.

## 3.8   THE MEGA-REGOLITH

The present 10-m-thick regolith in the highlands overlies a zone of brecciation and fracturing due to the intense early bombardment of the highland crust. All surfaces older than about 3.9 aeons are saturated with craters 50–100 km in diameter. Most estimates for the thickness of rubble produced during these events fall within the range of 1–3 km[63]. Some of the older maria surfaces have also been affected, and many of the early, now buried lava flows are probably much broken up by the declining stages of the bombardment. Such fracturing would account for much of the scattering of seismic signals observed in the upper 25 km but concentrated in the upper 2 km.

The calculations depend also on the thickness of ejecta from the large ringed basins. The difficulties in extrapolating to these giant events have been noted earlier and will be apparent throughout the book. The various estimates of ejecta thickness, which differ by a factor of five or greater[64] depend on arguments over basin dimensions as well as ejecta ballistics. Table 3.7 shows one set of estimates, but other interpretations are possible. Discussion of these grades into the wider questions of lunar stratigraphy. Such widespread ejecta blankets would arguably give a more uniform surface chemistry than we now observe.

This ancient mega-regolith might reasonably be expected to contain some of the oldest accessible fragments of highland crust. The "light matrix" breccias, excavated by North Ray Crater at the Descartes site might represent such material. Indeed, there is support for this view from geochronology. Very old $^{40}$Ar-$^{39}$Ar ages (4.25 aeons) are reported for the "light matrix" breccias[65]. The possibility remains that extensive brecciation of the highland crust owing to the ringed basin-forming collisions extends to depths of 20–25 km (section 6.4).

**Table 3.7**  Estimated Total Accumulation of Ejecta from the Large Lunar Frontside Ringed Basins at the Apollo Landing Sites[64].

|  | Total accumulation (m) |
|---|---|
| Apollo 11 | 560* |
| 12 | 278* |
| 14 | 280 |
| 15 | 1760 |
| 16 | 349 |
| 17 | 1939 |
| Tycho (Surveyor VII) | 115 |

*Buried by mare basalt flows.

### 3.9  CRATERS AND CRATERING RATES

Objects of all sizes from the large asteroids down to dust grains have impacted the lunar surface, and information about meteorite flux, planetary accretion, and cosmic dust can be gained from the impact evidence. Following suitable calibration, a relative chronology can be established, which is useful in extending the time-scale established by radioactive dating techniques. The first order observation, made by Baldwin, Urey, Hartmann, and others[66], that the highlands contained evidence of an early intense bombardment unrecognized on the earth, and hence older than the existing geological record, has been substantiated.

It is convenient to divide the discussion into three sections, one dealing with the major (1–100 km diameter) craters, a second discussing craters in the kilometer to centimeter range, and a final section on the microcraters observed in the returned lunar samples. The emphasis is on these latter—the first two categories have been dealt with by many workers before the Apollo missions. The large ringed basins have been dealt with earlier (section 2.7). There are 125 structures on the moon with diameters greater than 100 km.

**Major Craters (1–100 km diameter)**

These have been discussed in the chapter on lunar geology. Their relevance here is that they are nearly all primary craters, so that they should provide the best opportunity for constructing a relative crater chronology. This advantage is offset by their low density on younger maria surfaces, making the statistics less certain. They have been much studied. It is ironic that the earlier estimates gave ages around 3–4 billion years for the ages of the maria[66]. As the Apollo sample return became closer, the ages based on crater counts fell. Ages for the maria surfaces derived from this technique were very young, in the range of tens to hundreds of millions of years[67]. These estimates were 1–2 orders of magnitude too low. Such a wide spread in ages illustrates the inherent problems in the technique, principally due to the many uncertainties in the meteoritic flux rate, which restrict the usefulness of the method.

If the youngest maria surface (Ocean of Storms, 3.2 aeons), is given an arbitrary crater density of 1.0, then one of the oldest maria surfaces (Mare Tranquillitatis, 3.7 aeons) has 2.3 times as many of these large craters and has a thicker regolith. On the same scale, the southern highlands have a crater density of 32 and are effectively saturated. Thus the cratering rate steepens appreciably after about 3.5 aeons, and becomes very high after 3.8–3.9 aeons, as illustrated in Fig. 3.13. The general correlation between crater densities and radioactive age dates is clear from the data in Table 3.8 from the most recent summary by Hartmann[58]. The crater densities at the various sites cannot be fitted to a straightforward exponential decay curve of meteorites or asteroid populations: rather at least two separate groups of objects seem to be required.

The first is approximated by the present-day flux. The second is responsible for the intense early bombardment and decays rapidly in the period 3.8–3.5 aeons. The earlier (pre-4.0 aeons) bombardment history is still not clear. Some interpretations of the age data point toward a peak or cataclysm at about 4 aeons[68], with most of the visible ringed basins being produced in the interval 4.1–3.9 aeons. The older structures, which might have provided the information were obliterated by the saturation bombardment during this period, but the dimly seen record appears to continue backwards. Relics of former ages, preserved as the cores of plagioclase crystals in the highlands, tell of events back almost to 4.6 aeons. The evidence for a "spike" at 4.0 aeons may be more apparent than real.

The depth-diameter ratios of the larger craters, long used as prima facie evidence of their explosive impact origin, have been used in other contexts.

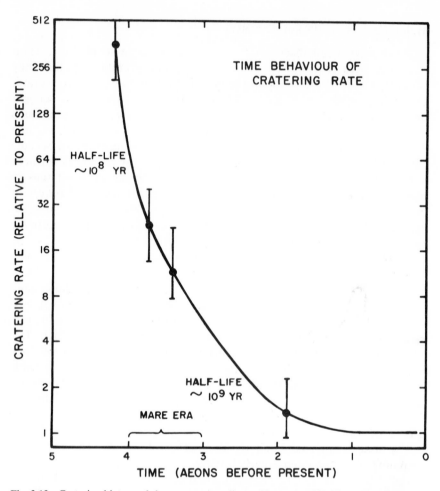

**Fig. 3.13** Cratering history of the moon, according to Hartmann[58]. The orbital half-lives of the proposed impacting bodies responsible for the cratering are indicated.

The oldest large craters are shallower, attributed by Baldwin[69] to isostatic readjustment, since mass wasting, erosion, collapse, or other features appeared to be inadequate explanations. The highlands do appear to be generally in isostatic equilibrium. Only a small gravity anomaly is observed, for example, across the great Apennine Mountain ridge[70]. Nevertheless, it is difficult to argue from the present crater morphology. The amount of filling of older craters by the plains-forming deposits (Cayley formation and equivalents) is considerable and widespread.

Most workers conclude that the oldest craters observed are not much older than 4.0 aeons[71] and that the earlier record has been erased. Whether a lunar cataclysm occurred at 3.9 aeons[68], whether we see a peak in ringed basin production or the terminal stages of accretion, it does not seem possible to extrapolate backward from the surface morphology much beyond 4.0–4.2 aeons. The combination of crater saturation and local redistribution of material, filling older structures, precludes this.

### The Smaller Craters (<1 km)

The smaller craters are composed of a mixture of primary and secondary craters formed by the impact of ejecta from the larger primary impacts. The crater field around Copernicus is a good example (Fig. 2.8) of this latter process. Such craters greatly complicate the establishment of relative age sequences, and most efforts to date surfaces using the smaller craters have been even less successful than those using the larger craters. They have been the object of much study since the early Ranger photographs revealed that the lunar surface was cratered at all scales[3].

Many of the smaller craters do not excavate bedrock but form entirely

**Table 3.8**  Crater Densities, Regolith Thickness, and Age Determinations.

| Region | Crater density | Regolith thickness (m) | Age (aeons) |
|---|---|---|---|
| Tycho | 0.06 | — | 0.1 |
| Copernicus | 0.3 | — | 0.9 |
| Oceanus Procellarum (Apollo 12) | 0.7 | 3 | 3.2–3.4 |
| Palus Putredinis (Apollo 15) | 0.75 | 5 | 3.3 |
| Mare Fecunditatis (Luna 16) | 0.6 | — | 3.45 |
| Mare Tranquillitatis (Apollo 11) | 1.6 | 5 | 3.7 |
| Taurus-Littrow (Apollo 17) | — | — | 3.8 |
| Fra Mauro (Apollo 14) | 4.0 | 8 | 3.9–4.0 |
| Apennine Front (Apollo 15) | 2.9 | — | 4.0 |
| Highlands | 32 | 10–15 | >4.0 |

Adapted from Hartmann, W. K. (1972) *Astrophys. Space Sci.* 17: 48.

within the regolith and contribute greatly to overturning and mixing. The craters in this size range are important for regolith production, and they make the major contribution toward reworking of the regolith. They are also responsible for the production of soil breccias. These received much prominence since half of the Apollo 11 rocks were in this category. In contrast, only two of the 45 rock samples returned by the Apollo 12 mission were soil breccias. This difference was related to the less mature and thinner regolith at the Apollo 12 site and to increasing sophistication in sampling. These breccias are essentially lunar soils, lithified by shock, with perhaps some examples of sintered material from base surge deposits. Glass coatings are common, and all degrees of induration are found. The soil breccias, although prominent in the mare sample return, are dwarfed in importance by the highland breccias (section 5.2).

### 3.10   MICROCRATERS AND MICROMETEORITES

Microcraters, occurring on rock and mineral surfaces as well as on glass spheres, are one of the most spectacular lunar features (Figs. 3.14, 3.15). These craters, ranging in size from less than 1 $\mu$m to more than 1 cm, are ubiquitous. Originally called "zap pits," they are caused by hypervelocity impacts of micrometeorites, which have struck every square centimeter of the lunar surface.

Information on the nature of the projectiles provides data on micrometeorite flux and on the nature and composition of "interplanetary" or "cosmic dust." The microcraters larger than about 3 $\mu$m typically consist of a glass-lined pit, a "halo" zone of fractured material surrounding and underlying the pit, and a "spall" zone concentric to the pit (Fig. 3.14). Spallation in this zone will sometimes leave the glass-lined pit standing on a pedestal of "halo" material. The hypervelocity nature of the impacts indicates that "primary" cosmic dust particles[72] are involved rather than "secondary" particles resulting from lunar impacts[73].

What conclusions can be drawn from the crater morphology? The first, and perhaps the most surprising, is that the objects were mostly spherical dispelling ideas that "cosmic dust" might be mainly irregular in shape. The densities lie within the range 1–7 g/cm$^3$, peaking in the range 2–4 g/cm$^3$. There is thus a lack of iron particles, and the composition is consistent with that of Type I carbonaceous chondrites[74].

The abundance of "frothy" rims is consistent with impacts of hydrated phyllosilicates, common constituents of carbonaceous chondrites. The higher density objects (5 g/cm$^3$) are probably magnetite grains. The most frequent mass range for the particles is from $10^{-7}$ to $10^{-4}$ g. Those in the

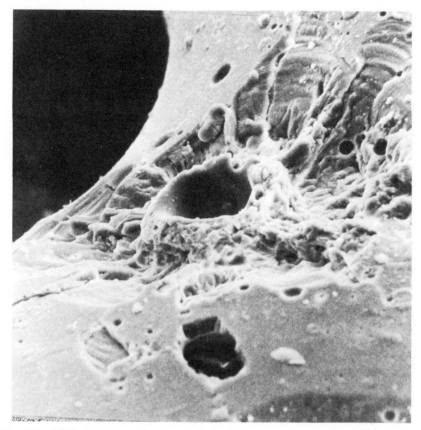

**Fig. 3.14**  SEM photograph of a hypervelocity impact crater. The glassy central pit is surrounded by a spall zone and is in sharp contrast to the smooth circular vesicles. The central pit is 30 $\mu$m in diameter. (NASA-S72-46943, courtesy D. S. McKay.)

size range $10^{-6}$ to $10^{-2}$ g contribute most energy and are responsible for most of the damage to the rock surfaces. The production rate is about 5 craters per cm per million years (with diameters $> 0.05$ cm). Thus, surfaces are effectively saturated at about 1 million years, and this limits the microcrater technique for exposure-age estimation. The impact velocities are nearly all $> 5$ km/sec and average 20 km/sec. The impacts cause erosion, ionization, vaporization, and lateral small-scale transport but little vertical mixing. The erosion rate is of the order of 1 mm per million years [75].

The masses of the micrometeorites are obtained from the crater diameters through empirically established correlations from laboratory

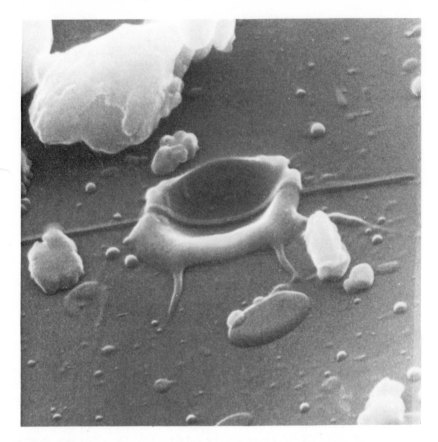

**Fig. 3.15**    Micrometeorite crater on the glassy surface of an Apollo 15 lunar rock. The crater is 1.7 $\mu$m in diameter. The line through the crater is a contamination line purposely applied to enable depth measurements to be made. Craters smaller than about 3 $\mu$m have a different morphology than the larger micrometeorite craters. (NASA S-73-18445, courtesy D. S. McKay.)

data. Craters from 1 mm to 100 $\mu$m in diameter correspond to a mass ranging from $10^{-3}$ to $10^{-6}$ g. Those craters with diameters from 100 to 0.1 $\mu$m are caused by particles in the mass range $10^{-6}$ to $10^{-15}$ g. It has been thought previously that radiation pressure would have swept less massive particles out of the inner solar system, but there is a finite flux below $10^{-14}$ g. The lunar surface is indeed an excellent detector over many orders of magnitude and is probably unexcelled in this respect.

A cometary source for the cosmic particles seems most likely. The mean density of 2–4 g/cm³ is consistent with silicates, not iron particles. The only independent check on the chemistry is the geochemical observation[76] that the trace element chalcophile and siderophile abundances are consistent with Type I carbonaceous chondrites rather than with ordinary chondrites or iron meteorites. Most significant is the shape. The particles are spherical: "Needles, platelets, rods, whiskers and other highly asymmetric particle shapes can be excluded"[74]. This observation has implications for theories of cosmic dust origin and early planetary condensation and accretion.

The microcratering effects extend down from those caused by micrometeorites to sputtering by solar wind ions (Fig. 3.16). Table 3.9 indicates the density of microcraters spanning this range. The erosion rate due to the sputtering is about $10^{-8}$ cm (1 A) per year in the near surface ($< 0.1$ cm) regions, or about 0.1 mm per million years. This is about 1/10 of the mass erosion rate caused by the micrometeorite erosion[77].

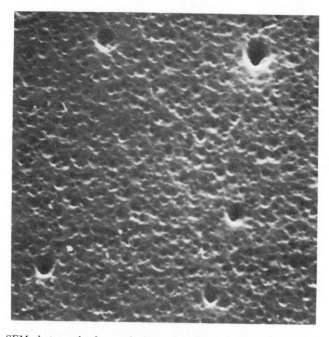

**Fig. 3.16**  SEM photograph of an etched green glass sphere from breccia 15086. The high density of small pits is due to solar flare iron nuclei. The large pits are attributed to nuclei of $Z > 26$. The width of field in this photograph is $\sim 26\ \mu$m. (Macdougall, D., et al. (1973) *PLC 4*, 2328, Fig. 5.)

**Table 3.9**   Crater Densities Due to Micrometeorites and Solar Wind Sputtering.

|  | Crater diameter | Crater density per cm$^2$ |
|---|---|---|
| Micrometeorites | } ≥ 0.3 mm | 20 |
|  | } ≥ 0.1 mm | 70 |
| Solar wind | } ≥ 1 $\mu$m | 1000–3000 |
| sputtering | } ≥ 0.25 $\mu$m | 10,000 |

## 3.11   METEORITE FLUX

Direct measurements of this important quantity have come from the seismic detectors deployed on the lunar surface[78]. Between 70 and 150 meteorite impacts per year are recorded, with masses in the range from 100 g to 1,000 kg. The present-day flux rate is given by

$$\log N = -1.62 - 1.16 \log m,$$

where $N$ is the number of bodies that impact the lunar surface per square kilometer per year, with masses greater than $m$ grams. The normal flux does not change during the year, but a set of larger than usual meteorites hit the moon during April, May, and June.

This flux is about one order of magnitude less than the average integrated flux over the past three aeons, calculated on the basis of crater counts on young lunar maria surfaces. It is also much lower than previous estimates of the present-day flux rate[79]. It is thus more difficult to extrapolate to rates in the past than previously believed. Although the overall meteoritic flux may be decreasing with time, this is by no means certain. It is more probable that there are large and random variations in the flux rate, a view that gives little help to age measurements based on crater counting. It accords with the evidence from the cosmic ray exposure ages of meteorites, which occur in clusters[80].

The question of the chemical identification of this material in the regolith is considered in the chapters on the maria and the highlands. The content of meteoritic material in mature lunar soils is about 1.5 percent, with a composition close to that of Type I carbonaceous chondrites[76]. Suggestions that the present rate, as measured by satellites, is higher than that for the past several million years are not supported by fossil track data[81].

## 3.12   SOLAR AND GALACTIC COSMIC RAYS

The moon's surface is much superior to meteorites as a recorder of exposure to cosmic radiation. It has been in its present orbit for a long time, whereas the orbits of meteorites are uncertain, extending probably inside the orbit of Venus and out to the asteroidal belt. The orbits of two chondritic meteorites, Pribram and Lost City, have been determined, since they were photographically recorded during entry. Both indicate an elliptical orbit extending to the asteroidal belt. These data help to dispose of the myth that meteorites come from beyond the solar system, an old suggestion rendered unlikely by a mass of chemical and isotopic evidence.

Meteorites suffer from much surface ablation loss during atmospheric entry so that the record of low-energy cosmic radiation, preserved near the original surface, is largely lost. The lunar rocks are thus free of most of the difficulties associated with the interpretation of cosmic ray effects in meteorites.

Three sources of radiation (Table 3.10) interact with the lunar surface: (a) the high-energy, so-called "galactic" cosmic rays, which come from outside the solar system; they typically have energies in the range 1–10 billion electron volts (Bev)/nucleon; (b) the lower energy radiation from the sun, mainly associated with solar flare effects, producing particles with energies in the 1–100 million electron volts (Mev)/nucleon range; and (c) the solar wind, with energies of about 1,000 electron volts (ev)/nucleon.

The particle exposure record in the soils enables estimates to be made of mixing rates of the regolith although caution must be used in sampling. Deductions based on single-grain analyses are suspect on account of the complex history of such particles in the regolith. For core samples, deposition and erosion rates may be calculated. Rock samples exposed to cosmic radiation provide data on erosion rates. Rocks identified with a

**Table 3.10**   Lunar Surface Radiation Environment.

|  | Mev/nucleon | Proton flux $(P/cm^2/sec)$ | Proton penetration depth (cm) |
|---|---|---|---|
| Solar wind | $10^{-3}$ | $10^8$ | $10^{-6}$ (100 A) |
| Solar flares | 1–100 | $10^2$ | $1-10^{-3}$ |
| Galactic cosmic rays | $10^2-10^4$ | 1 | $1-10^3$ |

particular crater may yield information on the crater age, stratigraphy, and cratering rates.

Two main classes of phenomena result from the interaction of cosmic rays with the lunar surface. These are (a) solid-state damage as a result of penetration of ionizing particles, producing etchable tracks, and (b) production, through nuclear interactions, of new isotopic species, both radioactive and stable, in the lunar rocks. These two effects have been pursued by different investigators, using etching and microscopic techniques to study the tracks produced, and mass spectrometric and radiochemical procedures to investigate the cosmogenic isotopes.

## 3.13  FOSSIL TRACK STUDIES

The Apollo samples have stimulated much work in this field, and many improvements have occurred both in the techniques of fossil track measurements and their interpretation [82]. The lunar surface samples are particularly good recorders of the lower-energy cosmic ray nuclei. Most tracks are caused by ionizing particles of the iron group of nuclei (Z 18–28, the so-called very heavy, or VH, ions). Solar wind protons and helium nuclei do not produce tracks. Track lengths differ in differing minerals, in the order feldspar > pyroxene > olivine.

A distinctive feature of the tracks is needed to identify the nature of the particles. Workers have used either the total etchable track length or the track etch rate. The track length is in principle simply related to atomic number, but it has proved difficult to apply in practice [83]. Measurement of the track etch rate has been more useful and indicates that there appears to be no sharp threshold ionization value. Tracks from light ions (Z < 18) etch more slowly than those from heavier ions, and they are more readily erased by thermal annealing. Tracks in clinopyroxenes are more resistant to annealing. A useful development has been the use of very mild etching techniques to reveal tracks in olivines [83].

The study of tracks in lunar grains is complicated by the continuous removal of surfaces by microerosion, on the order of 1 A unit per year and by the removal of rock surfaces at the rate of about 1 mm per million years by micrometeorite impacts.

Thus only the "survivors" that escape the sputtering and erosion processes yield meaningful data about exposure ages. The intensity of the irradiation is shown by these few uneroded surfaces. Thus, a millimeter-sized crystal at the bottom of a vug from an Apollo 15 rock [84], estimated to have been uncovered and exposed about $2 \times 10^4$ years ago, has a track density of $5 \times 10^{10}$ tracks/cm$^2$ on its surface, and some soil grains that have escaped sputtering have surface track densities of $10^{11}/cm^2$. Unshielded rock and grain surfaces have track densities typically about $10^8$ tracks/cm$^2$. Because of experimental difficulties, the error in track counts from different investigators is on the order of $\pm 20$ percent[82].

The low-energy heavy nuclei from solar flares are stopped in the outer 1 mm of the crystals. Most of the fossil tracks in lunar samples are due to the iron-group ions from solar flare and galactic cosmic rays[85], and the cosmic ray record is dominated by the low-energy solar flare ions in the upper 1 mm. Solar flare tracks are identified by their strong depth dependence or by the high track densities ($\geq 10^8$ tracks/cm$^2$). In contrast, tracks due to galactic cosmic rays may extend to depths of 20 cm.

The cosmic-ray-produced tracks must be distinguished from fission tracks due to $^{238}U$ and to $^{244}Pu$. High uranium concentrations can contribute $> 10^8$ fission tracks/cm$^2$ at grain boundaries or in inclusions. However, their nonuniform distribution, differing etch pit characteristics, and the low fission track density in common minerals (where uranium is low in abundance or absent) enable them to be distinguished from the cosmic ray tracks[85].

Tracks due to the spontaneous fission of $^{238}U$ are commonly observed, but those from $^{244}Pu$ ($t_{\frac{1}{2}} = 82$ million years) are difficult to find in lunar rocks. Most of the maria basalts are too young to contain measurable amounts of decay products. A slightly more favorable environment exists in uranium-rich mineral phases in the older lunar rocks. Evidence has been presented[86] that tracks due to $^{244}Pu$ fission occur in a whitlockite crystal from the Fra Mauro breccias (14321). This sample was heavily shielded from cosmic rays until about 25 million years ago. The evidence for the existence of $^{244}Pu$ comes from xenon isotope abundance anomalies[82].

The previous existence of superheavy elements has been much debated[87]. The principal evidence advanced was the presence of long fission tracks. These $> 20 \mu m$ tracks, which were identified as due to extinct superheavy elements, are probably "fresh" tracks due to cosmic ray nuclei[88]. There is no definitive evidence for the existence of the superheavy elements around $Z = 114$[88].

## Composition of Cosmic Rays From Track Data

There is a consensus that the intensity of the solar wind has been constant for at least an aeon ($10^9$ years). There is also no good evidence for any order of magnitude change in composition in the ratio of very heavy (VH, Z 18–28) to very very heavy (VVH, Z > 28) ions for the past 4–5 aeons, and there seems to be no variation in the VH/VVH ratio with energy in the range 30–2000 Mev/nucleon[82, 89, 90].

Some track evidence has been used as evidence for an early active sun[91]. Some feldspar grains of highland derivation from Luna 16 soil were observed to have a fivefold increase in track densities compared with the maria-derived feldspars. This increase, however, may be due to local variation in exposure of grains at the lunar surface or even to etching techniques. Other samples (e.g., from Apollo 12) fail to show this effect[92]. There is accordingly no need to invoke an early ( $>4.0$ aeons) enhancement of solar radiation.

One surprising result is that the composition of the solar flares is not always the same as that of the photosphere. This first became apparent from the study of the tracks developed in the Surveyor III TV camera glass filter, returned by the Apollo 12 mission[93] after 31 months on the moon. The Fe/H ratio was an order of magnitude higher than the solar value. Thus, very low energy cosmic rays are enriched in iron group nuclei relative to the solar abundances, presumably due to preferential heavy ion acceleration during solar flares. This unanticipated result disappears at higher energies.

It should be recalled that the absence of a strong lunar magnetic field allows the solar wind to impinge directly on the surface. If a dipole magnetic field had existed at earlier times, shielding of samples might have occurred. Further, atmospheric pressures must have been less than $10^{-9}$ atmospheres (atm) for solar wind effects to be observed. These considerations lend special importance to the study of solar wind effects in old breccias, although the difficulties are considerable.

### Exposure Ages and Regolith History From Track Data

Much insight into exposure ages and regolith history has been obtained from the track studies. An advantage of the fossil track techniques is that the attenuation length of the tracks is very depth sensitive. Track production at shallow depths ($<0.5$ cm) is dominated by solar flares, while at greater depths, galactic cosmic ray tracks predominate[90]. The "sun tan" exposure time is defined as the period during which a rock was at the surface of the moon (usually less than 3 million years), while the "sub decimeter" exposure time is the period during which a rock was within 10 cm of the surface (typically 1–100 million years)[90]. This latter time can be measured, since galactic track production is appreciable up to a 10-cm depth in lunar rocks.

High track densities, indicating surface exposure at some stage, are found throughout the core samples. Although the early interpretations were of a high rate of regolith turnover, it quickly became clear that the regolith was stratified, and models involving deposition of thin layers, stirring of the surface, and burial by subsequent layers were adopted[94]. Thus "throwout" models became preferred to "gardening" models. This became clear from the study of the Apollo 15 deep core, which contained 42 strata. High track densities were distributed throughout the 242-cm core length and were independent of depth.

Many micrometer-sized particles with very high track densities have an amorphous surface layer from the solar bombardment. Each layer in the core contains grains throughout it that were once at the "very surface," indicating good mixing of each layer before burial. This mixing is accomplished by the micrometeorite bombardment[95]. Thus stirring takes place to a depth of a few centimeters. Deeper stirring is rare. Instead, overturning of layers by cratering occurs. Surface layers seem to survive for periods of from 1 to 50 million years before burial, as indicated by cratering studies[19].

Surface rock exposure ages have been measured. Most (80 percent) have a complex exposure history[95]. Erosion by the micrometeorite bombardment and solar wind sputtering exposes fresh surfaces at rates of about 1 mm/million years.

In addition to the surface effects observed now, information about the exposure of old highland breccia fragments may be obtained, but this is offset by annealing due to heating during breccia formation. Because of this, the use of mare basalt rocks or individual grains in the regolith is preferred in cosmic ray studies. The tracks in the Apollo 14, 15, 16, and 17 breccias are largely inherited from the original parent materials of the breccias, which thus must have had exposure at the very top surface[96]. Grains with track densities of $\geq 10^8/cm^2$ occur as grains within the breccia matrix.

The track densities correlate with metamorphic grade. Low track counts due to thermal annealing have occurred. Examples of high track densities occur in 14301 and 15086, and low track densities in 14315, 14318, and 14321[96]. Tracks are absent in the well-recrystallized breccias (e.g., 15418, 61016, 66055, 67015)[97]. Tracks vanish first from the glasses during annealing, then generally from olivine, pyroxenes, and feldspar in that order with increasing temperature, with the least affected breccias being heated below 300°C.

There are a number of similarities between the lunar breccias and the gas-rich meteorites (e.g., Kapoeta, Fayetteville), which also contain grains exposed before incorporation in the meteorite with track densities $\geq 10^{10}$ tracks/$cm^2$. Preserved solar flare tracks are seen even in the most recrystallized chondrites (e.g., LL6 grade)[97, 98], suggesting that even the most metamorphosed chondritic meteorites correspond only to Group 2 or 3 of the lunar breccias[99]. However, some of those tracks may be postmetamorphism. The data seem consistent with the formation of the gas-rich meteorites in a regolith-type environment, possibly on asteroid surfaces[97]. In this context, recent observations on the asteroid, Toro, suggest that it has a lunar-type regolith[100].

### 3.14   COSMOGENIC RADIONUCLIDES

A wide variety of radioactive nuclides are produced by the cosmic ray interaction (Table 3.11). These range from $^{52}$Mn with a half-life of 5.6 days to $^{53}$Mn with a half-life of 3.7 million years. The production of the various species is a function of cosmic ray and solar flare activity as well as the chemistry of the target material[101]. On the surface, the solar flare

**Table 3.11**   Important "Spallogenic" Radioisotopes in Lunar Samples.

| Radioisotope | Half-life | Princial target element | Effective energy* |
|---|---|---|---|
| $^3$H | 12.5 yr | O, Si, Fe, Mg, Al, Ca | High |
| $^{10}$Be | $1.6 \times 10^6$ yr | O, Si, Mg, Fe | High |
| $^{14}$C | $5.7 \times 10^3$ yr | O, Si, Mg, Fe | Low |
| $^{22}$Na | 2.6 yr | Na, Mg, Al, Si, Fe, Ca | Low |
| $^{26}$Al | $7.4 \times 10^5$ yr | Al, Si, Mg, Ca, Ti, Fe | Low |
| $^{36}$Cl | $3 \times 10^5$ yr | Cl, S, Fe, Ca | High |
| $^{37}$Ar | 35 days | Ca, K, Ti, Fe | Low |
| $^{39}$Ar | 269 yr | K, Ca | Low |
| $^{48}$V | 16 days | Ti, Fe | Low |
| $^{49}$V | 550 days | Ti, Fe | Low |
| $^{52}$Mn | 5.6 days | Fe | Low |
| $^{53}$Mn | $3.7 \times 10^6$ yr | Fe, Cr | Low |
| $^{54}$Mn | 312 days | Fe | Low |
| $^{55}$Fe | 2.5 yr | Fe | Low |
| $^{56}$Co | 77 days | Fe, Ni, Co | Low |
| $^{57}$Co | 270 days | Ni, Fe, Co | Low |
| $^{58}$Co | 71 days | Fe, Ni, Co | Low |
| $^{59}$Ni | $8 \times 10^4$ yr | Co, Ni, Fe | Low |
| $^{60}$Co | 5.3 yr | Ni, Co | Low |
| $^{81}$Kr | $2 \times 10^5$ yr | Sr, Y, Zr | High |

Adapted from Lal, D. (1972) *Space Sci. Rev.* 14: 25. These nuclides are produced by proton and neutron reactions mainly. $^{26}$Al, $^{58}$Co, $^{50}$Co, and $^{59}$Ni may also be produced from $\alpha$ particle reactions.

*Low < 40 Mev; high > 40 Mev.

protons account for most of the production. Below about 1 cm, secondary particles from the galactic cosmic rays dominate. The longer-lived nuclides provide information about the past activity of the sun, while the shorter-lived species yield data on the recent solar flares.

The Apollo missions were well timed in this respect. Large solar flares occurred in November, 1968, and April, 1969, before the Apollo 11 mission in July, 1969. Large flares were absent before the Apollo 15 mission. A small solar flare, which enhanced the particle flux by a factor of $10^3$, occurred during the Apollo 16 mission. In August, 1972, before the December, 1972, Apollo 17 mission, the most intense solar flares observed during the past 15 years occurred.

There is a very strong depth dependence, mainly because of the large surficial production from the solar flare protons[102]. The $^{39}$Ar activity is consistent with steady solar flare activity for the past 1,000 years. The ancient cosmic ray flux seems to have been about the same as the present flux and compositionally similar[103].

There were no observable differences at the Apollo 16 site between samples collected from the Cayley and the Descartes formations[104], although it is possible that the latter was not sampled. This result is consistent with the absence of chemical variation observed at the site.

Work on some of the larger rocks[105] show that the contribution from galactic cosmic rays can be separated at depth from the solar cosmic radiation[106].

Production of $^{236}$U $(t_{\frac{1}{2}} = 2.34 \times 10^7$ years) and $^{237}$Np $(t_{\frac{1}{2}} = 2.14 \times 10^6$ years) by solar proton reactions with $^{238}$U have recently been reported[107]. The differences in the half-lives of $^{236}$U and $^{237}$Np provides a monitor of solar cosmic ray activity by comparison of the ratios. Although no direct evidence of plutonium was found, the fission track evidence in uranium-rich minerals such as whitlockite points to its presence[86].

The effect of low-energy neutrons produced by cosmic rays results in the enhanced abundances of those nuclides, such as excess $^{80}$Kr, $^{82}$Kr, $^{158}$Gd (from $^{157}$Gd), $^{156}$Gd (from $^{155}$Gd), $^{150}$Sm (from $^{149}$Sm), $^{131}$Xe (from $^{130}$Ba), $^{187}$Re, and others[108–110]. These data provide information both about the history of the regolith and the neutron flux.

## 3.15   RARE GASES

The rare, or noble, gases—helium, neon, argon, krypton, and xenon— are so-called because they are strongly depleted on the earth. Since the heavier ones could not be lost from the earth at present, it is the consensus that they have always been deficient, here. They are abundant cosmically and were present in the original solar nebula in amounts comparable to neighboring nonvolatile elements. On the moon, there is no evidence of rare gases, which might be residual from a primitive atmosphere. This is consistent with the general depletion of volatile elements, and, based on the low abundances of elements such as Pb and Tl, it may safely be concluded that the primordial rare gas content of the moon was effectively zero.

Thus the large quantities of rare gases found, particularly in the lunar soils, must be of secondary origin and preserve the record of much nuclear and cosmic activity. The rare-gas inventory records a complex variety of origins. Although these relate to differing processes (e.g., solar wind trapping, cosmic ray interaction, fission products, and radioactive decay), it is convenient and customary to treat the rare-gas studies as a group. This largely reflects the historical development of the studies.

There are several distinct sources for the rare gases. These include:

(a) trapped solar wind ions[111];

(b) implanted solar flare ions;

(c) isotopes produced by solar proton spallation and by high energy cosmic ray interactions (e.g., $^3$He, $^{21}$Ne, $^{38}$Ar);

(d) isotopes from radioactive decay (e.g., $^{40}$Ar from $^{40}$K);

(e) fission-produced isotopes (e.g., $^{131}$Xe from $^{244}$Pu fission);

(f) Neutron capture produced isotopes (e.g., $^{131}$Xe from $^{130}$Ba).

The concentration of rare gases in the solar fines is typically in the range $0.1$–$1.0$ cm$^3$ STP/g, corresponding to about $10^{19}$–$10^{20}$ atoms/cm$^3$. These are very large amounts and were one of the surprises encountered during the Apollo 11 Prelimnary Examination Team study. The detailed composition of the gases is given in Table 3.12.

The location of such large volumes of gas is intriguing. The gas occurs in bubbles, typically 50–100 A in diameter in soil grains, under high ($\sim 5000$ atm) pressures[112]. The penetration of the solar wind as shown by surface etching is on the order of 1,000 A, while the solar flare ions penetrate to millimeter depths.

The rare gas contents increase with decreasing grain size[113]. The inverse relation between the concentration of trapped gas and grain size is shown in Fig. 3.18.

### Solar Wind Composition

A solar wind ion detector was flown on missions 11 through 16. This simple and elegant experiment[114] (a sheet of metallic foil deployed to

**Table 3.12**  Comparison of Inert Gas Contents (cm³STP/g) and Elemental Ratios of Regolith Fines.

| Site | $^4$He $10^{-2}$ | $^{20}$Ne $10^{-4}$ | $^{36}$Ar $10^{-4}$ | $^{84}$Kr $10^{-8}$ | $^{132}$Xe $10^{-8}$ | $^4$He/$^{20}$Ne | $^{20}$Ne/$^{36}$Ar | $^{36}$Ar/$^{84}$Kr $\times 10^{-3}$ | $^{84}$Kr/$^{132}$Xe |
|---|---|---|---|---|---|---|---|---|---|
| Apollo 11 | 11–25 | 20–31 | 3.3–4.1 | 16–38 | 2.1–10 | 55–104 | 5.2–9.2 | 1.0–2.2 | 2.1–8.6 |
| Apollo 12 | 4–38 | 7–61 | 1.2–3.1 | 4–20 | 1.1–2.6 | 55–72 | 4.9–6.6 | 1.2–3.1 | 3.5–8.5 |
| Apollo 14 | 5–9 | 9–16 | 2.4–4.4 | 9–24 | 1.4–4.6 | 52–64 | 3.0–4.2 | 1.6–2.8 | 3.6–12 |
| Apollo 15 | 4–10 | 7–22 | 0.9–4.1 | 4.4–24 | 0.6–3.3 | 38–58 | 4.4–7.7 | 1.5–2.9 | 4.8–8.1 |
| Apollo 16 | 0.6–5.1 | 2.4–13 | 1.3–6.0 | 4.5–34 | 1–6.5 | 26–50 | 1.6–3.2 | 1.5–3.2 | 2.3–7.2 |
| Luna 16 | 18 | 34 | 5.4 | 22 | 8.5 | 53 | 6.3 | 2.5 | 2.6 |
| Luna 20 | 3.81 | 10.1 | 2.88 | 10.9 | 2.25 | 32–39 | 2.4–3.5 | 2.6–3.0 | 4.8–6.6 |

From Walton, J. R., et al. (1973) *PLC 4*: 2086.

catch the solar wind) (Fig. 3.17) has revealed that the He/H ratio of the solar wind (0.04) is much lower than that of the solar photosphere (~0.1). Thus the solar wind is being fractionated with respect to the outer surface of the sun by unknown mechanisms. Table 3.13 compares the solar wind data with that observed in the lunar surface in contrast to the terrestrial atmosphere. The differences between the solar wind data from the foil and the lunar fines are probably due to diffusive losses from the soil and possibly retrapping.

**Fig. 3.17**  The Apollo 16 solar wind composition foil deployed at the Descartes site. The difficulties of lunar dust contamination were overcome by use of layered foils and by incorporating platinum strips, which facilitated acid washing techniques, in the aluminum foil. (NASA AS-16-117-18849.)

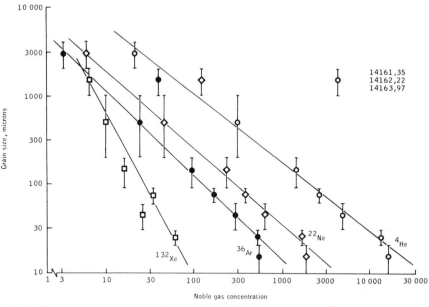

**Fig. 3.18** Inverse relation of grain size and rare gas content in soils from Apollo 14. (Bogard, D. D., and Nyquist, L. E., 1972, *PLC 3*: 1804.)

The variation in $^{20}Ne/^{22}Ne$ ratios between the solar wind and the terrestrial atmosphere is most likely due to fractionation during the evolution of the earth's atmosphere. The deuterium/hydrogen ratio is very low, so that the sun now has very little deuterium. According to current stellar evolution models, the sun has converted D to $^3He$. There is still a deficiency, however. $^3He/^4He$ ratios in the solar wind are at least four times less than indicated for the earth's D/H ratio. Thus, deuterium may have been enriched in the planets relative to the sun early in the formation of the solar system[115].

### The Argon-40 Anomaly

There is very little primordial $^{40}Ar$—the ratio of $^{40}Ar$ to $^{36}Ar$ is about $10^{-3}$. The major source of $^{40}Ar$ is the radiogenic decay of $^{40}K$. However, the lunar soils contain about two orders of magnitude more $^{40}Ar$ than can be accounted for by the *in situ* decay from potassium. What is the nature of the enrichment mechanism?

An early suggestion[116] was that $^{40}Ar$ atoms, resulting from the $^{40}K$ decay, escape from the lunar surface and are ionized by solar radiation.

**Table 3.13** Comparison of Weighted Averages of Solar Wind Ion Abundances Obtained from the SWC* Experiments with Abundances in Surface-Correlated Gases of Lunar Fines Materials, A Breccia and in the Atmosphere of the Earth.

| Source | $^4$He/$^3$He | $^4$He/$^{20}$Ne | $^{20}$Ne/$^{22}$Ne | $^{22}$Ne/$^{21}$Ne | $^{20}$Ne/$^{36}$Ar |
|---|---|---|---|---|---|
| Solar wind (average from 5 SWC experiments) | $2350 \pm 120$ | $570 \pm 70$ | $13.7 \pm 0.3$ | $30 \pm 4$ | $28 \pm 9$ |
| Lunar fines 10084 | $2550 \pm 250$ | $96 \pm 18$ | $12.65 \pm 0.2$ | $31.0 \pm 1.2$ | $7 \pm 2$ |
| Ilmenite from 10084 | $2720 \pm 100$ | $218 \pm 8$ | $12.85 \pm 0.1$ | $31.1 \pm 0.8$ | $27 \pm 4$ |
| Ilmenite from 12001 | $2700 \pm 80$ | $253 \pm 10$ | $12.9 \pm 0.1$ | $32.0 \pm 0.4$ | $27 \pm 5$ |
| Ilmenite from breccia 10046 | $3060 \pm 150$ | $231 \pm 13$ | $12.65 \pm 0.15$ | $31.4 \pm 0.4$ | — |
| Terrestrial atmosphere | $7 \times 10^5$ | 0.3 | $9.80 \pm 0.08$ | $34.5 \pm 1.0$ | 0.5 |

From Bogard, D. D., and Nyquist, L. E. (1972) *PLC 3*: 1804.
*SWC = Solar wind composition.

After ionization, the particles are then subject to rapid acceleration by the magnetic fields associated with the solar wind and strike the lunar surface with energies of 100–1,000 ev within a few seconds. At low energies, they are neutralized but not trapped and hence recycled. Ions with impact energies >1 kev are trapped in the fines, thus building up an excess of $^{40}$Ar.

Recently some criticism of this theory has been advanced[117] based on apparent absence of excess $^{40}$Ar in near-surface regions of grains and the apparently low amounts of $^{40}$Ar released at low temperatures. One alternative, but less likely, suggestion[117] is that potassium, volatilized during impact, has coated the grain surfaces and produces the excess $^{40}$Ar. Alternatively, it has been argued that most of the excess argon was implanted 3–4 aeons ago and that arguments based on the present-day flux, solar wind, and magnetic fields are not relevant[118]. The resolution of this problem calls for more detailed investigations, some of which are under way[119].

## Exposure Ages From Rare Gases

The exposure history of the regolith and of surface rocks was one of the first applications of the rare gas studies. Of the various age methods, the most reliable[120] are $^{81}$Kr–$^{83}$Kr, $^{21}$Ne, and $^{38}$Ar ages. The $^3$He ages are subject to loss of He by diffusion[121]. The ages[122] calculated for a number of larger craters whose ejecta blankets were sampled by the Apollo astronauts are given in Table 3.14. The agreement between the various workers, using different techniques, is excellent. The dating depends on the proper sampling of the ejecta blanket. Much confusion arose over the age of South Ray (Apollo 16), one of the freshest craters on the lunar surface. The ages of about 2 million years quoted in Table 3.14 are from rocks and are in accord with the geological criteria[123]. Many of the soils, interpreted as South Ray ejecta, are far removed from the crater rim. South Ray is 640 m in diameter. The astronaut traverses came no closer than about 3 km, and it is exceedingly doubtful that they sampled any fine ejecta from South Ray, at about 5 crater diameters distant[123]. On this interpretation, the astronauts found only scattered blocks from South Ray. This has some consequences for photogeologic mapping, basing ejecta blankets on the light-colored material surrounding craters. Much of this material, at distances greater than 2 crater diameters, may be local material ploughed up by ejected blocks[123]. This question has wider significance, if extrapolated to the ringed-basin-forming impacts (section 2.7) and bears on the debate surrounding the local versus distant origin of the Cayley formation.

The exposure ages of regolith soils from the various missions typically show averages of about 400 million years with much spread. Individual

**Table 3.14**   Rare Gas Exposure Ages of Ejecta Blankets From Sampled Craters.

| Mission | Crater | Age ($\times 10^6$ yr) |
|---|---|---|
| Apollo 14 | Cone | 26* |
| | | 25† |
| | | 26.2‡ |
| Apollo 16 | South Ray | 2* |
| | | 2§ |
| | North Ray | 46* |
| | | 50.6§ |
| | | 48.9‡ |
| | | 35‖ |
| Apollo 17 | Camelot | 90* |

*Turner, G. (1973) *PLC 4:* 1903.
†Kirsten, T., et al. (1972) *PLC 3:* 1865.
‡Lugmair, G. W., and Marti, K. (1972) *PLC 3:* 1891; Marti, K., et al. (1973) *PLC 4:* 2037.
§Behrmann, C., et al. (1973) *PLC 4:* 1957.
‖Hussain, L., and Schaeffer, O. A. (1973) *PLC 4:* 1847.

soil grains with ages up to 1,700 million years have been encountered, and rock exposure ages extend from 1 million to greater than 700 million years[121].

## 3.16   VOLATILIZATION OF ELEMENTS AT THE LUNAR SURFACE

Volatilization has been invoked as a lunar phenomenon ever since the initial report that the lunar basalts contained very low concentrations of alkali elements and that the other volatile elements (Pb, Tl, Bi, etc.) were also depleted. Two distinct problems arose. The first concerned the possible loss of volatiles during the basaltic flooding of the maria basins. The second was how much volatilization and redistribution of elements occurred during impact events.

The lunar impact events are so much larger than terrestrial examples that extrapolation is difficult. During glass formation, the loss of volatiles appears to be small but may be critical. Experience from terrestrial impact craters shows that only the very volatile components are lost and that the major element chemistry of the parent materials is preserved. Gibson and Hubbard[124, 125] find that both Pb and Rb may be volatilized during glass formation and deposited in the lunar soils. Isotope workers have found that some Pb (and Rb) are readily leachable from soils[126]. Volatile loss during the actual impact process from glasses is probably small, since these solidify from a melt phase. A larger amount of volatilized material will be ejected and will condense on the soil particles, leading to the observed increase of leachable material with decreasing grain size.

Gibson and Hubbard[124] note that 1.5 percent of the Rb is very easily leached from the soils and is possibly vapor deposited, along with a larger amount (~5 percent) of the lead. These amounts are sufficient to upset the isotopic calculations for age determination (see section 3.5).

The question of volatile loss is discussed again, both with respect to the extrusion of the maria basalts (see section 4.5) and to the behavior of elements in hot ejecta blankets formed during giant cratering in the highlands (see section 5.4).

## 3.17   LUNAR ATMOSPHERE

A mass spectrometer was deployed on the lunar surface during the Apollo 17 mission to measure the lunar atmosphere[127–129]. This is extremely tenuous and is in fact a collisionless gas. There are a number of possible sources for a lunar atmosphere. These include volcanic activity, argon-40 and radon-222 produced by radioactive decay, the solar wind particles, which impact the surface with energies of 1 kev per mass unit, and the spacecraft itself. Degassing of the spacecraft produces artifacts at nearly all mass numbers. The primary components are derived either from the solar wind or from radioactive decay, and no components due to volcanic activity have been detected. During the lunar night, when the temperature falls below 100°K, many of the species outgassed from the spacecraft condense, and measurement of the noncondensible species becomes possible.

Positive confirmation of hydrogen, helium, neon, and argon have been obtained. Table 3.15 gives a summary of the concentrations of the gases in the lunar atmosphere. These are compared with the model abundances assuming that the solar wind is the source. For helium, the agreement is excellent. The abundances of the other gases are compatible with a solar wind source, except of course the $^{40}$Ar abundances, derived by radioactive decay from $^{40}$K. Upper limits are given for $O_2$ and $CO_2$, and their presence is uncertain.

The total nighttime gas concentration is $2 \times 10^5$ molecules/cm$^3$, which is the same value obtained by the cold cathode gauge experiment carried on Apollo 12, 14, and 15 to measure total gas concentration[130]. Both $^{40}$Ar

**Table 3.15**  Abundance of Gases in Lunar Atmosphere Compared to Model Abundances with Solar Wind as Source.

| Gas | Concentration (molecules/cm³) | | Model (molecules/cm³) | |
|-----|-----|-----|-----|-----|
|  | Day | Night | Day | Night |
| $H_2$ | — | $6.5 \times 10^4$ | $2.1 \times 10^3$ | $1.2 \times 10^4$ |
| $^4$He | $2 \times 10^3$ | $4 \times 10^4$ | $1.7 \times 10^3$ | $3.7 \times 10^4$ |
| $^{20}$Ne | — | $8 \times 10^4$ | $4-7 \times 10^3$ | $1.2 \times 10^5$ |
| $^{36}$Ar | — | $3 \times 10^3$* | — | — |
|  |  | $3.5 \times 10^4$* |  |  |
| $^{40}$Ar | — | $7-8 \times 10^3$† | — | — |
| $O_2$ | — | $<2 \times 10^2$ | — | — |
| $CO_2$ | — | $<3 \times 10^3$ | — | — |

Adapted from Hoffman et al., *PLC 4*: 2874, Table 2.
*Sunrise terminator.
†Sunset terminator.

and $^{36}$Ar show a predawn enhancement, consistent with their being condensible gases during the lunar night, rereleased into the atmosphere at the sunrise terminator.

### Short-lived Radioactivity Over the Lunar Surface

An alpha particle spectrometer on board the Apollo 15 and 16 command modules observed the distribution of radon-222 over the lunar surface[131]. $^{222}$Rn, a noble gas produced as one nuclide in the radioactive decay sequence of uranium, has a half-life of 3.7 days. A second radon isotope ($^{220}$Rn) with a 56-sec half-life is produced during the decay of thorium. Lead-210, a descendant of $^{222}$Rn, has a half-life of 21 years and may be detected through alpha-particle emission from its granddaughter $^{210}$Po.

The distribution of both $^{222}$Rn and $^{210}$Po are nonuniform. Peaks are observed over Aristarchus and Grimaldi, and generally high count rates over Oceanus Procellarum and Mare Imbrium. The general trend is parallel to the U and Th values observed in the gamma ray experiment. One of the most dramatic features was the correlation of the $^{210}$Po decay with the edges of the maria, except for Serenitatis. $^{210}$Po and $^{222}$Rn are not in radioactive equilibrium, implying that the processes responsible for transporting radon to the lunar surface vary with time.

The correlation with features such as Aristarchus, where lunar transient phenomena have been reported, with Grimaldi (Fig. 3.19) and with the edges of the maria, where rilles are concentrated indicates that in these areas escape of radon to the surface is facilitated, perhaps along ring fractures.

### 3.18  EXOBIOLOGY

the Moon has no air or atmosphere surrounding it as we have, [and I] cannot imagine how any plants or animals whose whole nourishment comes from fluid bodies, can thrive in a dry, waterless, parched soil

(C. Huyghens, *Cosmotheoros*, 1757)

The possibility of life on other planets holds an understandable fascination for the human species. Much scientific effort was expended on the examination of the lunar samples with the object of finding life forms or complex organic molecules, which might be suitable precursors. No forms of life were discovered in the lunar samples, and, after extensive

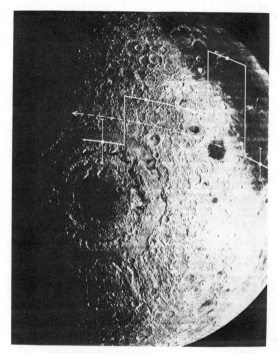

**Fig. 3.19** The observed $^{210}$Po count rate superimposed on a photograph of the moon. The dashed line represents the average ground track and is used to represent the background counting level. The crater directly beneath the local increase in count rate is Grimaldi. The large ringed basin is Orientale. (Ref. 131, Fig. 6.)

search, no unequivocal detection of complex hydrocarbons of lunar origin was made.

### Organisms

Three thousand tests for viable organisms were carried out on Apollo 11 samples with nine nutrient media, at four temperatures, in three different atmospheric mixtures of nitrogen, oxygen, and carbon dioxide. No viable life forms were found, not even terrestrial contaminants [132].

The lunar soil failed to show the presence of microfossils that would have indicated the one-time presence of lunar life. Glass spheres were observed with a size distribution similar to that of sexually reproducing microorganisms. These were not of organic origin, however, but were produced by melting of the lunar rocks during meteorite and micrometeorite impacts[50]. Micropalaeontological studies confirmed the foregoing observations. Thin sections contained elongate, spheroidal, spinose, and actinomorphic structures superficially resembling terrestrial microfossils, but there was no evidence of indigenous biological activity[133]. It was agreed by all investigators that optical and electron microscope studies showed a total absence of structures that could be interpreted to be biological in origin[134, 135].

No unfavorable reactions were observed when terrestrial organisms were exposed to lunar samples despite extensive testing of both plants and organisms[135, 136]. No increased rates of plant growth were observed during botanical testing using lunar soil[137].

### 3.19   ORGANIC GEOCHEMISTRY

No single organic compound of biological significance has been identified with certainty in the lunar samples[138], and, as noted, no organisms or fossil traces of organisms were found. These results, although not unexpected by many investigators, dashed hopes that the moon might be a rich source of organic matter[139]. Because such possibilities could not be ruled out with certainty, the sample allocation for biological and organic analyses was generous. A total of 2,095 g of the lunar sample return was used for biomedical testing alone[140]. In contrast, much smaller amounts were used for the physical sciences experiments. The lower limit of 3 g of the Luna 16 sample available to U.S. investigators proved sufficient to provide complete data on chemistry, mineralogy, petrology, and age.

**The Organogenic Elements**

All of these are present in low abundance on the moon, carbon being particularly scarce, so that the prerequisites for a hydrocarbon-rich environment are lacking. The search for low molecular weight compounds of these elements was a little more successful. A few parts per million of methane ($CH_4$) were discovered. Ethane ($C_2H_6$) was present at about 0.1 ppm.

Three methods of investigation on lunar fines were carried out: (*a*) vacuum pyrolysis, (*b*) acid hydrolysis, and (*c*) crushing under vacuum. Vacuum pyrolysis yielded a number of species. Methane ($< 6$ ppm) and ethane ($< 0.1$ ppm), CO, $CO_2$, $N_2$, $H_2$, $H_2S$, $H_2O$, and $SO_2$. Acid hydrolysis yielded methane ($< 5$ ppm), ethane, CO, $CO_2$, $H_2S$, COS, $CS_2$ and $SO_2$, while crushing yielded methane (1 ppm), ethane, $H_2$, $N_2$, and $H_2S$[141].

What is the origin of these various species, all of which are present only in very small amounts, in the lunar soils? Possible sources are:

(*a*) Species are indigenous to the lunar samples. The only confirmed indigenous material is low amounts of methane.

(*b*) They are derived from the solar wind.

(*c*) They are the products (chemical) of reaction of the solar wind with lunar minerals.

(*d*) They are terrestrial contaminants.

Most of the products observed are probably produced by reactions of lunar minerals. Carbides (cohenite) and sulfides (troilite) react with oxides and hydrogen to give the various species CO, $CO_2$, $H_2S$, $SO_2$. The interaction of carbides and the solar wind hydrogen yields methane and ethane. No carbonates have been positively detected, although a carbonate phase may exist[142].

The sources of the various elements are the following. Hydrogen comes from the solar wind; carbon is derived partly from meteoritic carbides and from the solar wind; nitrogen comes from the solar wind, but may also be partly indigenous to the moon. It is a possible candidate, along with CO, for the vesicle-forming gas. Sulfur is derived from troilite (FeS)[141]. There is little direct evidence of carbon derived from carbonaceous chondrites[142]. There is a general correlation of carbon content with the amount of agglutinate in the soils indicating that the amount of carbon is related to surface exposure[143].

### Isotope Abundances for Carbon and Sulfur

The fractionation of the carbon and sulfur isotopes is discussed in sections 4.10 and 4.12, but some brief mention is appropriate here. Compared to *reduced* compounds in meteorites or in terrestrial samples, the lunar fines are greatly enriched in $^{13}C$ and $^{34}S$. In each case, the fines are enriched relative to breccias and lunar basalts[143].

Carbon in the lunar soil is enriched in $^{13}C$ relative to the belemnite (PDB) standard by about 19 per mil. The carbon of breccias is lighter, about $\pm 5$ per mil, and that of fine-grained rocks still lighter at $-20$ to $-25$ per mil. Meteoritic organic carbon (noncarbonate) is commonly $-15$ per mil; terrestrial organic carbon is $-20$ to $-30$ per mil. During pyrolysis of lunar carbonaceous material, some fractions of the evolved gas were enriched in $^{13}C$ and others depleted in $^{13}C$ relative to the $\delta$ $^{13}C$ of the total sample[143, 144].

In studies on sulfur isotopes, all of the sulfur appeared to be evolved as

$H_2S$ on treatment with acid; this suggested the presence of troilite, and the isotopic distribution showed the same pattern as did the carbon: the lunar soil is more enriched in the heavy isotope, and the basaltic rocks are the least enriched. For a given soil sample, the smaller grain sizes are more enriched in the heavy isotope than the coarser material[143–145].

The enrichment of the heavy C and S isotopes in the lunar fines is attributed to a "stripping" effect by the solar wind protons[143]. Selective loss from the surface of $^{12}C$-enriched $CH_4$ and $^{32}S$-enriched $H_2S$ is the proposed mechanism. Some evidence for such an effect has been demonstrated from other isotopic studies[144]. Time-controlled etching studies reveal that the outer surfaces of grains in the lunar fines are strongly enriched in the heavy oxygen and silicon isotopes $^{18}O$ and $^{30}Si$. Such stripping may be highly efficient. The fines are much lower in total sulfur than are the rocks, even though meteoritic troilite is presumably being added to the soils. The net removal of sulfur from the lunar surface thus is an important process.

### Carbides

The presence of carbides in the lunar fines was inferred by the organic geochemists from the production of hydrocarbons during acid treatment of the soils. Heating with HCl yielded methane, ethane, ethene, acetylene, propane, and propene; and small amounts of unidentified $C_3$ and $C_4$ hydrocarbons were detected by gas chromatography in the products of the hydrolysis. Yields were estimated to represent an appreciable proportion of the total carbon present—from 3 to 15 percent. Decomposition of the lunar mineral matrix with hydrofluoric acid resulted in the evolution of methane, ethane, and other gases. Most of this yield of gases was attributed to acid decomposition of carbides[146].

The meteoritic carbide mineral cohenite (Fe Ni)$_3$C has been identified as a trace component in the lunar fines[147]. No other carbides have been identified. Cohenite is known only from iron meteorites and enstatite chondrites[148], and it is probably not very abundant on the lunar surface as a result.

### Aromatic Hydrocarbons

In the Apollo 11 samples the presence of nanogram quantities of toluene, $C_8$ alkyl benzene, phenol, and diphenyl were judged to be contaminants[149]. The conclusion is that the aromatics found were not indigenous to the moon.

Heating of the sample to 400°C failed to show the presence of a series of hetero-aromatic systems such as pyridines, furanes, and thiophenes, but pyrolysis to higher temperatures produced benzene and toluene above 500°C. At still higher temperatures other alkyl benzenes and naphthalenes were observed, and these were accompanied by styrenes, indenes, thiophenes, and diphenyl. A number of laboratories observed aromatic compounds of the foregoing types and little doubt exists as to their origin as pyrolysis products. In summary, benzene and toluene were detected at very low (parts per billion) levels in lunar samples by several laboratories, but these compounds are terrestrial contaminants[149].

## Alkane Hydrocarbons

A particular search was carried out for n-alkanes in the range above $C_{15}$ by combined gas chromatography–mass spectroscopy[150]. In no instance was evidence obtained for the presence of alkanes. In the most exhaustive analysis a 50-g sample of Apollo 11 fines was examined. No $C_{15}$ to $C_{30}$ alkane was present at concentrations exceeding 1 ppb. The consensus is that such compounds are absent from the lunar surface. It is important to note that the analyses apply not only to normal alkanes but in addition to branched alkanes including isoprenoid hydrocarbons and a variety of other organic compounds of biogenic or prebiotic significance, important as "biological markers."

## Porphyrins

Porphyrins are tetrapyrrole pigments, which are the molecular skeletons for the colored components of chlorophyll and hemoglobin. They are of particular interest in terms of both fossil and prebiotic biochemical structures. In the Apollo 11 samples, Rho[151] reported that porphyrins were not detected. Other workers[152] reported porphyrinlike pigments well above background levels. Similar pigments, however, were detected in the rocket exhaust along with other fluorescent pigments, and these are the probable cause of the conflicting observations.

No porphyrins were observed in the Apollo 14 samples, during collaborative experiments[153], and earlier reports of the presence of porphyrins in Apollo 12 samples well removed from the rocket exhaust[154] are probably an instrumental artifact[155]. It is concluded that less than $10^{-14}$ moles/g of extractable metalloporphyrin is present in the Apollo 14 samples[156].

## Amino Acids and Their Precursors

Considerable interest was focused on amino acids, which terrestrially are the structural elements of proteins. Traces of amino acids are produced from unknown precursors in the lunar soil by hydrolysis[157, 158]. Only the chemically most simple amino acids are formed in the experiments. The principal constituent is glycine, with smaller amounts of alanine and glutamic acid. The source of these precursors in the lunar fines is still in dispute. The quantities involved are minute (<20 ppb). Synthesis from inorganic compounds[159] during the analysis cannot be ruled out. Contamination at the very low levels encountered[160] is very likely.

The survival of free amino acids on the lunar surface[139] is a remote possibility. The extremes in lunar temperature, the raining meteorite bombardment, the hard vacuum, solar and cosmic radiation, unfiltered by any atmosphere, and the lack of water, all combine to produce a most unfavorable environment for the survival of the delicate and complex organic structural compounds. Possibly some material, derived from meteoritic (carbonaceous chondrites) or cometary impact, reactions involving the solar wind[161], or possibly a combination of all of these, may combine to produce a more or less steady-state production of amino-acid precursors. The lack of water[162] and the harsh environment preclude further development[163, 164].

> In the want of water and air, the question as to whether this body is inhabited is no longer equivocal. Its surface resolves itself into a sterile and inhospitable waste, where the lichen which flourishes amidst the frosts and snows of Lapland would quickly wither and die, and where no animal with a drop of blood in its veins could exist.
>
> (James Breen, *The Planetary Worlds*, 1854)

## REFERENCES AND NOTES

1. Fielder, G. (1961) *Structure of the Moon's Surface*, Pergamon, p. 46.
2. Piddington, J. H., and Minnett, H. C. (1949) *Aust. J. Sci. Res.* 2A: 643; Jaeger, J. C. (1953) *Aust. J. Phys.* 6: 10; Linsky, J. L. (1966) *Icarus.* 5: 606.
3. See papers by G. P. Kuiper, E. M. Shoemaker, and E. A. Whitaker (1966) in *The Nature of the Lunar Surface*, Johns Hopkins Press, Baltimore.
4. Gold, T., ibid.
5. Hörz, F. (1973) NASA SP-315: 7-24.
6. Keihm, S. J., et al. (1973) *EPSL.* 19: 337; (1973) *PLC 4*: 2503.
7. Saari, J. M. (1964) *Icarus.* 3: 161; Mendell, W. W., and Low, F. J. (1970) *JGR.* 75: 3319.
8. Gold, T. (1971) *PLC 2*: 2675.

9. The extreme case is the presence of the layer of "light gray fines" (12033) at Apollo 12, a KREEP-rich layer of exotic origin.

10. The XRF experiment samples only the top few micrometers ($< 10$) of the surface. The gamma ray experiment looks somewhat deeper (10–20 cm). Adler, I., et al. (1973) *PLC 4*: 2783; (1974) *LS V*: 1, 611; Metzger, A. E., et al. (1973) *Science.* 179: 800; (1974) *LS V*: 601.

11. McCoy, J. E., and Criswell, D. R. (1974) *LS V*: 475.

12. NASA SP-289: 5-23 (1972); Oberbeck, V. R., et al. (1973) *Icarus.* 19: 87.

13. Watkins, J. S., and Kovach, R. L. (1973) *PLC 4*: 2572.

14. Eberhardt, P. (1973) *Moon.* 8: 104.

15. Apollo 17 deep core was 294.5 cm.

16. Core tube samples from Apollo 11, 12, and 14 missions produced disturbed samples, but on Apollo 15, 16, and 17 missions, use of thin-walled tubes resulted in almost undisturbed samples of lunar soil with 90–95 percent core recovery (Carrier, W. D., 1973, *PLC 4*: 2403).

17. Houston, W. N., et al. (1974) *LS V*: 363.

18. Carrier, W. D., et al. (1973) *PLC 3*: 3213; Houston, W. N., et al., ibid., 3255; Mitchell, J. K., et al., ibid., 3235; Mitchell, J. K., et al. (1973) *PLC 4*: 2437.

19. Gault, D. E., et al. (1974) *LS V*: 260.

20. Bhandari, N., et al. (1972) *PLC 3*: 2811.

21. Terrestrial erosion reduces continents to base level in 30–50 million years. Judson, S., and Ritter, D. F. (1964) *JGR.* 69: 3395; Taylor, S. R. (1967) *Tectonophysics.* 4: 17.

22. Schmitt, R. A., and Laul, J. C. (1973) *Moon.* 8: 190.

23. Schonfeld, E., and Meyer, C. (1972) *PLC 3*: 1415.

24. Shoemaker, E. M., et al. (1971) *PLC 1*: 2399.

25. Wood, J. A., et al. (1970) *PLC 1*: 965.

26. Schonfeld, E., and Meyer, C. (1973) *PLC 4*: 125.

27. LSPET (1973) *Science.* 182: 659, 672.

28. Schmitt, H. H. (1973) ibid., 686.

29. See orange glass section. Lucchitta, B. K. (1973) *PLC 4*: 149.

30. Heiken, G., et al. (1974) *GCA 38*, 1703; Schaeffer, O. A. (1973) *EOS.* 54: 614.

31. Hussain, L., and Shaeffer, O. A. (1973) *Science.* 180: 1358.

32. Schonfeld, E., and Meyer, C. (1972) *PLC 3*: 1397.

33. The higher $Al_2O_3$ content in the soils than in most maria basalts is only partly due to the anorthositic component from the highlands. See section on aluminous maria basalts.

34. Papanastassiou, D. A., and Wasserburg, G. J. (1970) *EPSL.* 8: 1, 269; (1971) *EPSL.* 11: 37; 12: 36; (1972) *EPSL.* 13: 368; 17: 52.

35. Cliff, R. A., et al. (1972) *JGR.* 77: 2007; Mark, R. K., et al. (1973) *PLC 4*: 1785; Murthy, V. R., et al. (1972) *PLC 3*: 1503; Compston, W., et al. (1971) *PLC 2*: 1481.

36. Wetherill, G. W. (1971) *Science.* 173: 389.

37. The $^{87}Sr/^{86}Sr$ ratio of 0.69898 is the Basaltic Achondrite Best Initial (or BABI) ratio[34].

38. Nyquist, L. E., et al. (1973) *PLC 4*: 1839.

39. Tatsumoto, M. (1973) *Science.* 180: 1279; Oversby, V. (1974) *Nature.* 248: 132.

40. Evensen, N. M., et al. (1974) *LS V*: 220.

41. See section on volatile loss.

42. McKay, D. S., et al. (1972) *PLC 3*: 988.

43. Arrhenius, G., et al. (1971) *PLC 2*: 2583; Crozaz, G., et al. (1972) *LS III*: 167; McKay, D. S., et al. (1971) *PLC 2*: 755.

44. McKay, D. S., et al. (1974) *LS V*: 480.
45. Taylor, S. R. (1966) *GCA*. 30: 1121.
46. Dence, M. R. (1974) *Meteoritics*. In press; and personal communication.
47. Gold, T. (1969) *Science*. 165: 1345.
48. See section 5.4.
49. Macdougall, D., et al. (1974) *Science*. 183: 73.
50. Cloud, P. (1970) *PLC 1*: 1794.
51. See section on exobiology.
52. Taylor, S. R. (1973) *Earth Sci. Rev.* 9: 101.
53. O'Keefe, J. A. (1970) *Science*. 168: 1209.
54. King, E. A., et al. (1970) *Science*. 170: 199.
55. Frey, F., et al. (1970) *Science*. 170: 845.
56. Showalter, D., et al. (1971) *Science*. 175: 170, 172.
57. Roedder, E., and Weiblen, P. W. (1970) *PLC 1*: 801.
58. Hartmann, W. K. (1972) *Astrophys. Space Sci.* 17: 48.
59. Taylor, H. P., and Epstein, S. (1970) *PLC 1*: 613.
60. Schnetzler, C. C. (1970) *Meteoritics*. 5: 221.
61. O'Keefe, J. A. (1970) *Science*. 168: 1209.
62. Verbeek, R. D. M. (1897) *K. Ned. Akad. Wet.* 5: 421.
63. Hartmann, W. K. (1973) *Icarus*. 18: 634; Taylor, G. J., et al. (1973) *PLC 4*: 566.
64. McGetchin, T. R., et al. (1973) *EPSL*. 20: 226.
65. Hussain, L., and Schaeffer, O. A. (1973) *LS IV*: 406.
66. Baldwin, R. B. (1949) *The Face of the Moon* (Chicago); Hartmann, W. K. (1965) *Icarus*. 4: 164; (1966) *Icarus*. 5: 406.
67. Fielder, G. (1965) *Lunar Geology* (Dufour). Baldwin, R. B. (1969, *Icarus*. 11: 320) gives 640 million years for the age of the maria. Gault, D. E. (1970, *Radio Sci*. 5: 289) records many age estimates from 50 to 300 million years, with some extremely young ages of 3–6 million years for parts of Oceanus Procellarum.
68. Tera, F. (1974) *LS V*: 792.
69. Baldwin, R. B. (1970) *Science*. 170: 1297.
70. Sjogren, W. L., et al. (1973) NASA SP-315, 24-1.
71. For a recent extrapolation of the cratering rate to give ages of 4.4 aeons for the southern highlands, and 4.6 aeons for the far side, see Neukum, G., et al. (1972) *PLC 3*: 2806. See also reference 66.
72. Hörz, F., et al. (1971) *JGR*. 76: 5770; Hartung, J. B., et al. (1973) *PLC 4*: 3213; Morrison, D. A., et al., ibid., 3235; Neukum, G., et al., ibid., 3255; Schneider, E., et al., ibid., 3277; Morrison, D. A., et al. (1972) *PLC 3*: 2767; Neukum, G., et al., ibid., 2793; Gault, D. E., et al., ibid., 2713; Hartung, J., et al., ibid., 2735.
73. Frondel, C., et al. (1970) *PLC 1*: 445; Fredriksson, K., et al., ibid., 419.
74. Brownlee, D. E., et al. (1973) *PLC 4*: 3197; Hörz, F., et al. (1974) *Planet. Space Sci*. In press.
75. Schneider, E., and Hörz, F. (1974) *LSV*: 666; Hörz, F., et al. (1974) *PLC5*. In press.
76. See Anders, E., et al. (1973) *Moon*. 8: 3; Morgan, J. W., et al. (1974) *LS V*: 526.
77. Ashworth, D. G., and McDonnell, J. A. M. (1973) Space Research XV, COSPAR, Konstanz.
78. Latham, G., et al. (1973) *PLC 4*: 2515.
79. McCrosky, R. E. (1968) *Smithsonian Astrophys. Obs. Spec. Report*. 280.

80. Taylor, G., and Heymann, D. (1969) *EPSL.* 7: 151; Wood, J. A. (1968) *Meteorites and the Origin of Planets,* McGraw-Hill, N.Y., p. 55; Hartmann, W. K. (1972) *Moons and Planets,* Bogden and Quigley, N.Y., p. 205.

81. Crozaz, G. (1974) *LS V*: 157.

82. Price, R. B., Fleischer, R. L., and Walker, R. M. (1974) *Nuclear Tracks.* Univ. Calif. Press.

83. Price, P. B., et al. (1973) *EPSL.* 19: 377; Lal, D. (1972) *Space Sci. Rev.* 14: 45; idem. (1972) in *From Plasma to Planet,* Wiley, p. 49; Battacharya, S. K., et al. (1973) *Moon.* 8: 253.

84. Phakey, P. P., et al. (1972) *PLC 3*: 2905.

85. Arrhenius, G., et al. (1971) *PLC 2*: 2583; Crozaz, G., et al. (1972) *PLC 3*: 2917; MacDougall, D., et al. (1973) *PLC 4*: 2319; Storzer, D., et al. (1973) *PLC 4*: 2363; Hutcheon, K. D., et al. (1972) *PLC 3*: 2863.

86. Walker, R. M., and Yuhas, D. (1973) *PLC 4*: 2379; Crozaz, G., et al. (1972) *PLC 3*: 1623; Hutcheon, I. D., and Price, R. B. (1972) *Science.* 176: 909.

87. Bhandari, N., et al. (1971) *PLC 2*: 2599; *Nature.* 230: 219.

88. Fleischer, R. L., and Hart, H. R. (1973) *Nature.* 242: 104.

89. Bhandari, N., et al. (1974) *LS V*: 54.

90. Lal, D. (1972) *Space Sci. Rev.* 14: 3; Bhandari, N. (1971) *PLC 2*: 2611.

91. Poupeau, G., et al. (1973) *GCA.* 37: 2005.

92. Crozaz, G., et al. (1974) *LS V*: 154.

93. Nickle, N. L. (1971) *PLC 2*: 2683; Crozaz, G., and Walker, R. M. (1972) NASA SP-284, 209; Price, P. G., et al. ibid., 217; Barber, D. J., et al., ibid., 220.

94. Arrhenius, G., et al. (1971) *PLC 2*: 2583.

95. Bhandari, N., et al. (1973) *PLC 4*: 2275.

96. Hart, H. R., et al. (1972) *PLC 3*: 2831, 2842; Hutcheon, I. D., et al., ibid., 2845, 2863; Dran, J. C., et al. (1972) *PLC 3*: 2883; Yuhas, D. E., et al. (1972) *PLC 3*: 2941.

97. MacDougall, D., et al. (1973) *PLC 4*: 2319.

98. Van Schmus, W. R., and Wood, J. A. (1967) *GCA.* 31: 747.

99. Williams, R. J. (1972) *EPSL.* 16: 250; Warner, J. L. (1972) *PLC 3*: 623.

100. Dunlap, J. L., et al., (1973) *Astron. J.* 78: 491; Goldstein, R. M., et al., ibid., 508.

101. Eldridge, J. S., et al. (1972) *PLC 3*: 1651; Keith, J. E., et al., ibid., 1671; Begemann, F., et al., ibid., 1693; Herr, W., et al., ibid., 1763; Clark, R. S., and Keith, J. E. (1973) *PLC 4*: 2105; Eldridge, J. S., et al., ibid., 2115.

102. Yokoyama, Y., et al. (1972) *PLC 3*: 1733; O'Kelley, G. D., et al., ibid., 1659; Fireman, E. L. (1973) *PLC 4*: 2131; Rancitelli, L. A., et al. (1972) *PLC 3*: 1681.

103. Yokoyama, Y., et al. (1973) *PLC 4*: 2209.

104. Wrigley, R. C. (1973) *PLC 4*: 2203; Lal, D. (1972) *Space Sci. Rev.* 14: 88, 95.

105. Wahlen, M., et al. (1972) *PLC 3*: 1719.

106. Reedy, R. C., and Arnold, J. R. (1972) *JGR.* 77: 537.

107. Fields, P. R., et al. (1973) *PLC 4*: 2123; (1972) *PLC 3*: 1637.

108. Lingenfelter, R. E., et al. (1972) *EPSL.* 16: 355; Kornblum, J. J., et al. (1973) *PLC 4*: 2171.

109. Russ, G. P. (1972) *EPSL.* 13: 384, ibid., 53; (1973) *LS IV*: 642.

110. Marti, K., and Lugmair, G. W. (1971) *PLC 2*: 1591.

111. The solar wind in the neighborhood of the moon under normal conditions consists mainly of ionized hydrogen moving from the sun with velocities in the range 300–500 km/sec. The average density is about 10 ions/cm$^3$. The particles have energies in the kilovolt range, much less energetic than the cosmic rays or solar flares.

112. Phakey, P. P., et al. (1972) *PLC 3*: 2911.
113. Eberhardt, P., et al. (1972) *PLC 3*: 1821; Hintenberger, H., and Weber, H. W. (1973) *PLC 4*: 2012; Heymann, D., et al. (1970) *Science.* 167: 555.
114. Geiss, J., et al. (1972) NASA SP 315, 14-1.
115. Geiss, J., and Reeves, H. (1972) *Astron. Astrophys.* 18: 126.
116. Heymann, D., and Yaniv, A. (1970) *PLC 1*: 1261; Manka, R. H., and Michel, F. C. (1970) *Science.* 169: 278; Eberhardt, P., et al. (1970) *PLC 1*: 1037.
117. Bauer, H., et al. (1972) *PLC 3*: 1947; Megrue, G. H., and Steinbrunn, F., ibid., 1899; Frick, U., et al. (1973) *PLC 4*: 1987.
118. Yaniv, A., and Heymann, D. (1972) *PLC 3*: 1967.
119. Bogard, D. D., and Nyquist, L. E. (1973) *PLC 4*: 1975.
120. Marti, K. (1967) *Phys. Rev. Lett.* 18: 264; Lugmair, G. W., and Marti, K. (1972) *PLC 3*: 1891; Marti, K., et al. (1973) *PLC 4*: 2037.
121. Kirsten, T., et al. (1972) *PLC 3*: 1865.
122. Crater ages based on fossil track ages show less internal consistency than the rare gas data. See Phakey, P. P., et al., (1972) *PLC 3*: 2910.
123. McKay, D. S., and Heiken, G. H. (1973) *PLC 4*: 41; Oberbeck, V. R. (1971) *Moon.* 2: 263.
124. Gibson, E. K., and Hubbard, N. J. (1972) *PLC 3*: 2003.
125. Gibson E. K., et al. (1973) *PLC 4*: 1263.
126. Silver, L. T. (1972) *LS III*: 701; Doe, B., and Tatsumoto, M. (1972) *PLC 3*: 1981.
127. NASA SP-330.
128. Hodges, R. R., et al. (1973) *PLC 4*: 2854, (1974) *Icarus*, 21, 415.
129. Hoffman, J. H., et al. (1973) *PLC 4*: 2865.
130. Johnson, F. S., et al. (1972) *PLC 3*: 2231.
131. Bjorkholm, P. J., et al. (1973) *PLC 4*: 2793; see also NASA SP-289, 18-1 and NASA SP-315, 20-1.
132. Oyama, V. I., et al. (1970) *PLC 1*: 1921.
133. Schopf, J. W. (1970) *PLC 1*: 1933.
134. Barghoorn, E. S. (1970) *PLC 1*: 1775.
135. Oyama, V. I. (1972) *Space Life Sciences.* 3: 377.
136. Silverman, M. P., et al. (1971) *Nature.* 230: 169; Taylor, G. R., et al. (1971) *PLC 2*: 1939; Walkinshaw, C., et al. (1970) *Bioscience.* 20: 1297.
137. Shay, F. J., et al. (1974) *LS V*: 700.
138. Ponnamperuma, C. (1972) *Space Life Sciences.* 3: 493.
139. Sagan, C. (1961) NASA-757. Later comments by Sagan (1972, *Space Life Sciences.* 3: 484) indicate that the deeper parts of the lunar regolith might contain large amounts of organic material. This is an unlikely prospect in view of the bombardment history.
140. The amounts used were: Apollo 11, 700 g; Apollo 12, 528 g; Apollo 14, 589 g; Apollo 15, 144 g; Apollo 16, 73 g; and Apollo 17, 61 g.
141. Gibson, E. K., and Moore, C. B. (1972) *Space Life Sciences.* 3: 404.
142. Gibson, E. K., and Chang, S. (1974) *LS V*: 264; Chang, S. (1973) *PLC 4*: 1518; DesMarais, D. J., et al. (1974) *LS V*: 168.
143. Kaplan, I. (1972) *Space Life Sciences.* 3: 383.
144. Epstein, S., and Taylor, H. P. (1971) *PLC 2*: 1421; (1973) *PLC 4*: 1657; Clayton, R. N., et al. (1974) *LS V*: 129.
145. Friedman, I., et al., *PLC 2*: 1407: Kaplan, I., et al., ibid., 1397.

146. Eglinton, G. (1972) *Space Life Sciences.* 3: 497; Abell, P. I., et al. (1972) *Nature.* 226: 251; Chang, S., et al. (1971) *Science.* 171: 474.
147. Frondel, C., et al. (1970) *PLC 1*: 445; Anderson, A. T., et al. (1970) *Science.* 167: 587; Carter, I. D. (1970) *PLC 1*: 247.
148. Mason, B. (1972) *Meteoritics.* 7: 309.
149. Kvenvolden, K. A., et al. (1970) *PLC 1*: 1813.
150. Meinschein, W. G., et al. (1970) *PLC 1*: 1875.
151. Rho, J. H., et al. (1970) *PLC 1*: 1929.
152. Hodgson, G. W., et al. (1970) *PLC 1*: 1829.
153. Rho, J. H. (1972) *PLC 3*: 2149.
154. Hodgson, G. W., et al. (1971) *PLC 2*: 1865.
155. Rho, J. H. (1971) *PLC 2*: 1875.
156. Rho, J. H. (1972) *Space Life Sci. 3*: 415.
157. Fox, S. W., et al. (1972) *PLC 3*: 2109; Gehrke, C. W., et al. (1972) *PLC 3*: 2119.
158. Gehrke, C. W., et al. (1974) *LS V*: 262.
159. Biemann, K. (1972) *Space Life Sci.* 3: 469.
160. Flory, D. A., ibid., 457.
161. Hayes, J. M., ibid., 474.
162. Epstein, S., and Taylor, H. P. (1973) *PLC 4*: 1559.
163. Fox, S. W., *Space Life Sci. 3*: 425; Hamilton, P. B., and Nagy, B., ibid., 432; Gehrke, C. W., et al., ibid., 439.
164. See section 5.4 on rusty rock and on lunar water content.

CHAPTER 4

# *The Maria*

Selenographers are not the only students of the Moon's face. There are also selenologists, who use the telescope comparatively little, but cogitate much, and who have evolved theories of great ingenuity and variety.

G. K. Gilbert (1893)

## 4.1 THE LAVAS

The maria basalts, forming the dark patches on the face of the moon, have long been objects of interest (Figs. 4.1, 4.2, 4.3). In less scientific ages, they have formed the features of the man in the moon, an agreeable anthropomorphism, whose eyes were Mare Imbrium (Fig. 2.2) and Mare Serenitatis (Fig. 4.1). In other interpretations, Oceanus Procellarum is a rabbit's head, while Mare Crisium forms the tail of a celestial bunny. The reality is less exotic. Originally considered seas by the early selenographers on account of their smoothness relative to the rugged highlands, more recent theorizers speculated that they were asphalt[1] (being smooth and dark, they seemed to have characteristics of terrestrial car parking areas), dust[2], or sedimentary rocks[3, 4]. The more acute observers[5–7] detected the resemblance to terrestrial basaltic lavas, although the vast extent of the flooded areas (Mare Imbrium is the size of Texas) did not seem in accord with experience of terrestrial basalt viscosity.

The first sample return resolved these questions[8] but posed others. The mare material did indeed resemble terrestrial basaltic lavas, albeit of unusual chemistry and fluidity[9]. They were also ancient, fulfilling a few

120

**Fig. 4.1** Mare Serenitatis, a typical circular mare, 680 km in diameter. Note the wrinkle ridges and the dark outer ring of basalt (the dark mantle), including the Apollo 17 site. Note that the dark lavas extend southeastwards into Mare Tranquillitatis. The Apennine Mountains form the wall between Serenitatis and Imbrium to the west (middle left margin). The Apollo 15 site is in shadow at the west foot of the Apennines. The highland ridges radiating from the Imbrium basin are well shown in the lower left portion of the photograph. These form the Haemus Mountains. A light-colored ray, from Tycho about 2,000 km to the southwest, crosses the region, passing through the young crater Bessel (16 km diameter) located in the south-central portion of the basin. Sulpicius Gallus is the young crater west-southwest from Bessel, inside the mare. (Lick Observatory photograph.)

predictions[5, 10, 11] but dispelling other suggestions of youthful ages based on crater counting[12]. The subsequent sample returns extended this picture. Apollo 12 brought chemically distinct, somewhat younger (3.3 aeons) basalts from Oceanus Procellarum[13], closer to terrestrial analogues. The samples from the Hadley Rille site (Apollo 15)[14], important because of a cross section exposing mare fill, resembled those from the Ocean of Storms both in age and chemistry. The final samples from the Taurus-Littrow Valley (Apollo 17)[15], with a dark mantle, brought a return to the older Ti-rich basalts, close to the original Apollo 11 samples.

Numerous questions arose. Firstly, how representative a sample was gathered in four missions? While Apollo 11 and 12 had visited the open maria plains, Apollo 15 and 17 had sampled embayed marginal regions. There did not seem to be any effects due to the differing structural setting. Thus the Apollo 11 and 17 rocks were similar but distinct from the Apollo 12 and 15 samples.

Analyses of soil glass particles, however, and the slightly higher Al/Si ratios observed in the orbital data indicate that there are more aluminous basalts ($\sim$12–13 percent $Al_2O_3$)[16], as yet only sparsely sampled. Since there is considerable diversity in detail in the chemistry and petrology of the returned samples, no doubt other types await discovery by keen-eyed petrographers.

A second question concerns the volumetric importance of the high Ti basalts. Did Apollo 11 and 17 sample small areas of a special rock type (all Apollo 11 samples were collected within about 100 feet of the lunar module). However, the characteristic dark terrain extends widely across Tranquillitatis into Serenitatis (Fig. 4.1) and the Ti-rich basalts appear to be an important and widespread mare-filling unit on the eastern limb of the moon. The great extent of individual lava flows (section 2.10), the fluidity of the lavas, and the large areas of uniform lavas mapped by photogeologic techniques all encourage the view that the basalt samples are neither special nor trivial samples of the lunar surface.

The mode of eruption or extrusion of the lavas has been discussed in chapter 2. The most likely (section 2.10) mechanism seems to have been fissure eruptions, accompanied by fire fountaining analogous to the great eruption in Hekla, Iceland, in 1783[17].

What was the rate of filling of the great white amphitheaters? Were there great lakes of lava 10 or even 20 km deep, crystallizing in the raining meteorite bombardment in the hard lunar vacuum, glowing red under the black sky? The available evidence indicates instead that the basins were filled by many successive thin flows (section 2.10) with some regolith formation between flows. The eruptions seem to have been rapid, with vast effusions of fluid basalt flooding across hundreds of thousands of square kilometers and tongues of lava seeking the mild declivities among the older flows (Figs. 2.18, 2.19).

## 4.2  TYPES OF MARIA BASALTS

The Apollo missions returned a feast of interesting basalt varieties for the terrestrial petrographers. The initial samples from Apollo 11 provided, in addition to the high contents of Ti and refractory elements, two distinctive low- and high-K compositions[18, 19]. They contained evidence of extremely reducing conditions. The Apollo 12 basalts from the Ocean of Storms[13], in addition to being several hundred million years younger, were much lower in Ti, provided new textural types, and were separable into two new species, one with pyroxene and the other with olivine phenocrysts[20, 21]. Among the samples were the first examples of chilled or quenched basalts (e.g., 12009), indicating that they were present on the surface as a liquid. The Apollo 14 Fra Mauro samples provided evidence for another class of aluminous maria basalts (11–14 percent $Al_2O_3$) with distinctive REE patterns[16, 22, 23]. These occurred as clasts in the Fra Mauro breccias resulting from the Imbrium collision and indicated that mare basalt extrusion overlapped with at least the last stages of the cataclysmic events forming the ringed basins.

The greatest diversity of chemistry and texture in a single mission came from the Apollo 15 samples[14, 24–26]. Two major types, quartz-normative (or plagioclase phyric) and olivine-normative were recognized, with other highly vesicular rocks. These resembled the Apollo 12 basalts in age and chemistry.

The Apollo 15 mission returned some samples (e.g., 15597) consisting primarily of pyroxene and glass, apparently representing chilled examples of quartz-normative basalts, which arrived at the surface essentially in an entirely molten state. Such samples, which have not lost mineral phases due to fractional crystallization, provide the least equivocal information about their source region in the lunar interior.

An important new type was represented by the emerald green glass, the most primitive lunar basaltic composition yet sampled[27]. The Luna 16 basalts, from Mare Fecunditatis, were high $Al_2O_3$ types, resembling the clasts from the Apollo 14 breccias[23]. In contrast, the Apollo 17 samples from the Taurus-Littrow Valley were even more Ti-rich than the Apollo

**Fig. 4.2**  View along the western margin of Mare Humorum, looking south. Note the sinuous rilles and wrinkle ridges at the edge of the mare. (NASA AS16-120-19337.)

11 rocks and were the oldest (3.8 aeons) basalts sampled in place [15, 28–30]. An outstanding feature of the Apollo 11 samples is that many varieties were brought back, although the areas sampled were small. The diversity of chemistry and texture at each site is greater than would be encountered at terrestrial sites.

The classification of these diverse rocks presents a challenge to petrologists. Many different names are in vogue. Here, a general scheme is adopted, which attempts to take into account the chemistry and mineralogy of the rocks. Textural evidence is judged of less importance, being heavily influenced by local conditions of crystallization. Thus, for example, the highly vesicular Apollo 15 "seat belt" rock 15016 (Figs. 4.4,

4.5) is identical in chemistry to the well-crystallized rock 15555 (Figs. 4.6, 4.7), extensively used for an interlaboratory comparison of age dating techniques.

The classification adopted here distinguishes olivine normative basalts (Figs. 4.4–4.8), quartz normative basalts (Figs. 4.9–4.10), high-K Ti

**Fig. 4.3** Oceanus Procellarum, an example of an irregular mare, near the Apollo 12 landing site. The prominent crater with the central peak is Landsberg (39 km in diameter). The ridges in the foreground belong to the Montes Riphaeus. (NASA 16-2515.)

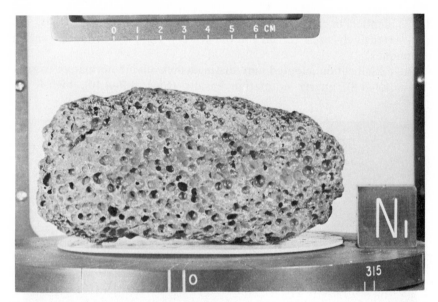

**Fig. 4.4**  A highly vesicular olivine basalt (15016). (Weight, 924 g; length, 13.5 cm.) (NASA S71-45477.)

basalts (Fig. 4.11), low-K Ti basalts (Figs. 4.12–4.15), and aluminous maria basalts (Figs. 4.16–4.17).

## Mineralogy

The number of mineral species on the moon is limited compared with the multitude of terrestrial minerals. More than 2,000 minerals are known on the earth; on the moon, about 100 have been identified (Table 4.2). This is a consequence of the lack of volatile elements, water, and weathering processes. The number of primary minerals, in the sense of having crystallized from silicate melts, rather than having developed by alteration of preexisting species, is not greatly different in terrestrial and lunar basalts. The modal compositions are given in Table 4.1 for the nine distinct mare basalt types. Principal minerals are clinopyroxene and plagioclase with olivine and ilmenite as important minor phases.

Lunar plagioclase is distinctive in being Ca-rich, with compositions usually between 80 and 90 percent anorthite. The range in the basalts is from $An_{60}$ to $An_{98}$, almost pure anorthite. The crystals are commonly zoned, showing variations in Ca within single crystals.

The variations in the plagioclases are comparatively simple in contrast to the complexity of the other major mineral group, the pyroxenes[31]. These show extreme zoning within single crystals, indicating that extreme element fractionation occurs over very small scales once crystallization begins. The amount of variation in single crystals in lunar pyroxenes far exceeds that observed in those from terrestrial basalts. Some also show well-developed exsolution lamellae, indicative of rapid cooling.

The olivine compositions are magnesian-rich (mostly $Fo_{50}$-$Fo_{70}$). Zoning is again very common. Iron-rich olivine is often present, associated with the last phases to crystallize.

Ilmenite (nearly pure $FeTiO_3$) is the common opaque mineral phase (Figs. 4.11–4.15). Tridymite and cristobalite (high temperature forms of $SiO_2$) are occasionally abundant in the lunar basalts.

Three new minerals, armalcolite, pyroxferroite, and tranquillityite have been added to the lengthening list (Table 4.2). These were first identified in

**Fig. 4.5**   Thin section of 15016 showing vesicle (Width of field = 4 mm.) Major minerals are clinopyroxene (65 percent), plagioclase (20 percent), olivine (10 percent), ilmenite (1 percent). (NASA S71-52221.)

**Table 4.1** Modal Mineralogy of Maria Basalts. (Values in percentages.)

| | Olivine basalt Apollo 12 | Olivine basalt Apollo 15 | Quartz basalt Apollo 15 | Quartz basalt Apollo 12 | High-K basalt Apollo 11 | Low-K basalt Apollo 11 | High-Ti basalt Apollo 17 | Aluminous maria basalt Apollo 14 | Aluminous maria basalt Luna 16 |
|---|---|---|---|---|---|---|---|---|---|
| Olivine | 10–20 | 6–10 | — | — | 0–5 | 0–5 | <5 | — | — |
| Clinopyroxene | 35–60 | 59–63 | 64–68 | 45–50 | 45–55 | 40–50 | 45–55 | 50 | 50 |
| Plagioclase | 10–25 | 21–27 | 24–32 | 30–35 | 20–40 | 30–40 | 25–30 | 40 | 40 |
| Opaques | 5–15 | 4–7 | 2–4 | 5–10 | 10–15 | 10–15 | 15–25 | 3 | 7 |
| Silica* | 0–2 | 1–2 | 2–6 | 3–7 | 1–5 | 1–5 | — | 2 | — |

*Tridymite, cristobalite.

**Fig. 4.6**  "Great Scott," a crystalline Apollo 15 olivine basalt (15555) identical in composition to 15016 (Fig. 4.4). (Weight, 9.6 kg; length, 30 cm.) (NASA S71-43393.)

the lunar samples, but at least one, armalcolite, has been found subsequently in terrestrial rocks[32].

The rather large number of accessory minerals contrasts with the few major species and reflects in general the high content of refractory elements such as Zr, Y, and the rare earths. Many elements present in lunar rocks are unable to enter the principal rock-forming minerals in significant amounts, and so concentrate to form their own mineral phases. This gives the lunar mineralogy a truly exotic flavor.

Much detailed work was carried out on the lunar minerals in the earlier stages of the Apollo program and the broad outlines of lunar mineralogy were established at that time. An extensive and detailed treatment of this early descriptive stage is given in a previous book[33] and a text on lunar mineralogy is in preparation[34]. *A Glossary of Lunar Minerals* [35] is available. There is not space here to cover the descriptive mineralogy, and the interested reader is directed to the above references. The emphasis here is on the interpretation of the mineralogical evidence for the origin and evolution of the maria and highland rocks.

**Fig. 4.7** Thin section of "Great Scott" (width of field = 4 mm), showing phenocrysts of clinopyroxene (1–2 mm) set in a groundmass of plagioclase, olivine, and pyroxene. (NASA S71-52213.)

### Vesicles in Maria Basalts

Spectacular examples of vesicular basalts occur among the maria samples, as illustrated in Fig. 4.4. The nature of the gas phase causing the bubble formation is not known[36]. Many of the bubble pits or vesicles are plated with late-crystallizing minerals and accordingly show strong reflection from the crystal faces.

One explanation is that the gas phase was carbon monoxide. This is produced by reaction of oxidized iron with carbon or carbides in the magma, leading to the production of CO and metallic iron. Such reactions could occur at depths of about 3 km in the moon, as the magma rose toward the surface[37]. It should be recalled, however, that the carbon content of the lunar basalts is very low (10–70 ppm).

### The Reduced Nature of Maria Basalts

The presence of metallic iron, FeS, and the absence of ferric iron in the maria basalts immediately led to the conclusion that the lunar basalts were strongly reduced relative to their terrestrial counterparts. Early estimates of oxygen fugacity values of about $10^{-13}$ at 1,150°C have been confirmed by experimental data[38]. Fig. 4.18 gives the measured total rock oxygen fugacity values for Apollo 12 and 15 basalts. At a given temperature, there is very little change in the oxygen fugacity, and the values appear to be independent of the texture, mineralogy, or chemistry of the basalts. The values lie about midway between the iron-wustite and the iron-rutile-ferropseudobrookite buffers and are several orders of magnitude lower than oxygen fugacity values for terrestrial basalts, which are typically about $10^{-8}$ at about 1,100°C.

The lunar basalts appear to have been strongly reduced at the time of extrusion, judging from the similarity in oxygen fugacity values in olivine

**Fig. 4.8**  Ilmenite-bearing olivine basalt (12057) showing ophitic texture. (Width of field = 4 mm.) (NASA S70-801-X.)

and groundmass for the Apollo 12 basalt 12009, which reached the surface as a liquid, before crystallization set in. The experimental studies do not favor the loss of the alkali elements by volatilization [39, 40]. At the low oxygen fugacities of lunar magmas, sodium would volatilize as the metal [38], rather than as the oxide, oxidizing the magma and producing $Fe^{3+}$. That this has not occurred is good evidence against extensive alkali loss by volatilization.

The highly reducing conditions account for the presence of $Eu^{2+}$ (about 70 percent of Eu is divalent) [41]. There is also evidence [42] for the existence of $Ti^{3+}$ and $Cr^{2+}$.

**Table 4.2**   Lunar Minerals.

| Common and abundant species | |
| --- | --- |
| Clinopyroxenes | $(CaMgFe)_2Si_2O_6$ |
| including   Augite | |
|          Sub-calcic augite | |
|          Titanaugite | |
|          Hedenbergite–ferrohedenbergite | |
|          Pigeonite | |
| Orthopyroxenes* | $MgSiO_3$-$FeSiO_3$ |
| Plagioclase feldspar | $(An)CaAl_2Si_2O_8$-$NaAlSi_3O_8(Ab)$ |
| Ilmenite | $FeTiO_3$ |
| Olivine | $(Fo)Mg_2SiO_4$-$Fe_2SiO_4(Fa)$ |

| Important accessory minerals | |
| --- | --- |
| Apatite | $Ca_5(PO_4)_3(F,Cl)$ |
| *Armalcolite* | $(FeMg)Ti_2O_5$ |
| Baddeleyite | $ZrO_2$ |
| Chromite | $FeCr_2O_4$ |
| Cristobalite | $SiO_2$ |
| Iron-Nickel | $FeNi$ |
| Potassium Feldspar | $KAlSi_3O_8$ |
| *Pyroxferroite* | $CaFe_6(SiO_3)_7$ |
| Spinels | $MgAl_2O_4$ |
| *Tranquillityite* | $Fe_8(Zr,Y)_2Ti_3Si_3O_{24}$ |
| Tridymite | $SiO_2$ |
| Troilite | $FeS$ |
| Whitlockite | $Ca_9MgH(PO_4)_7$ |
| Zirconolite | $CaZrTi_2O_7$ |

**Table 4.2**    (Continued)

| Rare lunar minerals | |
| --- | --- |
| Amphibole | |
| *Cohenite | $(FeNi)_3C$ |
| Copper | Cu |
| Goethite | FeOOH |
| Rutile | $TiO_2$ |
| *Schreibersite | $(FeNiCO)_3P$ |
| Zircon | $ZrSiO_4$ |

| Doubtful or tentative identifications still awaiting confirmation | |
| --- | --- |
| Ansovite | $Ti_3O_5$ |
| Calcite | $CaCo_3$ |
| Chalcocite | $Cu_2S$ |
| Chalcopyrite | $CuFeS_2$ |
| Chalcopyrrhotite | CuFeS |
| Corundum | $Al_2O_3$ |
| Garnet | |
| Graphite | C |
| Hematite | $Fe_2O_3$ |
| Iron carbide | FeC |
| Mackinawite | FeS |
| Magnetite | $Fe_3O_4$ |
| Mica | |
| Pentlandite | $(FeNi)_9S_8$ |
| Silicon carbide | SiC |
| Sphalerite | ZnS |
| Thorite | $ThSiO_4$ |
| Titanite | $CaTiSiO_5$ |
| Wustite | FeO |

*Highlands only.
New species unique to moon are in italics.


## 4.3   EMERALD GREEN AND ORANGE GLASSES

These varieties of beautiful glass spheres are found in association with the maria basalts. They are distinct from the wide range of glasses of impact origin found in the soils and provide important clues to lunar processes, and they are discussed in several places in the book.

**Fig. 4.9** Apollo 15 quartz-normative basalt (15058). (Weight, 2673 g; length, 16 cm.) (NASA S71-44205.)

### Emerald Green Glass (Hadley-Apennines)

The Apollo 15 astronauts collected "green clods" on the Apennine Front at Spur Crater. These samples (15425, 15426, 15427) were rich in emerald green glass spheres (Figs. 4.19, 4.20), which also occurred in the neighboring soils. These were of extremely uniform composition[27] (Table 4.3) and the most primitive lunar composition yet found. The spheres were most abundant in the 0.1–0.3 mm diameter size range. In the soil samples around Spur Crater they contribute up to 20 percent of the soil by volume. Their exposure age is 300 million years[43], which is taken as the age of Spur Crater. The age of the green glass is 3.3 aeons, similar to that of the Apollo 12 and 15 basalts[44]. The significance of this age is that the origin of the glass is firmly related to the extrusion of the maria basalts in the Swamp of Decay (Palus Putredenis) than to either younger volcanism, older highland crust, or impact events.

**Fig. 4.10** Thin section of quartz-normative basalt 15076, showing zoned clinopyroxene and plagioclase with cores of pyroxene. The inner zone is pigeonite, the outer zone is augite. Ilmenite is the opaque mineral. (Field of view 3 mm.) (NASA S71-52494.)

**Table 4.3**   Maria Basalt Compositions.

| | Green glass Apollo 15 | Olivine basalt Apollo 12 | Olivine basalt Apollo 15 | Quartz basalt Apollo 15 | Quartz basalt Apollo 12 | High K basalt Apollo 11 | Low K basalt Apollo 11 | High Ti basalt Apollo 17 | Aluminous maria basalts Apollo 12 | Luna 16 |
|---|---|---|---|---|---|---|---|---|---|---|
| $SiO_2$ | 45.6 | 45.0 | 44.2 | 48.8 | 46.1 | 40.5 | 40.5 | 37.6 | 46.6 | 45.5 |
| $TiO_2$ | 0.29 | 2.90 | 2.26 | 1.46 | 3.35 | 11.8 | 10.5 | 12.1 | 3.31 | 4.1 |
| $Al_2O_3$ | 7.64 | 8.59 | 8.48 | 9.30 | 9.95 | 8.7 | 10.4 | 8.74 | 12.5 | 13.9 |
| $FeO$ | 19.7 | 21.0 | 22.5 | 18.6 | 20.7 | 19.0 | 18.5 | 21.5 | 18.0 | 17.8 |
| $MnO$ | 0.21 | 0.28 | 0.29 | 0.27 | 0.28 | 0.25 | 0.28 | 0.22 | 0.27 | 0.26 |
| $MgO$ | 16.6 | 11.6 | 11.2 | 9.46 | 8.1 | 7.6 | 7.0 | 8.21 | 6.71 | 5.95 |
| $CaO$ | 8.72 | 9.42 | 9.45 | 10.8 | 10.9 | 10.2 | 11.6 | 10.3 | 11.82 | 12.0 |
| $Na_2O$ | 0.12 | 0.23 | 0.24 | 0.26 | 0.26 | 0.50 | 0.41 | 0.39 | 0.66 | 0.63 |
| $K_2O$ | 0.02 | 0.064 | 0.03 | 0.03 | 0.071 | 0.29 | 0.096 | 0.08 | 0.07 | 0.21 |
| $P_2O_5$ | — | 0.07 | 0.06 | 0.03 | 0.08 | 0.18 | 0.11 | 0.05 | 0.14 | 0.15 |
| $S$ | — | 0.06 | 0.05 | 0.03 | 0.07 | — | — | 0.15 | 0.06 | — |
| $Cr_2O_3$ | 0.41 | 0.55 | 0.70 | 0.66 | 0.46 | 0.37 | 0.25 | 0.42 | 0.37 | — |
| $\Sigma$ | 99.4 | 99.77 | 99.46 | 99.08 | 100.23 | 99.67 | 99.85 | 99.58 | 100.2 | 100.42 |
| Sample no. | 15426 | 12009 | 15555 | 15076 | 12052 | Ave. | Ave. | 71055 | 12038 | B-1 A-35 |

Major elements expressed as oxides in weight percent.

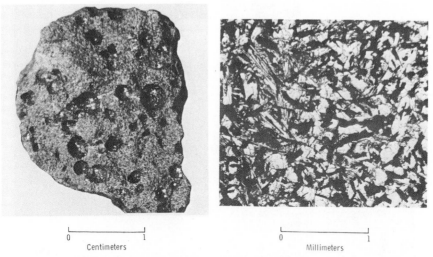

0                    1
Centimeters

0                    1
Millimeters

**Fig. 4.11**   (a) High-K Apollo 11 basalt 10022. (NASA S69-45223.) (b) Thin section of 10022. (NASA S69-47908.)

0       1       2
Centimeters

0                    1
Millimeters

**Fig. 4.12**   (a) Low-K Apollo 11 basalt 10047. (NASA S69-45633.) (b) Thin section of 10047. (NASA S69-47907.)

**Fig. 4.13**  High-Ti basalt from Apollo 17 (70035). (Weight, 5765 g; length, 23 cm.) (NASA S72-56383.)

**Fig. 4.14**  Thin section of high-Ti basalt 70035 showing coarse grain size and plagioclase, pyroxene, and ilmenite. (Field of view = 4 mm.) (NASA S73-19848.)

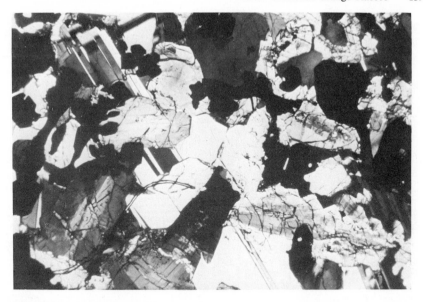

**Fig. 4.15** Thin section of 70149, an ilmenite-rich basalt from Apollo 17. (Field of view = 4 mm.) (NASA S-73-19854.)

Much effort and ingenuity has been expended on theories of their origin. Before discussing these, consideration is necessary of the related question of the orange glasses at Apollo 17, with which they share much in common, although of differing chemical composition. Note, however, that both glasses have high contents of zinc and other volatile elements.

### Orange Glass (Taurus-Littrow)

The finding of orange soil (74220) by the Apollo 17 astronauts was a spectacular part of the mission, since it carried with it hopes of water, oxidation, young volcanic activity, and the possibility that "Shorty" Crater, on whose rim the glass was found, might be the young lunar volcanic vent so eagerly awaited by some astrogeologists. All these hopes were dampened by the examination of the glass.

The soil consisted almost entirely of fine glass spheres, averaging about 0.1–0.2 mm diameter. The color is mainly orange but ranges from yellow to black. They have a high titanium content ($\sim$9.3 percent $TiO_2$), which

**Fig. 4.16**    Aluminous mare basalt 14053. (Weight, 251 g; length, 8 cm.) (NASA S71-21353.)

causes the orange color, and they are similar in composition both to the Apollo 11 orange glasses and to the Apollo 11 and 17 basalts, although somewhat richer in MgO, zinc, chlorine, copper, lead, and other volatile components[45, 46]. Gibson and Moore[47] found very low carbon contents (4 ppm) in the orange glass, compared with earlier values of 100 ppm. They conclude that the carbon (and, by inference, many of the other volatiles) is present as a surface condensate. A further characteristic is the chemical homogeneity of the glass spheres. The surface of the spheres is coated with adhering droplets of similar composition, indicating low-velocity spattering. The major element composition is close but not identical to that of the Apollo 17 basalt. There is no evidence of the presence of ferric iron[48, 49].

The age of the glass spheres is 3.8 aeons, which links them directly to that of the Apollo 17 basaltic rocks[50]. Thus, they are not young but old. Their lead content is high (2.5 ppm), but 80 percent of it is leachable. The lead content is too high to be derived from the U and Th present (0.16 and 0.56 ppm, respectively). This lead is among the most nonradiogenic on the moon. Tatsumoto[51] calculates that the $^{238}U/^{204}Pb$ ($\mu$) for the source was 34.5, compared to values of 100–300 for source of the maria basalts. Similar parentless lead appears in the rusty rock 66095.

The occurrence of the orange glass at Shorty Crater in the Taurus-Littrow valley was only the most spectacular facet of a related series of phenomena, embracing as well the dark mantle and the emerald green glass from the Apennine Front. The dark mantle (section 2.13) at the Apollo 17 site is at present part of the regolith. Shorty Crater penetrated through the highland landslide and excavated the famous orange soil from underlying layers within the mare basalt. The soil is unique since it is composed mostly of orange and black spherules, with an absence of the rock fragments so characteristic of other lunar soils. The individual

**Fig. 4.17**   Thin section of aluminous mare basalt 12038. (Field of view = 4 mm.) (Courtesy A. M. Reid.)

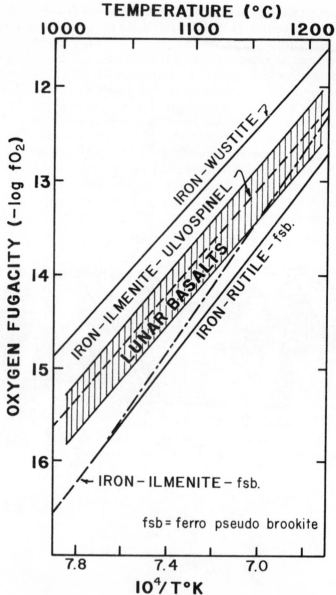

**Fig. 4.18** Measured bulk oxygen fugacity (fo$_2$) values for maria basalts fall in the shaded zone, superimposed on the buffer curves of the Fe-FeO-TiO$_2$ system[37]. (Courtesy M. Sato.)

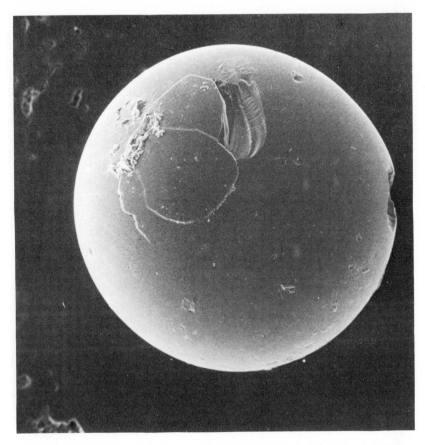

**Fig. 4.19**  Scanning electron microscope (SEM) photograph of a green glass sphere (175 $\mu$m diameter); a chip has been spalled from the surface. Splashes of molten and partially hardened glass of the same composition adhere to the surface. (NASA S72-53599, courtesy D. S. McKay.)

spheres show no evidence of high velocity impact pits, so they have not been exposed at the surface.

### Origin of the Orange and Emerald Green Glasses

Most of the lunar glasses originate as splash during meteorite impact, but several features of the orange and green glasses raise doubts about such an origin. The glasses do not show a wide range of size; both are notably uniform in composition; both contain high concentrations of

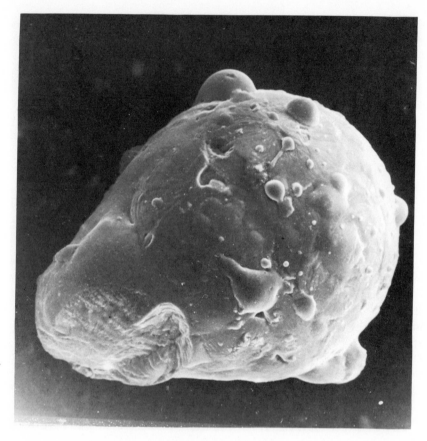

**Fig. 4.20**  Composite green glass droplet, 950 $\mu$m long, with mounds of the same material adhering to the surface. (NASA S73-18505, courtesy D. S. McKay.)

volatile elements; both were last liquid at, or close to, the time of extrusion of the maria basalts with which they are associated; both occur in valleys close to highland ridges and at the extreme edges of the mare basalt flooding. Conventional impact hypotheses seem ruled out by their abundance and uniformity of composition.

The ingenious suggestion that they are formed by meteorite impact into a lava lake neatly resolves the various problems noted above [52, 53]. That such events occur is undisputed: that the evidence of this brief moment survives is less likely, particularly since *both* green and orange glasses have to be explained. The lack of rock fragments from the frozen crust of the proposed lake is a serious defect in the hypothesis. The same mechanism would need to act widely across the moon along the margins of the maria basins to explain the dark mantle deposits generally. The similarities in volatile element content, the occurrence in areas where lavas may be ponded, the lead isotope evidence, and the absence of a demonstrated meteoritic component in the glasses all point to an internal, rather than an external process of origin. The absence of shock effects and the great homogeneity of the glasses are similarly strong evidence against the impact hypothesis.

Most of the criteria can be explained as resulting from fire fountaining[54, 55]. In such a process, multiple droplets are built up by low velocity impacts of material with the same composition (Fig. 4.20). Orange colors were observed in the dark albedo areas near basin margins. The observation that the last flows flooding across the broad plains of Mare Imbrium came from a 20-km-long fissure near one edge is relevant here as well, as is the distribution of the sinuous rilles, interpreted here as lava cut channels.

All these phenomena are consistent with lava effusions flooding out from fissures near the edges of the basins. During this massive outpouring, some fire fountaining occurs, spraying the homogeneous glass spherules in layers over the nearby surfaces. Often, they will be buried by subsequent flows and later excavated by impacts as at Shorty Crater, to produce locally a glass-rich regolith.

The minor differences with the products of terrestrial fire fountains, such as lack of vesicles, can be ascribed to the lower viscosity of the lunar basalts and to the lower gravity field. The appropriate pressure is provided by a local concentration of volatiles. The glass compositions are not extreme differentiates, but on the contrary, primitive and unfractionated, except for the volatile contents. In their constancy of composition, the green and orange glasses bear a strong resemblance to glasses from Hawaiian lava fountains[55].

## 4.4  COMPOSITION OF MARIA BASALTS

A great amount of data are available. The approach used here has been to select rocks typical of the various basaltic types. Nine distinct types are recognized on a chemical and mineralogical basis. Rather than provide averages of data of varying quality, from rocks of varying modal mineralogy and sample size, it has been judged more appropriate to quote data from specific rock samples, hopefully avoiding the above problems.

Makers of averages are perennially prone to mix apples and oranges. Only in the case of the Apollo 11 high-K and low-K rocks are averages of data given.

The major elements (Table 4.3) are usually defined as those elements present as principal constituents of the main rock-forming minerals, with abundances exceeding 1 percent by weight. In the lunar rocks, seven elements, O, Si, Al, Fe, Mg, Ca, and Ti are major constituents. K, Na, Mn, and Cr are minor constituents within the concentration range of 0.1–1.0 percent. Other constituents at levels between 100 and 1,000 ppm (0.01–0.1 percent) include Zr, Ba, Sr, Y, and total rare-earths (and Ni in the fines). The other elements are generally present at levels below 100 ppm (0.01 percent) and do not contribute significantly to the total.

Although all data are given here as weight percent, parts per million ($10^{-4}$ weight %), or parts per billion ($10^{-7}$ weight %), it should be recalled that alternative representations in terms of atomic percent or volume percent give a different picture. In terms of volume, the large cation, potassium, is much more important than its weight percentage would indicate. On a volume basis, all the cations are reduced to occupying interstices among a packing of oxygen anions, comprising more than 90 percent of the volume.

The trace elements are divided into several groupings in which the elements exhibit similar geochemical behavior. This classification is based on the geochemical distribution of elements in minerals, where the size of the cations is a critical factor in determining element behavior. Thus the normal periodic classification of the elements, while remaining the ultimate base, needs some modification to allow for such effects due to the strict geometric requirements for entry into crystal lattices. The abundance of the major elements, Si, Al, Fe, Mg, Ca, Ti (and Na and K), control the type of mineral lattices that form and that the trace elements can enter on the basis of similarity in ionic size, valency, bond type (ionic-covalent-metallic) and, for the transition elements, crystal field effects. The advantages of this classification are:

(*a*) Elements whose geochemical behavior is similar are brought together. This is preferable to groupings such as Large Ion Lithophile (LIL) elements, which brings together many unlikely geochemical bedfellows and is too broad a classification to be of use in detailed geochemical discussions[56].

(*b*) Tables are arranged in order of decreasing ionic size, and this order is preserved within each table except for the ferromagnesian elements, where a tabulation based on crystal field site preference energy is used.

(c) The large number of elements is broken up into tables of convenient size.

The siderophile and chalcophile elements are excluded from the compilation of abundance data for the maria basalts. Their chief significance lies in the information they provide on the origin and evolution of the moon, rather than in the detailed considerations on the formation and subsequent history of the maria basalts. Accordingly, they are considered separately later.

## Major Element Comparisons

The maria basalts are completely distinct in composition from typical upper crustal rocks on the earth, such as granodiorites and granites (Table 4.4). Other materials that are dissimilar include sedimentary rocks, ultrabasic rocks, iron and chondritic meteorites, and tektites.

The closest resemblances in element abundances are to the terrestrial basalts and to the basaltic achondrites (eucrites and howardites). It was long suggested that some classes of meteorites were derived from the moon. The Apollo 11 data effectively ruled out the chondrites, since the element abundances are widely different. The basaltic achondrites, however, although too low in Ti (and differing in some trace elements), show

Table 4.4   Range in Composition of Maria Basalts and the 10–90 percent Frequency Range of Terrestrial Continental Basalts.

|          | Moon      | Earth*       |
|----------|-----------|--------------|
| $SiO_2$  | 37–49     | 44–53        |
| $TiO_2$  | 0.3–13    | 0.9–3.3      |
| $Al_2O_3$ | 7–14     | 13–19        |
| FeO      | 18–23     | 7–14         |
| MnO      | 0.21–0.29 | 0.09–0.3     |
| MgO      | 6–17      | 4–10         |
| CaO      | 8–12      | 8–12         |
| $Na_2O$  | 0.1–0.5   | 1.8–3.8      |
| $K_2O$   | 0.02–0.3  | 0.3–2.0      |
| $P_2O_5$ | 0.03–0.18 | 0.04–0.6     |
| $Cr_2O_3$ | 0.12–0.70 | 0.005–0.04 |

*Data from Schmitt, R. A., and Laul, J. C. (1973) *Moon*. 8: Table 2.

some remarkable similarities in chemistry. The aluminous basalts (e.g., 12038) are particularly close in composition, although Ti is still too abundant in the lunar rocks. Decisive differences, particularly for the oxygen isotope ratios, rule out the moon as a source for the basaltic achondrites, but as with the close comparisons between some lunar breccias and meteorites (see section on chondrules), analogous processes to those seen on the moon must have occurred elsewhere in the solar system in the source regions of the basaltic achondrites.

Among the terrestrial basalts, the low potassium "oceanic tholeiites," which appear to form most of the oceanic crust, are the most primitive lava being extruded from the earth's interior, and immediately invite comparison with the lunar basaltic rocks. Although there are some similarities, the sodium content of the terrestrial basalts is much higher, and the iron and titanium contents much lower than the lunar lavas.

The significance of these abundances, when taken in conjunction with the more informative trace element data and the experimental work, indicate that the lunar basalts, like their terrestrial counterparts, are products of local partial melting deep in the interior. The chemical differences among the resulting lavas indicate that the parent material is different, so that the lunar interior does not have the same composition as the earth's mantle.

## 4.5   THE LARGE CATIONS

The large cations comprise the elements that mainly accompany potassium. In contrast to most terrestrial surface rocks, potassium is so low in the lunar rocks as to constitute a minor or trace element and resembles the concentration levels in low-K oceanic tholeiites or in chondritic meteorites. In the lunar rocks (Table 4.5), potassium and other large cations are principally contained in the interstitial material, or *mesostasis*, and enter the lattice sites in the main rock-forming minerals only to a minor degree. Nevertheless, potassium may concentrate in the residual phases (up to 9 percent K has been observed) with formation of K-feldspar.

The abundance of barium calls for special comment. In contrast to potassium, it is relatively much more abundant than in the earth. The cosmic or primitive abundance is about 4 ppm and at least 50 percent of all the barium in the earth is concentrated in the continental crust, which makes up 0.4 percent of the mass of the earth. The abundance levels of 200–300 ppm barium in the lunar basalts imply similar concentration in

**Table 4.5**  Elemental Abundances of Large Cations in Maria Basalts.

| | Green glass Apollo 15 | Olivine basalt Apollo 12 | Olivine basalt Apollo 15 | Quartz basalt Apollo 15 | Quartz basalt Apollo 12 | High K basalt Apollo 11 | Low K basalt Apollo 11 | High Ti basalt Apollo 17 | Aluminous maria basalts Apollo 12 | Luna 16 |
|---|---|---|---|---|---|---|---|---|---|---|
| $Rb^+$ | 0.58 | 1.03 | 0.65 | 0.92 | 1.26 | 5.6 | 0.9 | 0.6 | 1.4 | 1.6 |
| $K^+$% | 0.017 | 0.053 | 0.025 | 0.025 | 0.059 | 0.24 | 0.08 | 0.06 | 0.06 | 0.14 |
| $Ba^{2+}$ | 18 | 60 | 32 | 60 | 70 | 280 | 100 | 84 | 128 | 220 |
| Eu | 0.21 | 0.94 | 0.69 | 0.98 | 1.04 | 2.2 | 1.9 | 1.45 | 2.6 | 2.5 |
| $Pb^{2+}$ | 1.3 | 0.40 | 0.20 | 0.27 | 0.65 | 1.7 | 0.4 | 0.6 | 1.3 | — |
| $Sr^{2+}$ | 41 | 96 | 85 | 112 | 115 | 155 | 170 | 176 | 180 | 435 |
| $Ca^{2+}$% | 6.23 | 6.73 | 6.75 | 7.72 | 7.79 | 7.3 | 8.3 | 7.36 | 8.30 | 8.25 |
| $Na^+$% | 0.089 | 0.17 | 0.18 | 0.19 | 0.19 | 0.34 | 0.31 | 0.29 | 0.48 | 0.24 |

Data in parts per million except where indicated in weight percent.

the outer regions of the moon. This is evidence that much of the Ba has been selectively melted and concentrated upwards if the moon was originally homogeneous. The high Ba abundance in residual phases leads to the formation of Ba-rich K-feldspar[57].

Strontium is also strongly enriched by about 15 times over the chondritic abundances. This element is mainly contained in the plagioclase feldspars, where it readily substitutes for calcium. Divalent europium is similar in ionic radius to strontium and, like it, is concentrated in plagioclase feldspar. Strontium is less strongly enriched in the lavas than barium. This is consistent with its geochemical behavior, since it enters calcium sites rather readily. Hence it will occur in the main mineral phases in the interior of the moon and will be less readily partitioned into the liquid phase than barium.

Sodium is present at rather uniform abundance levels in contrast to the heavier alkalis, K, Rb, and Cs. This is a consequence of its entry into plagioclase, which the larger alkalis enter only with difficulty. It is depleted relative to terrestrial basalts by a factor of about five. Sodium will be partitioned into the liquid phase during partial melting, so that the source rocks will be depleted even more in sodium.

Some petrologists appealed to loss of Na and K to account for the order of magnitude depletion in sodium compared with terrestrial lavas, perhaps reluctant to believe that so fundamental a distinction could exist in basalt chemistry[40]. The lunar lavas were extruded at temperatures approaching 1,200°C into a hard vacuum of at least $10^{-9}$ torr. Although such conditions might be thought to favor loss of volatile elements, the lithospheric pressure of the lava exceeds that of the vapor pressure of the elements at depths greater than $10^{-3}$ cm. Thus loss could occur only from a thin skin[58]. Very thorough stirring, mixing, or bubbling would be needed to lose elements from depth.

Since the lavas are quite uniform in sodium content, a very efficient mechanism would be needed. The mineralogy of the samples shows no such effects. The zoned plagioclases become richer in Na toward the exterior, the reverse to that predicted by volatile loss. Also there seem to be no Na-rich concentrations in the soils or other likely repositories for the proposed very large amount of volatilized sodium. Loss of volatiles is of course inhibited by rapid freezing of the surface of the extruded lavas. The consensus is that volatile loss from the maria basalts during extrusion is trivial.

The Rb/Ba ratio is a good example of the coherence between the volatile [59] element, Rb, and the involatile element, Ba. Figure 4.21 illustrates this relationship. It is significant that this correlation holds for the highlands, as well as the maria samples discussed here. The significance of these and many similar observations will be dealt with in later sections. Rb and Ba are an example of a pair of elements whose close association is predictable on geochemical grounds. For many other relationships in the highland rocks, which we will discuss later, there are no simple similarities in geochemical behavior to account for them. In the maria basalts, considered here, many close element correlations arise from their presence together in residual phases or glassy mesostasis during crystallization of the basaltic melts.

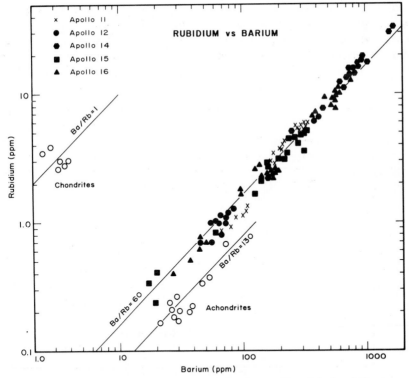

**Fig. 4.21**  The good correlation between the volatile element Rb and the involatile element, Ba, for both maria and highland samples.

## 4.6   THE RARE EARTH ELEMENTS (REE)

The significant geochemical difference is a regular decrease in ionic radii from $La^{+3}$ (1.14 A) to $Lu^{+3}$ (0.85 A). The only common cations close in size are $Ca^{+2}$ (1.02 A) and $Na^+$ (0.97 A). Substitution of the trivalent rare earth elements for sodium does not occur, but they substitute for $Ca^{+2}$ in a variety of minerals. However, valency difficulties ensure that they concentrate in residual phases, and a substantial portion occurs in the interstitial material in the lunar rocks. The REE data for the maria basalts are given in Table 4.6.

. The rare-earth patterns, relative to the chondritic abundances[60], are shown in Fig. 4.22. Several interesting features emerge. Firstly, is the europium depletion, which is discussed in the next section. Although there is a general decrease of the Eu depletion with decreasing total REE content, this is not systematic. Secondly, the abundance patterns are only broadly parallel to one another, with significant differences in detail. The main difference lies in the tendency for a decrease in the large REE (La-Sm) in Ti-rich basalts, reminiscent of the patterns observed in the Low-K oceanic tholeiites. The lack of enrichment of the large REE

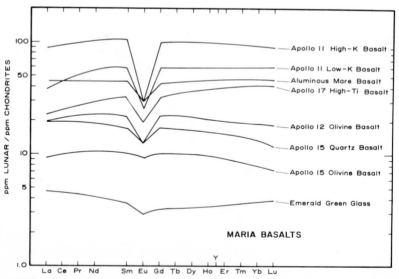

**Fig. 4.22** Rare earth patterns for maria basalts, plotted relative to chondritic abundances[60]. Note the variable degree of europium depletion and the tendency for the light rare earths (La-Sm) to decrease relative to the chondritic abundances.

**Table 4.6**  Rare Earth Element Abundances in Maria Basalts.

| | Green glass Apollo 15 | Olivine basalt Apollo 12 | Olivine basalt Apollo 15 | Quartz basalt Apollo 15 | Quartz basalt Apollo 12 | High K basalt Apollo 11 | Low K basalt Apollo 11 | High Ti basalt Apollo 17 | Aluminous mare basalt Apollo 12 |
|---|---|---|---|---|---|---|---|---|---|
| $La^{3+}$ | 1.4 | 6.1 | 3.5 | 5.4 | 6.3 | 27 | 11.4 | 6.0 | 14 |
| $Ce^{3+}$ | 3.8 | 16.8 | 8.06 | 15.1 | 18.8 | 76 | 36 | 19.2 | 36 |
| $Pr^{3+}$ | 0.53 | 3.0 | 1.2 | 2.2 | 2.6 | 13 | 7 | 3.2 | 5.3 |
| $Nd^{3+}$ | 2.2 | 12 | 6.3 | 10.6 | 14.7 | 63 | 33 | 17.4 | 26 |
| $Sm^{3+}$ | 0.76 | 4.5 | 2.1 | 3.52 | 4.9 | 21 | 12 | 6.85 | 9.4 |
| Eu | 0.21 | 0.94 | 0.69 | 0.98 | 1.04 | 2.2 | 1.9 | 1.45 | 2.6 |
| $Gd^{3+}$ | 0.91 | 6.9 | 2.90 | 4.95 | 6.87 | 27 | 17 | 10.3 | 13 |
| $Tb^{3+}$ | 0.15 | 1.11 | 0.51 | 0.83 | 1.2 | 4.6 | 2.5 | 1.87 | 2.9 |
| $Dy^{3+}$ | 1.1 | 7.13 | 3.27 | 5.6 | 7.74 | 32 | 20 | 11.8 | 15 |
| $Ho^{3+}$ | 0.27 | 1.4 | 0.78 | 1.24 | 1.34 | 6.8 | 3.3 | 3.16 | 3.9 |
| $Er^{3+}$ | 0.8 | 3.6 | 1.7 | 3.4 | 4.55 | 19 | 12 | 8.40 | 9.9 |
| $Tm^{3+}$ | 0.15 | 0.60 | 0.24 | 0.35 | 0.70 | 3.0 | 1.6 | 1.41 | 1.6 |
| $Yb^{3+}$ | 0.93 | 3.74 | 1.60 | 2.77 | 4.3 | 19 | 10 | 8.55 | 9.0 |
| $Lu^{3+}$ | 0.14 | 0.55 | 0.22 | 0.33 | 0.65 | 2.6 | 1.5 | 1.33 | 1.5 |
| $\Sigma$REE | 13.4 | 71 | 33 | 59 | 76 | 315 | 173 | 101 | 150 |
| $Y^{3+}$ | 7.2 | 34 | 18 | 29 | 40 | 184 | 104 | 75 | 80 |
| $\Sigma$REE+Y | 20.6 | 105 | 56 | 88 | 116 | 500 | 277 | 176 | 188 |

Data in parts per million.

relative to the smaller (Gd-Lu) contrasts with the terrestrial patterns, where extreme enrichments of large REE are observed. The lunar patterns are consistent with only a limited amount of fractional crystallization during cooling.

A significant portion of the REE is contained, not in the major mineral phases, but in the accessory minerals apatite, whitlockite, zirconolite, and tranquillityite. Note that the enrichment of the REE relative to chondrites reaches 100 times in the high-K Apollo 11 basalts. The generally parallel movement of the total REE patterns (excluding Eu) over more than an order of magnitude is attributed to two causes.

Firstly, small amounts of partial melting produce strong enrichment of REE in the melt, since the accessory phases containing the REE are among the first components to enter the melt. Increasing the degree of partial melting dilutes the total REE content with the addition of REE-poor phases. Secondly, the various classes of basalts come from differing depths in the lunar interior. Those from shallower depths are likely to come from an inherently richer REE source region, as discussed in the section of the geochemical evolution of the moon (see section 7.6). The REE are refractory elements and show an interesting relationship to the volatile elements. This is demonstrated by the K/La relationship (Fig. 4.23), although other elements would serve equally well. K/La is constant at about 70, not only in maria basalts but also in the highlands rocks, a fact fraught with significance for theories of lunar origin.

Yttrium is closely associated with the REE. The trivalent ion has the same radius as $Ho^{3+}$ (0.92A), and on the plots where the rare earths are normalized to chondrites, yttrium usually falls on the line displaying the same enrichment relative to chondrites as does Ho.

## 4.7  THE EUROPIUM ANOMALY

Although many geochemical and geophysical problems have been posed by the study of the lunar rocks, the europium anomaly exhibited by nearly all the lunar REE patterns has probably produced most controversy, conflicting explanations and interpretations of the geochemical, mineralogical, and experimental petrological results. The unique behavior of europium was immediately observed in the analysis of the Apollo 11 rocks, which showed a strong depletion in the element relative to neighboring rare earth elements Sm and Gd.

Under reducing conditions, the divalent state is stable[61]. The ionic radius ($Eu^{2+}$ = 1.25 A) is 28 percent larger than that for the trivalent state

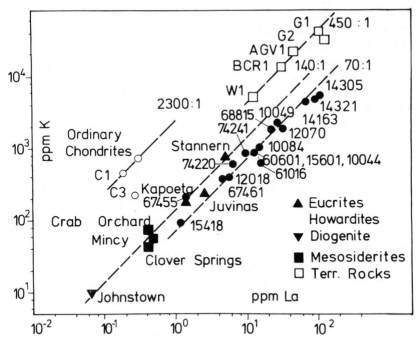

**Fig. 4.23** The close association between volatile potassium and involatile lanthanum, in both maria and highlands samples (K/La = 70). Note that the data for the achondrites is displaced, with a K/La ratio of 140. Common terrestrial ratios (W-1, G-1, line) are 450, while carbonaceous and ordinary chondrites have very high ratios (2300). (Courtesy H. Wänke.)

($Eu^{3+} = 0.98$ A). This increase in size and the change in valency completely alter the geochemical behavior of europium. It now enters larger lattice sites. On account of similarity in size and identity of valency to $Sr^{2+}$ ($r = 1.18$ A), divalent Eu and Sr show a close geochemical association, or coherence, readily entering Ca, Na, and K sites in feldspar lattices. This is fortunate since strontium is a particularly useful geochemical tracer, providing age, as well as geochemical information. The close coherence with Eu in lunar rocks is best shown by the similar depletion or enrichment of Sr and Eu in lunar rocks, relative to abundances in chondritic meteorites.

The $Sr^{2+}/Eu^{2+}$ coherence depends, of course, on the amount of $Eu^{2+}$ relative to $Eu^{3+}$. This is a function of temperature and oxygen fugacity[62]. A plot of Sr versus total Eu reveals that the Sr/Eu ratio is highest in plagioclase-rich samples, such as anorthosite, and falls in the total rocks. This is due to the preferential entry of $Eu^{2+}$ into feldspar while $Eu^{3+}$ remains with the trivalent REE. Sr/Eu is typically about 180 in plagioclase from highland samples, whereas the average total rock ratio is about 130. Philpotts[63] has made use of the geochemical coherence of $Sr^{2+}$ and $Eu^{2+}$, utilizing Sr distribution coefficients as an aid in calculating the $Eu^{2+}/Eu^{3+}$ ratios. In lunar samples, typically about 70 percent of the europium is divalent.

Several hypotheses have been advanced to account for the depletion in europium observed in the maria basalts. These are discussed in order of increasing probability.

(*a*) *The moon as a whole is depleted in Eu.* Was Eu selectively lost[64] from the moon at or before accretion, along with the volatile elements such as Pb? There is no evidence that Eu or its compounds differ significantly in volatility from those of the other REE. The close coherence with Sr indicates parallel behavior for these two elements. But Sr is notably involatile, and the moon is enriched in such refractory elements. Accordingly there is no *a priori* reason to suppose that Eu is separated from the other REE during accretion. There is a lack of europium anomalies in most meteorites and in the bulk earth[65]. The problem is not universal but a feature unique to the moon.

(*b*) *Eu is volatilized from lava lakes during mare basin filling* [66]. The objections noted above about the involatile nature of Eu and its geochemical coherence with Sr are valid. More telling is the general absence of evidence of loss of even such volatile elements as Rb. The Rb-Sr model ages do not allow much loss of Rb relative to Sr during the filling of the maria basins[67].

(*c*) *Plagioclase feldspar, incorporating Eu, is removed by near surface fractionation* [68]. Eu in the main lunar rock-forming minerals is concentrated in the plagioclase feldspar, and depleted in pyroxenes and ilmenite. From these observations, many workers concluded that plagioclase separation had occurred, thus depleting the residual liquid in Eu. The total rock samples show Eu depletions by factors of 2–3 relative to neighboring REE (Sm-Gd). To account for this depletion by crystallization and removal of plagioclase, 60–90 percent of plagioclase removal is necessary. For the Apollo 11 rocks, most of the chemical and mineralogical data are consistent with rapid chilling and crystallization, without wholesale separation of plagioclase. The Apollo 12 maria basalts show evidence of near-surface crystal fractionation, but this involves mainly removal of olivine, which has little effect either in Eu or the total REE patterns.

The evidence from experimental petrology caused a considerable controversy. The Canberra high pressure group[69, 70] concluded from their experimental studies that plagioclase was not a liquidus phase and so could not be responsible for depleting the total rock compositions in Eu. The Edinburgh group[71, 72] disputed this finding, claiming that there was both experimental and petrological evidence for the presence of plagioclase as an early crystallizing phase, and that near-surface crystal settling, and hence depletion, in Eu had occurred.

As discussed in the section on crystallization of the maria basalts, the weight of the available evidence indicates that plagioclase is a late, rather than an early, phase to crystallize in maria basalts. It is not a liquidus phase, except in the aluminous maria basalts (e.g., 14053). The possibility of massive separation of plagioclase, just prior to, or early in the course of eruption of the maria basalts, is remote and has not been widely accepted as an explanation of the Eu depletion.

(d) *Eu is selectively retained in plagioclase in the lunar interior during partial melting.* The experimental evidence[69, 70] shows that plagioclase is not a stable phase at the depth of formation of the lavas (200–300 km). The aluminous maria basalts come from shallower levels.

(e) *Eu is selectively retained in accessory minerals in the lunar interior during partial melting.* This model proposes that the trivalent REE were mainly contained in accessory phases, such as the phosphate mineral, whitlockite, in the lunar interior[70, 73–75]. During the partial melting process that produced the maria basalts, such accessory minerals preferentially entered the melt. Eu is selectively retained in the lunar interior in major mineral phases, such as pyroxene.

However, most pyroxenes have negative Eu anomalies[75]. Small degrees of partial melting involving the minor and interstitial phases will then produce a high concentration of REE with a large Eu depletion[70]. Increasing amounts of partial melting will involve the major phases and dilute the total REE content, and the relative Eu depletion will decrease (Fig. 4.22). This implies that partial melting takes place on a scale involving individual phases, and that equilibrium melting of all phases is not achieved. Partial melting in the lunar interior can be predicted to be very localized, at least in the initial stages, on account of the lack of water and other volatiles. Within the limiting assumptions noted above, this model can explain the depletion of Eu in a single stage, but some difficulties remain.

Several objections to this model have been advanced[65]. The abundance of phosphorus is only about 500–1,000 ppm in maria basalts. If all this is partitioned into the melt, then, for 5 percent partial melting, the source region contains 25–50 ppm P. This is a low concentration to exist as a separate phase.

Well-developed correlations are noted between, for example, Ba and the trivalent REE. Ba does not enter phosphate lattice sites, so that the correlation becomes fortuitous. "Analyses of Apollo 12 apatites and whitlockites do not report any K, let alone Ba. This is in accord with terrestrial apatite data. For example, an apatite with a matrix partition coefficient for Ce of 52 yields a Ba partition coefficient that is a factor of at least 2,500 times lower. Seemingly, the only way around this problem would be to postulate an additional trace phase that contains the Ba, but this cannot be K-feldspar (positive Eu anomaly) or zircon (high heavy rare earths); further, when more than one phase is involved the chances of coherence decrease. For these reasons the phosphate fusion model is rejected"[76].

Modifications to this model have recently been proposed[77]. These involve the distribution of the REE among refractory phases, resulting from condensation in the solar nebula. Thus the trivalent REE would enter minerals such as perovskite, while Eu enters melilite. These proposals avoid the difficulties with pyroxene[75]. It is difficult, however, to see how these phases might survive partial or complete melting of most of the moon following accretion (section 7.3).

(f) *Eu was concentrated in the highlands and depleted in the mare basalt source regions by early melting and differentiation.* Many of the difficulties associated with single-stage models for the Eu anomaly disappear when multistage explanations are considered. Thus, the debate whether or not plagioclase is a liquidus phase becomes irrelevant for the europium problem if Eu has already been mostly removed from the source regions of the maria lavas.

The question of single-stage versus multistage origins for the Eu anomaly has wider implications. Single-stage models derive the maria basalts from pristine lunar mantle: multistage models from already melted and fractionated (i.e., no longer primitive) material. In this case, evidence about the composition of the lunar interior as a whole has to be evaluated in terms of multistage models. In the former event, information about wide regions of the lunar interior may be inferred.

In the two-stage model (section 7.6), an initial melting at 4.6 aeons forms the highland crust. Eu (and Sr) is incorporated mainly in the plagioclase lattice sites. A complementary iron-rich cumulate underneath the highland crust forms the source material for the maria basalts.

This model has intuitive appeal. Variants of this theme were immediately suggested after the discovery of the Eu depletion. A fuller discussion of the two-stage model is given in the section of the origin and evolution of the highland crust. There is now a growing body of data to support the idea that the highland crust is the result of an early melting and fractionation episode.

## 4.8   THE LARGE, HIGH-VALENCY CATIONS

The large, high-valency cations, because of a combination of medium to large size and high valency, do not commonly enter the lattice sites available in the common rock-forming minerals (Table 4.7). The larger quadrivalent ions, which accompany $Ti^{+4}$ to a limited extent in sixfold coordination in ilmenite, prefer a larger lattice site and concentrate in the interstitial material, in accessory minerals such as apatite and zircon, as well as in several mineral species within the system $ZrO_2$-$TiO_2$-$FeO$ (Table 4.2)[78].

As a class, these elements are abundant in the lunar rocks, being concentrated by factors of 50–100 over their abundances in chondritic meteorites. This enrichment is rather uniform and occurs for many other "refractory" elements (Ba, Y, REE), which do not readily enter sixfold coordination sites in pyroxenes or olivine. These elements, dispersed in accessory minerals and in interstitial material along grain boundaries, are readily concentrated by processes of partial melting. They are strongly concentrated in the crust of the earth and a similar strong upward concentration appears to have operated on the moon (see section 7.6).

Thorium and uranium are of interest both because of their use in radioactive dating and because they are important sources of heat production. The high U and Th contents of the lunar surface rocks would produce enough heat to melt the entire moon. Since the shape of the moon indicates that it has been rigid for probably the past three aeons, U and Th must have been concentrated near the surface (as is the case for the earth). This is evidence of the efficiency of the process producing upward concentration of the elements.

Figure 4.24 shows the K/U relationships. K/U ratios for many terrestrial rocks are constant at about 10,000. This is not the consequence of any profound geochemical coherence, but rather that both elements are strongly concentrated in residual systems by fractionation processes. The K/U ratios[79] for chondrites are 50,000–80,000. The maria basalts, in contrast, average about 2,500 (O'Kelley, 1974). The highland samples have lower K/U ratios, typically about 1,600. This difference, discussed

**Table 4.7** Abundances of Large High Valency Cations in Maria Basalts.

| | Green glass Apollo 15 | Olivine basalt Apollo 12 | Olivine basalt Apollo 15 | Quartz basalt Apollo 15 | Quartz basalt Apollo 12 | High-K basalt Apollo 11 | Low-K basalt Apollo 11 | High-Ti basalt Apollo 17 | Aluminous maria basalts Apollo 12 | Aluminous maria basalts Luna 16 |
|---|---|---|---|---|---|---|---|---|---|---|
| $Th^{4+}$ | 0.08 | 0.88 | 0.05 | 0.59 | 1.15 | 3.4 | 1.0 | 0.54 | 0.90 | 0.30 |
| $U^{4+}$ | 0.02 | 0.24 | 0.15 | 0.13 | 0.30 | 0.8 | 0.25 | 0.17 | 0.25 | — |
| $Zr^{4+}$ | 22 | 110 | 94 | 71 | 120 | 560 | 360 | 180 | 200 | 295 |
| $Hf^{4+}$ | 0.42 | 4.0 | 2.0 | — | 4.2 | 19 | 11 | 5.70 | 6.5 | — |
| $Sn^{4+}$ | 0.12 | — | 0.19 | — | 0.16 | 0.5 | 1.0 | — | 0.3 | — |
| $Nb^{5+}$ | 1.5 | 6 | 6.2 | 4.9 | 6.0 | 25 | 20 | 20 | 8 | — |
| $Ti^{4+}$ % | 0.17 | 1.74 | 1.35 | 0.88 | 2.00 | 7.1 | 6.3 | 7.31 | 2.0 | 2.46 |

Data in ppm except for Ti in wt %.

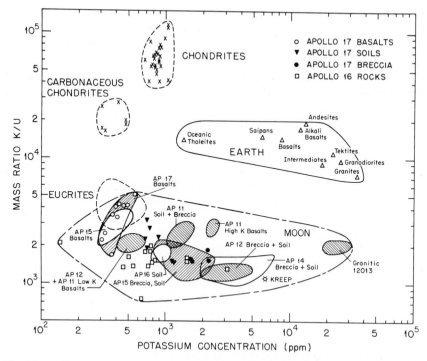

**Fig. 4.24**   K/U ratio plotted versus potassium, showing the separation of the lunar K/U ratios from those in the earth and most meteorites (excluding achondrites). There is a tendency for the maria basalts to have higher K/U ratios than the soil. (Courtesy G. D. O'Kelley.)

later, has been used as an argument for heterogeneous accretion of the moon, but the coherence of other volatile-involatile element ratios makes alternative suggestions more likely[80].

It is apparent from Fig. 4.24 that the K/U ratios provide a useful method of distinguishing the geochemistry of the moon from that of other units of the solar system. In contrast to the K/U ratios, the Th/U ratios for the moon, meteorites, and the earth are closely similar (3.5–4.0). Some exceptions occur on the moon, the Apollo 17 basalts having lower Th/U ratios (~3) as well as some highland feldspathic rocks.

In contrast, the Zr/Hf in the lunar samples is more variable than the terrestrial ratios, typically about 50. The lunar ratios vary from 20–30 in the high-Ti basalts to 40–50 in the more conventional compositions. This may be because of reduction of some $Zr^{4+}$ to $Zr^{3+}$, with subsequent separation due to mineralogical control. It may also reflect a change in the ratio in the source regions between the high-Ti basalts, and the olivine- and quartz-normative basalts. The analytical data are not yet precise enough to explore these interesting possibilities.

The Zr/Nb ratio[81, 82] is (Fig. 5.18) surprisingly constant at about 13–15 in maria basalts. This constancy holds as well for many highland rocks, emphasizing the close relationship between the highlands and maria chemistry, a fact of much significance for theories of lunar origin. The enrichment of these elements relative to primitive solar nebula compositions is shown in Fig. 4.31. The question of the total enrichment in the moon is addressed in the section on geochemical evolution and appears to be about 5 times the chondritic abundances.

The high-Ti basalts from Apollo 11 and 17 show some exceptions to the constancy of the inter-element ratios (K/Zr, Zr/Nb, etc.) observed rather widely in lunar samples. The variations are in the direction of increased amounts of elements (e.g., $Zr^{4+}$) associated with $Ti^{4+}$. Thus Zr/K ratios increase with increasing Ti content. The evidence is consistent with the derivation of the high-Ti basalts from a source already enriched in Ti-Zr-Nb phases. This is consistent with at least a two-stage origin for the high-Ti basalts (see section 7.6).

## 4.9  THE FERROMAGNESIAN ELEMENTS

The elements in this category (Table 4.8) show both extensive deple- tions and enrichments compared with chondritic meteorites or with terrestrial basalts. Thus Ni, Cu, Ga, and V are strongly depleted, and Cr, Sc, and Ti, enriched. The depletion in Cu and Ni may be ascribed in part to entry into metallic phases under the strong reducing conditions of the partial melting and crystallization of the lunar lavas. In addition, probably Ni and the siderophile elements were depleted before accretion (see following sections and section 7.6 on geochemical evolution of the moon).

Nickel is strikingly depleted in the aluminous maria basalts and in the high-Ti basalts, where values of only 1–2 ppm are common. Fe/Ni ratios become extreme, reaching values on the order of 15,000–20,000, com- pared with 100–500 in terrestrial basalts and 20 in chondritic meteorites. The quartz-normative basalts, from deeper in the interior contain 10–20 ppm nickel (still very low by terrestrial standards). The olivine- normative basalts have 40–50 ppm Ni, while the emerald green glass (15426) has the highest amount—180 ppm. These values must all be distinguished from the high (100–300 ppm) Ni in the soils, or in the

Table 4.8 Abundances of Ferromagnesian Elements in Maria Basalts.

| | Green glass Apollo 15 | Olivine basalt Apollo 12 | Olivine basalt Apollo 15 | Quartz basalt Apollo 15 | Quartz basalt Apollo 12 | High-K basalt Apollo 11 | Low-K basalt Apollo 11 | High-Ti basalt Apollo 17 | Aluminous maria basalts | |
| | | | | | | | | | Apollo 12 | Luna 16 |
| --- | --- | --- | --- | --- | --- | --- | --- | --- | --- | --- |
| $Cr^{3+}$ | 2800 | 3790 | 4790 | 4520 | 3140 | 2500 | 1730 | 2900 | 2500 | — |
| $V^{3+}$ | 150 | 150 | 240 | 135 | 160 | 70 | 60 | 98 | 120 | — |
| $Sc^{3+}$ | 43 | 45 | 38 | 40 | 54 | 86 | 87 | 76 | 50 | — |
| $Ni^{2+}$ | 180 | 52 | 42 | 11 | 21 | ~2 | ~1 | 2 | 1 | — |
| $Co^{2+}$ | 72 | 49 | 60 | 42 | 42 | 29 | 15 | 22 | 29 | — |
| $Cu^{2+}$ | 3.5 | 14 | 7 | 9 | 5.0 | 4 | 15 | 4 | 5 | — |
| $Fe^{2+}$ % | 15.3 | 16.3 | 17.5 | 14.5 | 16.1 | 14.8 | 14.4 | 16.7 | 13.9 | 13.9 |
| $Mn^{2+}$ | 1600 | 2170 | 2300 | 2100 | 2000 | 1900 | 2200 | 1700 | 2100 | 2000 |
| $Mg^{2+}$ % | 9.98 | 7.0 | 6.76 | 5.71 | 4.89 | 4.6 | 4.2 | 4.95 | 4.1 | 3.59 |
| $Li^+$ | — | 6.0 | 6.4 | 5.6 | 8.0 | 18 | 11 | — | — | 10 |
| $Ga^{3+}$ | 4.7 | 5.0 | 3.0 | 4.1 | 3.9 | 4.9 | 5.5 | — | — | — |
| $Al^{3+}$ % | 4.06 | 4.55 | 4.49 | 4.92 | 5.26 | 4.6 | 5.5 | 4.6 | 6.61 | 7.35 |
| $Si^{4+}$ % | 21.3 | 21.0 | 20.7 | 22.8 | 21.5 | 18.9 | 18.9 | 17.6 | 21.8 | 21.3 |
| $P^{5+}$ | — | 300 | 260 | 130 | 350 | 790 | 480 | 220 | 600 | 650 |

Data in ppm except where shown in wt %.

highland rocks, due to a meteoritic contribution. The variation in nickel with basalt type is attributed to variations in the olivine content with depth in the source regions, rather than to entry into a metal phase (section 7.6). Again, one may draw the contrast with terrestrial basalts, indicating that the earth's mantle differs from the lunar interior.

Cobalt, which is less siderophile than nickel, shows a much more even distribution, as does manganese. The chief feature of the lunar geochemistry of manganese is the very close coherence with ferrous iron (Fig. 4.25), a consequence of the similarity in ionic radius between $Fe^{2+}$ and $Mn^{2+}$. The reducing conditions on the moon ensure that Mn will be divalent.

Vanadium shows a trend rather similar to nickel, increasing in the olivine-normative samples. It is probably retained in residual phases

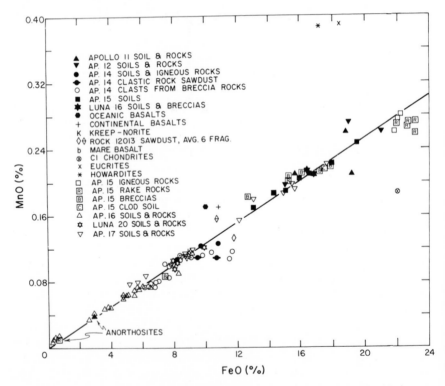

**Fig. 4.25**  The correlation between FeO and MnO in maria and highland rocks. Mn is more volatile than iron. (Courtesy R. Schmitt.)

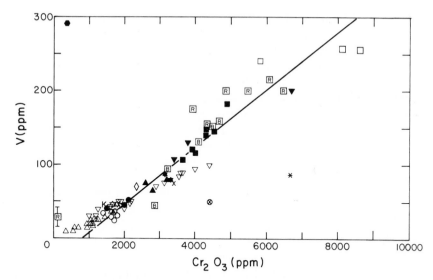

**Fig. 4.26**   The V-Cr$_2$O$_3$ correlation in maria and highland rocks. (Symbols as in Fig. 4.25.) (Courtesy R. Schmitt.)

during partial melting (Fig. 4.26). Chromium is a critical element in lunar geochemistry, both in the maria basalts and the highlands rocks. It is enriched over the concentrations in terrestrial basalts by an order of magnitude. Its abundance clearly distinguishes terrestrial and lunar rocks. The significance of the high Cr content, which is about the same order of magnitude as in chondrites, lies in the extreme sensitivity of chromium to crystal fractionation processes during cooling of silicate melts. Cr$^{3+}$ enters pyroxenes, and its abundance in the maria basalts indicates that it is retained in the moon at the high levels where the maria basalts originate by partial melting. It is also high in the highland rocks ($\sim$ 600 ppm), a fact whose significance will become apparent later in this story. The appearance of large amounts of Cr in the lunar basalts contrasts with the lower content of Cr in terrestrial basalts (typically an order of magnitude lower). Clearly the source region of the lunar maria basalts is enriched in Cr, which indicates that the deep interior is probably depleted. Although Cr is mainly present as Cr$^{3+}$, the highly reducing conditions in the moon [42, 83] produce some Cr$^{2+}$. Cr$^{2+}$ has similar chemical properties to Co$^{2+}$, having much lower crystal field site preference energy than Cr$^{3+}$. Thus, Cr$^{2+}$ does not preferentially enter Mg-rich olivine and is not concentrated in the deep lunar interior.

Scandium is also enriched in the lunar rocks, being enriched by a factor of about 10 over the cosmic abundances. It is also depleted during fractional crystallization, although not as rapidly as $Cr^{3+}$, but its usually high abundance indicates little near-surface fractionation in the maria basalts. It is highest in the high-Ti basalts, and the lower values in the quartz- and olivine-normative basalts are consistent with a lower pyroxene/olivine ratio in the source region.

Gallium is an element of great interest since it is somewhat volatile and may enter metallic, sulfide, or silicate phases. It is a factor of 4 lower than in terrestrial rocks and is rather constant at about 3–5 ppm. (It rarely varies outside the range 15–25 ppm in terrestrial rocks.) The depletion of Ga is due to an initial depletion, along with the other volatile and chalcophile elements, and its entry into metallic phases.

In contrast to the other alkali elements, lithium is not depleted in the lunar rocks relative to terrestrial basalts. It is present at levels of 10–20 ppm, enriched by a factor of 5–10 over cosmic abundances. Lithium, in contrast to the other alkali elements, is involatile, accounting for its enrichment in the lunar basalts.

## 4.10   SULFUR AND THE CHALCOPHILE ELEMENTS

Sulfur and the chalcophile elements, which in terrestrial rocks enter sulfide phases, are volatile at temperatures up to 1,500°C. The chalcophile elements are strikingly depleted in ordinary chondrites relative to the carbonaceous chondrites. In the lunar basalts they are generally low in abundance and are grossly depleted relative to the cosmic abundances and to the terrestrial abundances. The basic questions are whether these elements were ever accreted, were lost subsequent to accretion, were retained in the interior during partial melting, or entered an Fe-FeS core [84].

Surface loss of volatiles during extrusion or meteorite impact has not found much favor [85]. During surface extrusion of the lavas, freezing of the surface will rapidly occur, and loss of volatiles will not occur. Lead is not more strongly depleted than other much more volatile elements such as mercury, which would be more readily lost under such conditions. The case for some movement of lead has been discussed earlier [85]. The two most likely mechanisms to account for the depletion of the chalcophile elements are loss before accretion or retention in an Fe-FeS-type core. Since the chalcophile elements are volatile, it is more probable that they were never accreted in the moon. Definitive answers to these questions are difficult, since no refractory chalcophile elements, which could provide a key, are known.

The total lead abundances are low in comparison with terrestrial average crustal lead concentrations of 15 ppm and with the carbonaceous chondrite values of 3–4 ppm. The low abundance of lead parallels that of the other volatile elements and indicates loss of such elements at or before accretion of the moon. The comparatively high uranium and thorium contents mean that a major portion of the lunar lead is radiogenic in origin, so that the amount of common lead is very low. Thus contamination by terrestrial lead can be a serious problem.

The ratio $U^{238}/Pb^{204}$, ($\mu$), is distinct for terrestrial and lunar rocks. It is commonly in the range 5–10 for terrestrial rocks and rarely exceeds 30. The mean value is about 9. In contrast, in the lunar rocks, the values are, with minor exceptions, very much higher (Table 4.9). For the maria basalts, the usual range is from 200 to 1,000, while values for KREEP-type rocks are much higher, with values of 1,500–3,000 being recorded for rock 12013.

The extreme depletion of the chalcophile elements in the maria basalts allows their use as indexes of the contribution by carbonaceous chondrites. The abundances in the lunar rocks are about a factor of $10^3$–$10^4$ less than observed in the Type I carbonaceous chondrites[86]. These elements are abundant in the regolith, where they have been supplied during meteorite impact.

**Table 4.9** Values for the Ratio $\mu$
$^{238}U/^{204}Pb$ in Various Lunar Rocks.

|  | $^{238}U/^{204}Pb$ |
| --- | --- |
| Apollo 11 basalts | 220–1400 |
| Apollo 12 basalts | 450–990 |
| 12013 | 1500–3000 |
| Apollo 14 breccias | 145–1800 |
| 14310 (crystalline) | 280–3040 |
| Apollo 15 basalt | 380–610 |
| 15415 (anorthosite) | 1.5 |
| Apollo 16 breccias | 330–1360 |
| 67075 (anorthosite) | 16 |
| Apollo 17 basalt | 250 |
| 74220 orange glass | 35 |
| 15426 green glass | 16 |

**Sulfur and Sulfur Isotopes**

All sulfur appears to be present in the maria basalts as troilite (FeS). The abundance of the element varies with basalt type, being lower in Apollo 12 and 15 basalts. These typically contain 500–700 ppm, and have $\delta^{34}S$ values of $-0.1$ to $-0.3$ per mil. In Apollo 11 and 17 high-Ti basalts, the S values are about three times higher, averaging about 2,200 ppm, with $\delta^{34}S$ values of about $+1.2$ per mil.

These differences reflect other differences in chemistry, and constitute additional evidence for fractionation in the lunar interior[87]. The lunar sulfur data[88] contrast strongly with terrestrial sulfur abundances from basaltic rocks, which are typically in the range 10–200 ppm.

The inverse correlations of metallic iron with sulfur content[88] suggests that some of the metallic Fe in lunar basalts comes from reduction of FeS. The $\delta^{34}S$ values overlap those in meteoritic troilite and in terrestrial basalts. Significantly, the values for the Apollo 12 basalts resemble those in terrestrial tholeiitic basalts, while the Apollo 11 high-Ti values resemble those in terrestrial olivine alkali basalts[87, 89]. Such compositional differences are consistent with different source regions for the various types of maria basalts.

## 4.11   THE SIDEROPHILE ELEMENTS

The siderophile elements include gold, silver, and the platinum group. Exceedingly large depletions are observed for this group in the lunar basalts, relative to cosmic or terrestrial abundances[91]. A basic question is whether these low abundances observed in lunar rocks are due to preaccretion loss or to their removal in metallic core. An iron core for the moon has been judged unlikely by most workers, but an Fe-FeS core remains a possibility[84]. Formation of such a core would effectively deplete the outer portion of the moon in both siderophile and chalcophile elements. In the section on the geochemical evolution of the moon (section 7.6) this question is examined. Although such a core cannot be definitely excluded, the evidence for its existence is not strong. The preaccretion loss of the siderophile elements is more likely.

Internal variations are observed within the group. Compared with the earth, silver and gold are depleted by much larger factors in the moon than are the other siderophile elements. This is shown in Fig. 4.27 and indicates that Au is depleted more than Ir. It has long been recognized[91] that the difference in lunar and terrestrial Au/Ir ratios is a strong

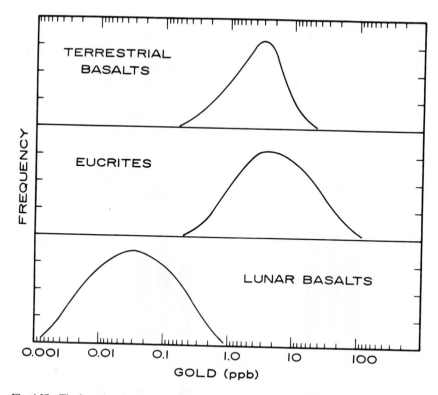

**Fig. 4.27**  The low abundance of gold in lunar basalts compared with terrestrial basalts and eucritic meteorites. (Courtesy E. Anders.)

constraint on the fission hypothesis, for the earth and the moon should have the same ratio in simple versions of the model.

The cause of the loss of the gold and silver, relative to the Ir and Ni has been the cause of much speculation. Since both Au and Ag are volatile, compared with Ir and Ni, a preferred explanation is that they were lost to a greater degree than the more refractory siderophile elements before accretion. This implies a two-stage process: loss of volatile elements followed by depletion of the siderophile elements. It is possible also that the strong reducing conditions within the moon may contribute to the Ag and Au depletion. The elements would be strongly concentrated in metallic phases at the prevailing low-oxygen fugacities observed in lunar rocks ($f_{O_2} = 10^{-13}$ bars at 1,150°C).

Whether much separation of metal takes place within the moon is a moot point. The formation of Fe metal in lunar basalts is probably a late near-surface phenomenon, rather than one that occurs in the source region[84, 91]. Since nickel is more readily reduced than iron, a small lunar core (e.g., 1.5 percent of the mass of the moon) would consist mainly of nickel[84] if the moon had chondritic abundances of that element. As was the case for the chalcophile elements, the very low abundance of the siderophile elements in the rocks has been a useful feature in deciphering the meteoritic contribution in the soils.

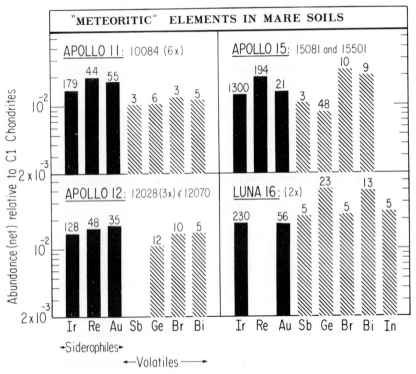

**Fig. 4.28**   All maria soils studied to date are enriched in "meteoritic" elements, relative to crystalline rocks. Net meteoritic component is obtained by subtracting an indigenous lunar contribution, estimated from crystalline rocks. Numbers above histogram indicate signal-to-noise ratio (i.e., ratio of net component to correction). Abundance pattern is flat, with siderophiles and volatiles almost equally abundant. Apparently the meteoritic component has a primitive composition (see Fig. 4.29). (From Anders, E. (1973) *Moon.* 8, Fig. 1, courtesy E. Anders.)

## Meteoritic Component in the Maria Soils

Pre-Apollo models for the formation of the lunar surface predicted rather large amounts of meteoritic debris on the surface. Little direct evidence was gained before the manned landings. A magnet attached to the Surveyor VI footpad found only minor amounts of magnetic material[92].

The search for meteoritic debris was aided by the extreme depletion of the lunar rocks in both siderophile and volatile elements. The lack of the former aids in the identification of iron meteoritic components; the great depletion of the volatile (and chalcophile elements) aids in the recognition of primitive carbonaceous chondritic components. The meteoritic compositions recognized in the maria soils turn out to be surprisingly uniform at about 1.5 percent. The abundance patterns (Fig. 4.28) are close to those for primitive unfractionated Type I carbonaceous chondrites.

They do not resemble the ordinary chondrites, the iron meteorites, or the stony-irons. Figure 4.29 shows the abundance patterns for these elements relative to those in Type I carbonaceous chondrites. The meteorite component is concentrated in the finer grain size, and in the agglutinates, and is readily leached. Possibly it is vaporized and condensed on impact. Most of this material is attributed to a micrometeoritic addition to the lunar soil. The large crater-forming meteorites contribute an unknown amount, possibly 10 per cent of the total. A further source of the exotic elements is the solar wind, which is estimated to contribute 3–4 percent of the total siderophile element content in the soil[93, 94]. The ultimate source of the material is in debate, with comets and asteroids about equally favored, although the evidence for Type I carbonaceous chondrite compositions in the asteroid belt is growing[95].

## 4.12  OXYGEN AND CARBON ISOTOPES

A remarkable feature is that the variation in $\delta^{18}O$ values[96] in maria basalts from all lunar sites is very small[97]. The range is from $+5.4$ to $+6.8$. No significant differences exist in the ratios between the lunar basalts, terrestrial basaltic and ultramafic rocks, and chondritic meteorites. The achondrites and stony-irons show very different ratios. Although the achondrites show many mineralogical and chemical similarities to the lunar rocks, they are derived from a separate oxygen isotope reservoir compared with the earth, moon, and chondrites.

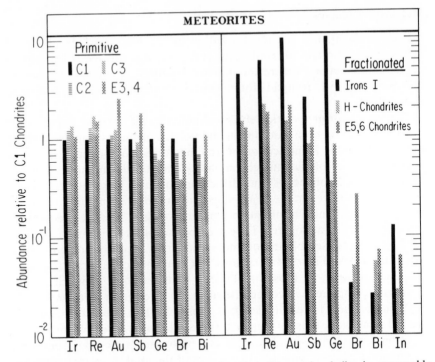

**Fig. 4.29** Primitive meteorites (left) contain siderophiles and volatiles in comparable abundance. Fractionated meteorites (right) are depleted in volatiles. (From Anders, E. (1973) *Moon.* 8, Fig. 2, courtesy E. Anders.)

The $\delta^{18}O$ values for the minerals increase in the sequence:

|  | $\delta^{18}O$ |
|---|---|
| Ilmenite | 3.8–4.1 |
| Olivine | 4.9–5.0 |
| Clinopyroxene | 5.34–5.95 |
| Plagioclase | 5.7–6.4 |
| Tridymite-cristobalite | 6.7–7.2 |

The $\delta^{18}O$ values for the minerals from different rocks are very similar, and there is no evidence of oxygen isotope exchange or equilibration during cooling following crystallization at temperatures estimated about 1,120°C. This effect is attributed to the very low water content of the lunar rocks. Although the rocks crystallized rapidly, and the minerals are often inhomogeneous, there is no sign of isotopic zoning in the minerals.

This lack of diversity in oxygen isotope chemistry in the moon contrasts sharply with the variations seen in the earth or the metamorphosed meteorites. There seems to be no sign of isotopic exchange at temperatures below that of crystallization. Thus the oxygen isotopic compositions in the lunar basalts are determined by igneous processes and are locked in, due to the absence of alteration processes[98].

Since the variations are very small, it is a reasonable conclusion that the $^{18}O/^{16}O$ ratio is rather constant in the moon. One group of workers consider it the "best-known chemical parameter for the moon"[98], and it is accordingly a constraint that theories of lunar origin must meet. It is particularly unfavorable for heterogeneous accretion theories, which seek to accumulate high temperature Ca-Al refractory phases, which have very low $\delta^{18}O$ ratios (−5 to −15 per mil). Thus a further conclusion is that the lunar interior is dominated by Fe-Mg silicates rather than Ca-Al silicates[98].

### Carbon and Carbon Isotopes

The carbon content in lunar basalts is low. The Apollo 11 samples average about 70 ppm, the 12 basalts from 16 to 45 ppm, the 15 lavas from 10 to 30 ppm, and the 17 basalts from 40 to 80 ppm (Fig. 4.30)[99]. These values are all much lower than those found in the soils, on which most interest has been focused (see section 3.19 on organic geochemistry). The carbon is apparently present in the lunar rocks as carbides, although mineralogical evidence of their presence is lacking. Their existence is inferred from the release of methane and other gases during acid hydrolysis. The $\delta^{13}C$ values[100] are in the range −20 to −30, closely resembling terrestrial basalts. The soils, in contrast, have values of +10 to +20.

### 4.13  COSMOCHEMICAL IMPLICATIONS OF THE TRACE ELEMENT ABUNDANCES

The trace element abundances in the maria basalts have provided many constraints on lunar processes. It is of immediate interest to compare the composition of lunar samples with primitive solar nebula compositions. These are conventionally taken as equivalent to the composition of Type I carbonaceous chondrites less water, organic compounds, and noble gases. The selection of the lunar sample is subject to the following considerations. The maria basalts represent the end-stage product of several processes. The element abundances have been altered from those in the

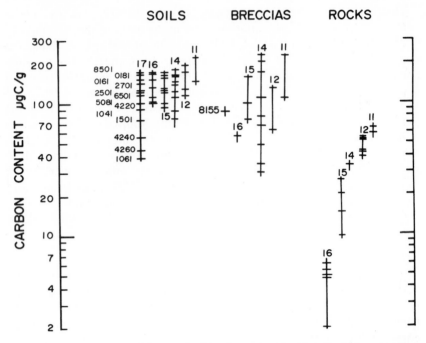

**Fig. 4.30** Carbon content of lunar soils, breccias, and rocks. Note the high and uniform abundances in the soils and the low and variable contents in the rocks. The Apollo 11 (and 17) high-Ti basalts have the most carbon. (Courtesy E. K. Gibson.)

primitive solar nebula in several steps. These include:

(*a*) Preaccretion fractionation. This resulted in loss of the volatile elements, and probable loss of the siderophile elements.

(*b*) After the accretion of the moon, it is inferred that widespread melting and fractionation occurred (see section 7.6 on geochemical evolution) and a zoned structure developed, in which the source regions of the maria basalts were enriched in some elements and depleted in others (e.g., Eu). This occurred shortly after formation.

(*c*) Much later, at 3.8–3.2 aeons, partial melting leading to element fractionation occurred in the source region of the maria basalts (due to radioactive heating), and the basaltic magma was extruded at the surface.

(*d*) En route to the surface, and during and following extrusion, crystallization occurs. If opportunity exists for removal of phases, further element fractionation may occur.

In the particular basalt (12009) selected, there is good petrographic evidence that it reached the surface in an essentially liquid condition, and so it is a good example of a pristine partial melt from the interior. Such rocks are the most primitive samples of the lunar interior to which we have access, but in making the comparisons with other samples, the previous multistage history of the maria basalts should be recalled.

The comparison with the Type I carbonaceous chondrites is instructive (Fig. 4.31). The most distinctive features are the wide dispersion, by factors up to $10^4$ from these primitive abundances. The first-order conclusion, reached from the study of the Apollo 11 samples and substantiated by later studies, was that the moon was not the primitive unfractionated sample of the solar nebula hoped for by some workers. As a corollary, the moon was ruled out as a source of chondritic meteorites.

A more detailed study of Fig. 4.31 reveals that the volatile and siderophile elements are depleted and the refractory elements are enriched in the lunar sample. Again, the conclusion was drawn from the first examination of the samples. The isotopic data indicate loss of Rb and Pb before accretion. By analogy, loss of the other volatile elements is inferred to have occurred before accretion. The evidence for the time of depletion of the siderophile elements is less clear, but the increasing consensus is that they were also lost before accretion. In contrast to the previous two groups, the refractory elements are enriched by factors of 10–20 over the chondritic abundances.

It should be recalled that the lunar basalt has undergone three stages of element fractionation. Thus, depending on one's views of the primitive accretionary process and its relation to primitive solar nebula abundances (see section on origin of the moon), some enrichment of refractory elements occurred when the volatile elements were lost. The extent of this enrichment varies depending on whether a simple loss of volatiles and siderophiles is considered or whether a condensation mechanism is invoked. Secondly, the geochemical zoning of the primitive moon concentrates the REE, U, Th, Zr, Hf, Ba, and so on, in the upper zones and produces a second enrichment in the source region of maria basalts. Thirdly, the partial melting process enriches the melt relative to the residue again in these elements, all of which are distinguished by their lack of ability to enter the sixfold Mg-Fe coordination sites, which probably dominate the deeper zones of the lunar interior.

Further insights can be obtained by comparisons of maria basalts with other analogous materials. Among all the meteoritic classes, only the eucritic class of the basaltic achondrites come close in composition. The

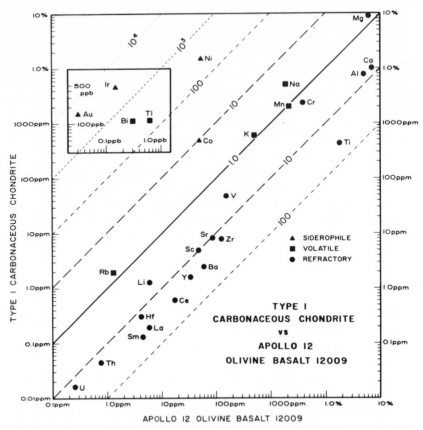

**Fig. 4.31** Comparison of the average composition of Type I carbonaceous chondrites (data from Mason) taken as representative of the abundances of the nonvolatile elements in the solar system nebula, with those in a primitive Apollo 12 olivine basalt 12009. This sample is one of the best examples of an unfractionated primary melt from the lunar interior. Points lying along the 45° diagonal full line indicate equality in composition. Increasing distance from the diagonal line indicates increasing disparity in composition. The dashed lines indicate limits for differences by factors of 10, 100, $10^3$, and $10^4$. Elements lying to the right of the equal abundance line are enriched in the lunar sample. Those lying to the left are depleted.

The volatile, siderophile and refractory elements are indicated by distinctive symbols.

Note the very wide dispersion of abundances, with some volatile and siderophile elements depleted in the lunar sample by factors of $10^3$–$10^4$. Note the rather uniform enrichment of the refractory elements by factors of 10–20. Three stages of fractionation separate 12009 from the primitive abundances. These are (a) preaccretion separation of volatile and siderophile elements, (b) differentiation following initial lunar melting at about 4.5–4.6 aeons to form source region of maria basalts, (c) partial melting in source region at 3.2 aeons to produce 12009. This olivine basalt reached the surface as a liquid, so that its composition is not affected by a fourth stage of subsequent fractional crystallization.

nearest lunar analogues are the aluminous maria basalts, which show a very good match for the major elements (Fig. 4.32). In particular, the chromium, sodium, and potassium concentrations, so typically lunar, match those of the eucrites. Even the trace volatile (Tl, Bi) and siderophile (Ir) elements cover about the same range in concentration, although gold is still depleted.

The refractory elements (Ba, Zr, Ti) are consistently higher and show their distinctive lunar enrichment. Other criteria (e.g., oxygen isotopes) are also distinctive in distinguishing the eucrites from the lunar samples,

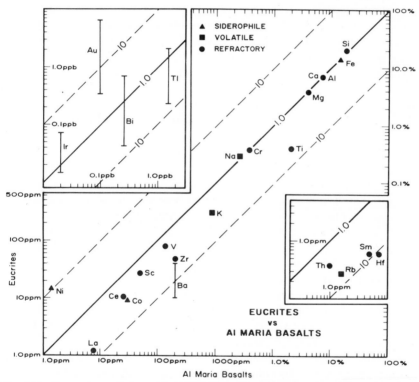

**Fig. 4.32** Comparison of the composition of eucrites (basaltic achondrites) (data from Mason 1970) and the closest lunar analogues, the aluminous maria basalts. There are many close resemblances in composition, particularly for the diagnostic lunar elements Cr, Na, and K (as well as Si, Al, Fe, Mg, and Ca). The rare volatile (Bi, Tl) and siderophile (Au, Ir) elements are also similar in abundance. Nevertheless, some critical differences remain. Ni is depleted in the lunar rocks, while many of the refractory elements (Ti, Ba, Zr, La) show the typical lunar enrichment.

so that this class of meteorite cannot be derived from the moon. Nevertheless, the eucrites contain evidence of many analogous processes, and the same major element chemistry is certainly being produced elsewhere in the solar system.

Major interest attaches to the comparison with terrestrial materials. We may immediately exclude many terrestrial rock types on grounds of gross incompatibility in element abundances. These include the granites and granodiorites. It should be noted that small amounts of K-rich granitic glasses, presumably residual late stage differentiates, formed during crystallization. Volcanic equivalents such as rhyolites and ignimbrites are not found. Neither are there any representatives of the great calc-alkaline suite of andesites, dacites, or rhyolites, so typical of the orogenic areas on the earth. Their origin is intimately related to the subduction zones, where down-going slabs of the lithosphere slide into the earth's mantle. The absence of plate tectonics on the moon effectively rules out the mechanism for the production of these rocks. Even the fairly common differentiated sequences known from basaltic magmas on the earth are not found. There is an absence of mugearites, hawaiites, trachytes, and other species.

The composition of primary melts from the earth's mantle have been widely used to infer the composition of the earth's mantle. Similar inferences can be drawn from the lunar rocks. Comparisons of primary, unfractionated melts from the lunar interior and the mantle of the earth are made in Fig. 4.33, using the low-K oceanic tholeiite as representative of an important terrestrial lava. The lunar analogue is the Apollo 15 olivine basalt 15555. It is clear that there are many similarities in composition. In studying these diagrams, differences should exceed a factor of two to be significant.

Decisive differences remain, notably in the high lunar abundance of Cr and in the depletion of the volatile elements (Na, K, Bi, Tl) and the siderophile elements (Au, Ir). These are important distinctions, indicating that the composition of the lunar interior is distinct from that of the earth's mantle. This is a powerful constraint on theories of origin of the moon by fission, for the compositions should be identical in the simplest version of the theory. The depletion of volatile and siderophile elements and the enrichment of chromium in the moon require specialized circumstances. Thus the earth's core cannot be used as a sink for the siderophile elements in the fission model. This removes one of the chief attractions of simple fission.

The Apollo 11 high-K basalts show strong concentrations of REE, Ba,

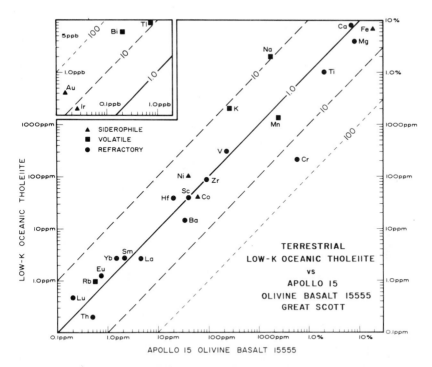

**Fig. 4.33** Comparison of the element abundances in low-K oceanic tholeiites (taken as representative of an important terrestrial primary magma) with that of Apollo 15 olivine basalt 15555, a typical lunar primary magma. Construction of the diagram as for Fig. 4.31.

Note that there are many similarities in composition but that a few decisive differences remain. These include the diagnostic lunar element Cr, greatly enriched in the lunar basalt, and the alkali elements Na, and K, which show their characteristic lunar depletion. The rare volatile (Bi, Tl) and siderophile (Au, Ir) elements also show a characteristic lunar depletion.

and many other elements. Their nearest terrestrial analogues are the continental basalts (Fig. 4.34). Although there are some similarities, wide differences persist. The lunar basalts show the typical depletion in Na and K, the trace volatile and siderophile elements. In contrast, they are enriched in the refractory elements including the small (Lu-Yb), but not the large (La-Sm), rare earth elements. The lack of fractionation of the REE patterns is noteworthy in the lunar samples, in comparison with terrestrial examples, and indicates a major difference in the partial melting conditions in the moon.

In summary, although there is some resemblance between eucrites and terrestrial basalts and their lunar analogues, the differences are decisive.

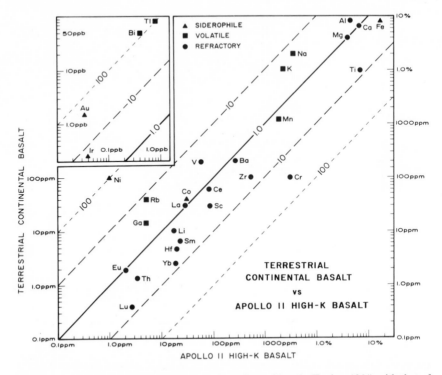

**Fig. 4.34** Comparison of the composition of continental basalt (Taylor, 1964) with that of high-K Apollo 11 basalt, the nearest lunar analogue. Construction of the diagram as in Fig. 4.31. Note that wide differences persist. The lunar basalts are depleted in Na, K, Rb, Tl, Bi, and Ga (all volatile) and in the siderophile elements Au and Ir. The lunar basalts are enriched in Ti, Cr, Zr, Hf, and the small REE (Lu, Yb) compared with the terrestrial basalts. Thus, significant differences in composition remain even between close analogues.

They indicate extensive fractionation both pre- and postaccretion in the moon. They place serious constraints on the fission hypothesis, in its simpler forms.

## 4.14  AGES OF MARIA BASALTS

The maria basalts are all old by terrestrial standards, even though they represent the youngest internally generated events on the moon. They show an age range from 3.16 to 3.96 aeons (Table 4.10). Reports of younger ages (e.g., 2.8 aeons for 12004) have not been substantiated. Although this period of time is usually remarked on as an episode or short period of lunar history, it spans a longer period of time than has elapsed since the beginning of the Cambrian period on earth.

In order to avoid interlaboratory bias, dates are selected from only a few laboratories[101–112]. This enables inter-comparison of ages with the least ambiguity. Only one serious discrepancy remains. The age of the

**Table 4.10**   Ages of Maria Basalts.

| | Age (aeons) | Rock type | Sample no. | Method | Reference | T BABI (p. 65) (aeons) |
|---|---|---|---|---|---|---|
| Apollo 14 | 3.96 | Al-basalt | 14053 | Rb-Sr | 101 | 4.60 |
| | 3.95 | Al-basalt | 14053 | $^{40}$Ar-$^{39}$Ar | 102 | — |
| | 3.95 | Al-basalt | 14321 | Rb-Sr | 101 | 4.24 |
| Apollo 17 | 3.83 | High Ti | 75055 | Rb-Sr | 103 | — |
| | 3.82 | High Ti | 70035 | Rb-Sr | 104 | — |
| | 3.76 | High Ti | 75055 | $^{40}$Ar-$^{39}$Ar | 102 | — |
| | 3.74 | High Ti | 75083 | $^{40}$Ar-$^{39}$Ar | 105 | — |
| Apollo 11 | 3.82 | Low K | 10062 | $^{40}$Ar-$^{39}$Ar | 106 | — |
| | 3.71 | Low K | 10044 | Rb-Sr | 107 | 4.52 |
| | 3.63 | Low K | 10058 | Rb-Sr | 107 | — |
| Apollo 11 | 3.68 | High K | 10071 | Rb-Sr | 107 | 3.86 |
| | 3.63 | High K | 10057 | Rb-Sr | 107 | 3.90 |
| | 3.61 | High K | 10024 | Rb-Sr | 107 | 3.84 |
| | 3.59 | High K | 10017 | Rb-Sr | 107 | 3.80 |
| | 3.56 | High K | 10022 | $^{40}$Ar-$^{39}$Ar | 108 | — |
| Luna 16 | 3.45 | Al-basalt | B-1 | $^{40}$Ar-$^{39}$Ar | 109 | — |
| | 3.42 | Al-basalt | B-1 | Rb-Sr | 110 | — |
| Apollo 15 | 3.44 | Quartz basalt | 15682 | Rb-Sr | 111 | 4.06 |
| | 3.40 | Quartz basalt | 15085 | Rb-Sr | 111 | — |
| | 3.35 | Quartz basalt | 15117 | Rb-Sr | 111 | — |
| | 3.33 | Quartz basalt | 15076 | Rb-Sr | 111 | — |
| | 3.32 | Olivine basalt | 15555 | Rb-Sr | 111 | — |
| | 3.31 | Olivine basalt | 15555 | $^{40}$Ar-$^{39}$Ar | 112 | — |
| | 3.26 | Quartz basalt | 15065 | Rb-Sr | 111 | — |
| Apollo 12 | 3.36 | Olivine basalt | 12002 | Rb-Sr | 107 | 4.56 |
| | 3.30 | Olivine basalt | 12063 | Rb-Sr | 107 | 4.33 |
| | 3.30 | Olivine basalt | 12040 | Rb-Sr | 107 | 4.64 |
| | 3.27 | Quartz basalt | 12051 | $^{40}$Ar-$^{39}$Ar | 108 | — |
| | 3.26 | Quartz basalt | 12051 | Rb-Sr | 107 | 4.48 |
| | 3.24 | Olivine basalt | 12002 | $^{40}$Ar-$^{39}$Ar | 108 | — |
| | 3.24 | Quartz basalt | 12065 | $^{40}$Ar-$^{39}$Ar | 108 | — |
| | 3.18 | Quartz basalt | 12064 | Rb-Sr | 107 | 4.98 |
| | 3.16 | Quartz basalt | 12065 | Rb-Sr | 107 | 4.38 |

Apollo 11 low-K rocks is 140–200 million years older by $^{40}$Ar-$^{39}$Ar dating[114, 115] than by Rb-Sr techniques. This may be a real effect, for different samples are involved[113].

A comparison of K-Ar and $^{40}$Ar-$^{39}$Ar dates for Apollo 14 and 15 samples [116] given in Table 4.11, shows that all samples have lost some radiogenic argon. Curiously, the crystalline maria basalts from Hadley Rille have lost far more radiogenic argon than the highland samples, which have had a violent history of cratering.

The oldest basalts are the aluminous clasts embedded in the Apollo 14 breccias. Their apparent absence in other highland rocks implies that basalt extrusion began not long before the Imbrium collision. Perhaps another older basin, of which "South Imbrium" (section 2.10) might be a remnant, occupied the site of the great cataclysm and had begun to fill with basalt before the immense projectile struck.

The oldest post-Imbrium (and post-Orientale) basalts are the Apollo 17 Taurus-Littrow and the Apollo 11 low-K basalts in the Sea of Tranquillity. Both are titanium-rich. Although the Taurus-Littrow valley fill is younger than the last flows filling the Sea of Serenity, the Apollo 11 basalts must cover a substantial thickness of earlier flows. They cannot be a thin veneer over Imbrium (or Orientale) ejecta, for underlying ridges radial to the Imbrium basin would surely be reflected in the surface lavas. Instead, structures concentric to the basins (wrinkle ridges, for example, see section 2.12) predominate. Somewhat younger are the Apollo 11 high-K high-Ti basalts. If these, and the low-K suite, are near surface samples, as is judged likely from the absence of nearby large craters and our experience at other sites, then we have a picture of an extended period of final mare flooding. The orange glasses show the same age as the Apollo 17 basalts (Table 4.12).

**Table 4.11**   Comparison of K-Ar and $^{40}$Ar/$^{39}$Ar Dates[116].

|  |  | $^{40}$Ar/$^{39}$Ar (aeons) | K-Ar (aeons) |
|---|---|---|---|
| Hadley Rille | 15555 | 3.28 | 2.87 |
|  | 15668 | 3.15 | 2.50 |
|  | 15683 | 3.27 | 2.86 |
| Spur Crater | 15415 | 4.09 | 3.95 |
| Fra Mauro | 14310 | 3.78 | 3.68 |
|  | 14053 | 3.92 | 3.69 |

**Table 4.12**   Ages of Orange and Green Glasses and
Associated Basalts [44, 50].

|  |  | Age (aeons) |
| --- | --- | --- |
| Taurus-Littrow | ⌠Orange glass | 3.8 |
|  | ⌡Apollo 17 high-Ti basalt | 3.83 |
| Hadley-Apennines | ⌠Emerald green glass | 3.3 |
|  | ⌡Apollo 15 basalt | 3.28–3.44 |

The next youngest lavas sampled are the Sea of Fertility (Luna 16) aluminous basalts. The younger age than the other Al basalts seems well established by the agreement of Rb-Sr and $^{40}$Ar-$^{39}$Ar techniques. The Apollo 15 basalts show a distinct spread in ages, with no spread in the initial $^{87}$Sr values. The ages overlap with those from the Ocean of Storms (Apollo 12), which in contrast do show a spread in this ratio. The emerald green glass ages overlap those of the Apollo 15 basalts (Table 4.12). The last major flooding so far measured took place at about 3.2 aeons. The youngest rock dated is an Apollo 12 basalt (12065) with an age of 3.16 aeons.

What are the chances of finding younger rocks? The Marius Hills volcanics are probably younger. So too are the last flows in Imbrium (Figs. 2.18, 2.19). Geological mapping indicates that a zone of young basalts occurs in the far west of the Ocean of Storms, not sampled by a mission. How much younger is uncertain, but our past experience with age estimates based on crater counting and surface morphology must engender caution.

In this reviewer's opinion, maria basalts younger than 3.0 aeons are not likely to be found in significant amounts. Maria volcanism occurs as floods of rapidly extruded fluid basalt. The late stages (Apollo 12 and 15 olivine basalts and the Apollo 15 green glass) come from great depths (200–300 km). The dying stages of thermal activity are likely to lead to a rather sudden shutdown of surface volcanic activity, since the declining quantities of the last melts will find increasing difficulty in reaching the surface.

### Rb-Sr Dating [117]

The Rb-Sr dating method measures the time that has elapsed since Rb-Sr fractionation took place. At least two rock samples with differing

Rb-Sr ratios are needed to determine this age, and they must have been cogenetic. In the case of the lunar rock samples, which are scattered from random meteorite impact craters, there is no prima facie case that they are from the same rock unit, or have an identical age of formation.

This problem is overcome by separating and analyzing mineral phases. Individual minerals within each rock formed at the same time, and so meet the cogenetic criterion. Hence a meaningful age of crystallization may be established. This approach (Fig. 4.35) was successfully adopted for the Apollo 11 basalts and for subsequent maria basalts.

We have noted the requirement that mineral isochrons are needed to establish the crystallization age. However, this requires that the phases containing radiogenic Rb and Sr be separated. In the maria basalts, most of the Rb is contained in residual fine-grained or glassy interstitial material, variously called "mesostasis" interstitial material or, poetically, "quintessence"[119]. This phase, largely a mixture of K feldspar and $SiO_2$, is trapped in various mineral phases during crystallization, thus explaining why such an inhospitable host for Rb as ilmenite, which commonly contains much interstitial material, is separated and analyzed. However, this approach raises a more serious question. Do the mineral isochrons have age significance, or are they merely mixing lines representing successive dilution of a quintessence with, for example, Sr from plagioclase?

Papanastassiou and Wasserburg[111] have examined this problem. They measured K and Rb in mineral separates from 15555 with the following results:

|              | K/Rb  |
| ------------ | ----- |
| Plagioclase  | 4,300 |
| Pyroxene     | 500   |
| Quintessence | 395   |
| Ilmenite     | 325   |

These figures provide evidence of enrichment of Rb relative to K, hence fractional crystallization, and hence a meaningful separation of Rb and Sr during crystallization. Particularly noteworthy is the decrease in K/Rb between the separated quintessence and that trapped in the ilmenite.

Although it would be desirable to have much more information of this sort, it can be concluded that the mineral isochrons give the date of crystallization. This conclusion is reinforced by the general agreement with ages calculated from other methods, in particular the $^{39}Ar/^{40}Ar$ method, except for the Apollo 11 low-K data[113].

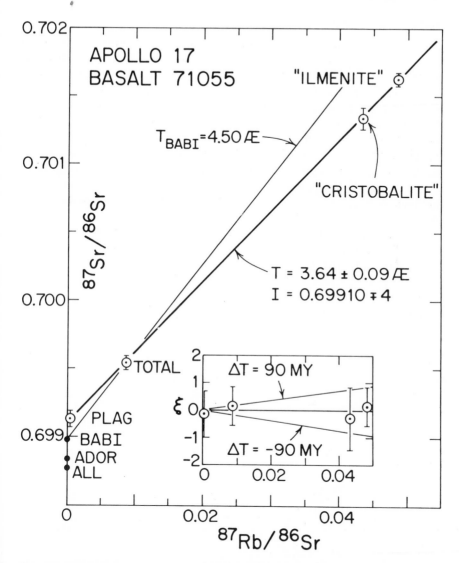

**Fig. 4.35** Rb-Sr evolution diagram for a low-K Apollo 17 high-Ti basalt (71055). The age of crystallization is 3.64 aeons. The initial ratios for basaltic achondrites (BABI), Angros dos Reis (ADOR), and Allende (ALL) are shown. Note that the Allende ratio is significantly lower, a stumbling block for models making the moon from Allende-type material. "One picture is worth 1,000 words"[118]. (Courtesy G. J. Wasserburg.)

### Initial $^{87}Sr/^{86}Sr$ Ratios

A striking feature of the Rb-Sr age data is the low initial $^{87}Sr/^{86}Sr$ ratio (Fig. 4.36). The mineral isochrons, when extrapolated to zero $^{87}Rb/^{86}Sr$, yield initial values for the ratio, which are exceedingly primitive, being close to that observed in basaltic achondrites (BABI) of 0.69898. Refined evaluation of the data[111] point to a slightly lower value of 0.69894.

This ratio is very close to that inferred for the primordial solar nebula material at 4.6 aeons. This value will increase very rapidly in the presence of chondritic Rb/Sr ratios (~0.24), so that separation of Rb and Sr occurred very early in lunar history, and the source material for the lunar lavas was not in a high Rb environment from that time. This event could be the loss of volatile elements such as Rb, together with some fractionation.

The various basalts show at least four separate ratios. The Apollo 15 basalts appear to come from a single source, as do the Apollo 17 basalts[101, 103, 104, 107, 110, 111].

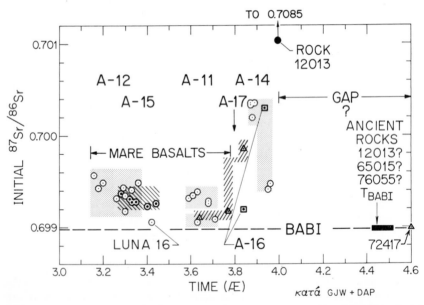

**Fig. 4.36**  Age versus initial $^{87}Sr/^{86}Sr$ ratio for all lunar samples that have internal mineral Rb-Sr isochrons[118]. Note the data point for dunite sample 72417. (Courtesy G. J. Wasserburg.)

There are wide differences in mineralogy, chemistry, and texture among the various classes of maria basalts. Do these differences reflect in the isotopic abundances? Some of these questions have been answered by a study[111] of the Great Scott sample (15555). Samples from various parts of this 9.6-kg boulder show no variations in the initial $^{87}Sr/^{86}Sr$ ratios. The extreme homogeneity rules out surficial contamination from the radiogenically enriched soil. Similarly, there is no evidence of postcrystallization redistribution of the Sr isotopes. If any crustal material was assimilated during eruption, it has been thoroughly homogenized. In view of the rapid crystallization of this rock, such effects must be minimal. Thus the isotopic evidence can be taken at its face value.

The Apollo 15 basalts provided much insight into the isotopic characteristics of maria basalts. All had nearly uniform I values even though many separate chemical and mineralogical types were sampled. This indicates that if any basalts were thrown in from distant impacts on maria (Autolycus and Aristillus are within range) (Fig. 2.23), then they had the same isotopic characteristics as the locally derived samples.

### Model Rb-Sr Ages

Although the Rb-Sr mineral isochrons yield the correct age of crystallization, as confirmed by other approaches, the model Rb-Sr ages give a much older age. The model ages are calculated by assuming an initial $^{87}Sr/^{86}Sr$ ratio. There is not, in fact, much choice available because of the very low values for the initial ratio. The mineral isochrons yield initial ratios close to that of basaltic achondrites at 4.6 aeons. The model ages calculated, assuming an initial $^{87}Sr/^{86}Sr$ value equal to BABI (0.69898), are given in Table 4.10. These are the so-called T BABI ages.

An early conclusion was that the model ages "are remarkably close to 4.6 aeons and indicate approximate closed system behavior and no fractionation in Rb/Sr for about 4.6 aeons"[101], although it was noted that the Apollo 11 high-K basalts gave much younger model ages (Table 4.10)[120].

The picture is consistent with the model of a two-stage Rb-Sr fractionation. Rb is initially separated from Sr at 4.5–4.6 aeons in the primitive fractionation. During the partial melting, about $10^9$ years later, fractionation of Rb from Sr is not marked. Nevertheless, it is not zero. The scatter of T BABI model ages is considerable (Table 4.10), and there are several basalts with young model ages[120]. Since these include the high-K Apollo 11 basalts, where the analytical uncertainties are least, clearly some separation of Rb from Sr occurs during the partial melting in the lunar interior. Implications of these data are discussed in the section on origin of maria basalts and in section 7.6 on the geochemical evolution of the moon.

## 4.15  SOURCES OF THE MARIA BASALTS

The origin of the volcanic basaltic rocks that flood the ringed basins and other areas of the moon has been the subject of much debate. It appears to this reviewer that a consensus is slowly being reached, although there are still areas of disagreement. Two questions may be asked: (a) What was the source of the lavas and how were they melted? (b) What was the subsequent history of the melt before and during solidification?

In examining these questions, various interpretations of the information available are possible, and this is reflected in the differing origins proposed. In the following discussion, we shall adopt what appears to be the most reasonable of the alternative hypotheses, recalling the adage that the progress of scientific research lies not in the proof of theories, but in their refutation.

### The Alternatives

Two major and mutually incompatible hypotheses have been proposed. One theory is that the lavas were produced by impact melting of preexisting surface rocks or of underlying mantle during the large impact events that formed the ringed basins.

The second view is that the lavas were formed deep within the moon by partial or selective melting, as is the case for terrestrial lavas, and were extruded onto the surface, filling the ringed basins long after they were formed. In this event, much information about the lunar interior is potentially available. Two contrasting opinions have arisen over this. One[71] holds that near-surface fractionation modified the compositions thus disguising the nature of the parental liquids. The other position[69] is that the original liquids or primary magmas can be identified, and hence, unequivocal information about the interior obtained from experiments at high pressure and temperature.

Further controversy has arisen over the nature of the source material. In one view, the interior of the moon from which the maria basalts are derived represents primary material, with a composition equivalent to that of the whole moon[69, 70, 73].

The alternate viewpoint is that the source regions of the basalts are themselves fractionated during initial melting of part [76] or whole [121] of the moon. Such views bear on the genesis of the europium anomaly, the origin of the highland crust, the thermal history of the moon, the nature of the accreting process, and the origin of the body itself.

## 4.16  IMPACT MELTING

The suggestion persists that the vast impacts forming the ringed basins were in some way responsible for the generation of the lavas. The fact that the density of the basalts is close to that of the whole moon has always lent a facile attraction to the hypothesis. However, the maria basalts cannot be representative of the whole lunar composition. The transformation of such a composition to the dense rock-type eclogite at shallow depths would mean a layered interior structure and a greater overall density for the moon [69, 122]. This is not consistent with the geophysical evidence [123]. Hence impact melting of near-surface material would have to be followed by fractionation to produce the basalts. It will be shown later that such large-scale near-surface fractionation is unlikely to have occurred, thus placing a severe restriction on the hypothesis.

A further major objection is that the composition of the maria basalts is totally distinct from that of the older highland crust, which was impacted. Such a composition could not produce the basalts either by partial or complete melting. It has been suggested [124] that in order to produce a sufficient amount of lava the rocks were near their melting temperature before impact. The extra energy provided by the impact was sufficient to raise the temperature above the melting point. However, as we have seen above, this melt must then undergo fractionation to produce the basalt chemistry [69]. Furthermore, a hot surface of the moon raises many problems. Some large ringed basin impacts occurred toward the final stages of the heavy cratering of the uplands. The surface of the moon was cool enough at that stage to support the Apennine Ridge and the Orientale basin, neither being totally isostatically compensated.

Alternative views suggested that the giant impacts broke through the highlands crust, melting the mafic substratum [125, 127]. In the impact melt hypothesis, the basin flooding occurs immediately after the creation of the basin. There is much evidence from stratigraphy and age dating to refute this view. Much of this has been discussed in chapter 2 on lunar geology, but the salient points are summarized here.

(*a*) The maria surfaces have lower impact crater densities than the ejecta blankets of the basins, and thus are younger.

(*b*) Within the basins, there are large craters now filled with lava. The crater Archimedes, in the Imbrium basin, is a typical example. It is clearly postbasin but prelava fill, being now flooded itself.

(*c*) The individual flows, for example, in Mare Imbrium, show that the basins were filled successively by individual flows, rather than by a single great pool of lava.

(*d*) The maria surfaces show no trace of impact debris from the great collisions[126]. For example, there is no debris from the collision that produced the Imbrium basin lying on the broad and smooth lava surfaces of Mare Serenitatis (Fig. 4.2).

This conclusion applies generally across the moon. None of the maria surfaces have debris on them from any of the great maria basin collisions. Thus, if the lavas filling the basins were produced by the impacts which dug the basins, *all* the events must have occurred at the same time. In this way, the collisional debris could sink from sight in the liquid lava lakes. This was an unlikely but not absurd hypothesis, since before the advent of dating of the samples, it was a possibility that most lunar events were telescoped together at 4.6 aeons and that the observed differences in crater rates occurred on a very short time scale.

A more reasonable point of view was that the basins were flooded long after they were formed. The impact-produced debris is covered up by successive flows from the interior of the moon. This sequence of events was strongly advocated by astrogeologists[128] on the basis of the apparent differences in ages as shown, for example, by the differing abundances of craters on the maria surfaces.

The radiometric age data from Apollo 11 was suggestive but not decisive in deciding between these two viewpoints. The Apollo 12 rocks provided a decisive answer. Their age is several hundred million years younger than those from Mare Tranquillitatis, indicating at least two widely separated epochs of maria filling. Samples from subsequent missions confirmed a long-continued history of these processes. Such a long time interval is totally inconsistent with the stratigraphic requirements for simultaneous or near simultaneous maria filling by impact-produced lavas. It indicates that the lavas that filled the maria basins and spilled over into adjoining regions, came over long intervals from the interior of the moon, in an analogous fashion to terrestrial lava flows[129].

There is some evidence that *small* amounts of impact-generated melts occur[130]. Thus the floors of Tycho and other large craters show material looking like lava flows, and there are the terrestrial analogies from large impact craters (e.g., Clearwater Lake, Manicouagan, and Mistastin)[130], as well as the small amounts of melt produced at the smaller craters. Possibly, and indeed probably, there may well be a lower zone of impact melt at the base of the great ringed basins. The volumes are insignificant, however, compared with the vast outpouring of the maria basalts.

## 4.17  PARTIAL MELTING IN THE INTERIOR

Various degrees of partial melting of material deep within the moon may explain the chemistry, mineralogy, the high pressure and melting studies on the lunar lavas. One requirement is that the melt be less dense than the overall density of the moon (assuming a uniform radial density distribution) so that it will rise to the surface. The density is about $3 \text{ g/cm}^3$ for the molten lava, which crystallizes at the surface to form the basalts with densities $3.3$–$3.4 \text{ g/cm}^3$.

Studies of the behavior of lunar basalts under high pressures have been carried out by several groups[69–72, 134–136] and typical phase relations are shown in Figs. 4.37 and 4.38. The most significant result is that material of lunar basalt composition transforms to the dense rock type, eclogite, at pressures above 12 kilobars at 1,110°C. At higher temperatures, the pressure needed to effect the transformation rises slowly, increasing at the rate of about 20 bars per degree centigrade.

The transition from basalt to eclogite involves changing from the mineral assemblage ilmenite-clinopyroxene-plagioclase to one composed of garnet-rutile-clinopyroxene. Thus, the transition is not sharp but is smeared out over a pressure and temperature interval as the different mineral phases react. However, in comparison with terrestrial rocks, the interval is surprisingly narrow (2 kilobars at 1,100°C). Thus, if the moon were composed of lunar basalt, it would possess a central core of dense eclogite. Since the transformation occurs at low pressures, estimates of a core radius of about 1,400 km have been made, overlain by an outer 350-km-thick shell of basalt. This is an unrealistic model from many lines of evidence. From the moment of inertia studies, it appeared that the moon has a uniform radial density distribution. These data constitute the principal line of evidence that the maria basalts are derived from small amounts of *partial* melting in the interior of the moon. Thus, the experimental data set broad limits of the amount and depth of the partial melting process. These compositions may be modified by fractional

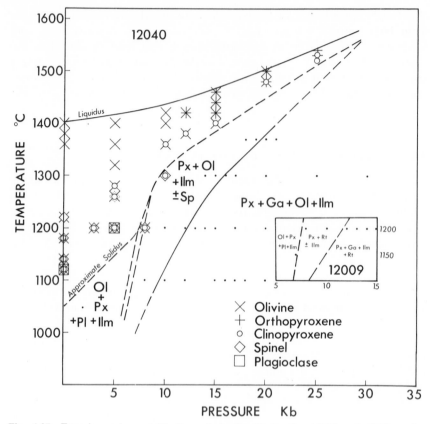

**Fig. 4.37** Experimental crystallization of Apollo 12 basalts 12009 and 12040 under subsolidus conditions at pressures up to 25 kbars[70]. (Courtesy D. H. Green.)

crystallization en route to the surface[137]. A number of constraints limit the depth of partial melting. The presence of the mascons indicates that they must have been emplaced in a crust strong enough, and hence cool enough, to support them. The preferred explanation for the mascons is that they are due to the excess mass resulting from the emplacement of the maria basalts. Isostatic adjustment has not occurred since then. The mascon constraint sets an upper limit of about 100 km, while partial melting at depths greater than 400 km are unlikely, since the experimental data[69, 70, 133] indicate that at that depth a melt of the composition of the maria basalts would be in equilibrium with a clinopyroxene and garnet. This mineral assemblage will have a density greater than 3.6 g/cm³,

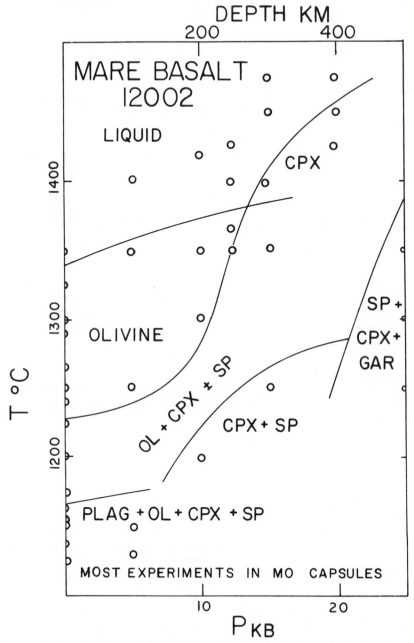

**Fig. 4.38** Experimental crystallization experiments on Apollo 12 basalt 12002 up to 25 kbars [136]. (Courtesy J. F. Hays.)

corresponding to eclogite. Thus, if the basalts come from very great depths, they would have to have been melted from a *source* rock denser than the overall density of the moon[122]. The nearly uniform distribution of density with depth precludes this, and there is no evidence for an eclogite core extending to within 500 km of the surface[131]. Thus the sources of maria basalts are constrained within a region of about 100–400 km depth in the moon.

The sources of heat are discussed in chapter 7. The main source is radioactive heating, due to the strong near-surface concentration of the radioactive elements K, U, and Th in the moon. Whether there was any contribution from residual accretionary heating is less certain. These sources were sufficient to raise the lunar interior to the melting point of basalt (~1,300°C) for about 1 billion years between 3 and 4 billion years ago. Since about that time, the interior has been too cold to produce basaltic lava flows, and the moon has remained a rigid body, supporting the mascons and its irregular shape.

The degree of partial melting in the lunar interior and the depth depend on models of the lunar interior[121]. Thus, if a primary unfractionated composition is inferred at depth, differing amounts of melting are required to account for the variations in the basalt types discussed earlier. An alternative view is that the lunar interior is zoned, and that the different species of maria basalts come from differing depths, which differ significantly in composition. These models depend on constraints other than those of experimental petrology and are discussed in the section on the geochemical evolution of the moon (section 7.6).

Such models must explain the high degree of enrichment of many trace elements (section 4.13) and the other chemical features. One constraint from the isotopic data is relevant here. The maria basalts have extrusion and crystallization ages in the range from 3.2 to 3.9 aeons (Table 4.10). The Rb-Sr model ages are older, indicating that separation of $^{87}$Rb from $^{87}$Sr was not a particularly effective process during partial melting.

It is clear from an examination of the model Rb-Sr ages based on BABI (Table 4.10) that they are mostly younger than 4.6 aeons. Although this might mean that the moon has a more primitive ratio than BABI, evidence for this is not very convincing[139, 140].

One reasonable interpretation of the mare basalt model ages is that there is some separation of Rb from Sr during partial melting, with Rb entering the melt more readily than Sr. Factors on the order of 2 are suggested[140]. The separation is not great, but is difficult to measure. The notion has arisen that no fractionation of Rb and Sr has occurred during partial melting to form the maria basalts, but this unlikely circumstance does not appear to be valid. This removes a constraint on theories of mare basalt origin.

As discussed in section 4.14 there is ample evidence for an early (~4.6 aeons) fractionation of Rb from Sr, both as a consequence of loss of volatile elements at or before accretion and because of early crustal formation.

## 4.18   COOLING AND CRYSTALLIZATION OF THE LAVAS

Did changes in the chemical composition of the lavas occur between the production of the melt and its crystallization as mare basalt? During the cooling and crystallization of the lava, separation of early formed mineral phases may change the composition. This may happen during the ascent of the lava to the surface and during the spreading of the lava across the maria, as well as during the final crystallization.

The extremely fluid nature of the lavas (the viscosity is in the range 5–10 poises, comparable to that of heavy engine oil at room temperature and about an order of magnitude lower than terrestrial lavas) enables them to spread out widely in thin sheets. These thin flows are not conducive to much crystal settling. They cool rapidly and crystallize quickly. Whenever a deep lava lake occurs, the opportunity is present for slow cooling and crystal settling, leading to compositional changes. Such conditions might occur occasionally on the moon, perhaps best of all where the lavas are confined within large craters (e.g., in the flooded craters such as Archimedes or Plato). The Taurus-Littrow valley and the Apollo 15 sites are also favorable structural situations for ponding lavas, but there are no indications of strong fractional crystallization in the returned samples.

Similar conditions might apply in the earliest flooding of the maria basins, when extensive ponding may occur. As the basins are filled, the extreme fluidity of the lavas allows them to flow freely over the lunar surface. Even vast outpourings will only rarely form deep lakes but instead will flood widely across the lunar surface forming the irregular seas, spreading out from the circular basins. Mare Tranquillitatis is one such, and Oceanus Procellarum, the Ocean of Storms, site of the Apollo 12 landing, is another. They are of shallow depth[142] compared with the circular maria, and do not have mascons.

Several workers have concluded that rocks such as 12002 and 12009 represent primary magmas, derived by partial melting from the lunar interior, which have arrived at the surface still totally liquid[70, 132, 133]. Contrary opinions have been advanced[71, 72, 141]. These relate the variations in chemistry of the maria basalts to crystal accumulation in large lava lakes, and these workers interpret rocks such as 12009 as impact melts[138].

Evidence bearing on these questions comes from experimental studies of the cooling behavior of the basaltic melts. Fig. 4.39 shows the crystallization sequence at 1 bar pressure for three Apollo 12 basalts. From these and similar studies[70, 143], it has proved possible to relate the chemistry of sequences of the Apollo 12 and 15 basalts to removal of olivine and pyroxene in a near-surface crystallization environment. Starting, for example, with 12009 as a parental magma, 12020 and 12018 are

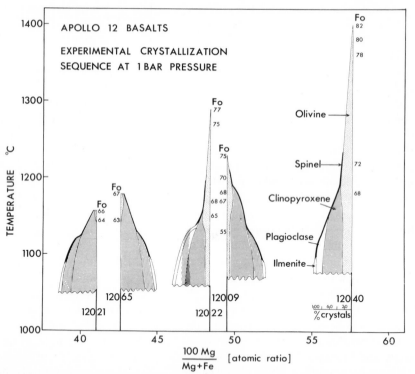

**Fig. 4.39** Crystallization sequence established experimentally for Apollo 12 rocks at 1 atm in equilibrium with metallic iron. The width of the shaded area for each mineral shows the visual estimation, from crushed and polished mounts, of the amount of crystallization of that phase (see 12040 composition for scale). (Courtesy D. H. Green.)

simply related by olivine accumulation and 12052 by removal of olivine[144]. Similar relationships can be found in the Apollo 15 suite[143]. The Apollo 15 olivine basalts show a range in compositions that can be simply related by removal or addition of olivine and some chromium-rich spinel.

### Liquid Immiscibility

A characteristic feature of lunar magmas is that at very late stages of crystallization, when about 95 percent of the rock has solidified, the residual liquid splits into two immiscible liquids[145, 146]. Typical compositions are (a) high in $SiO_2$, $K_2O$, and other selected elements, similar in many ways to a potassic granite, and (b) low in $SiO_2$ and $K_2O$ but very high in FeO and other elements characteristic of pyroxenite. In Table 4.13 the average chemical analyses of two immiscible phases, determined from analysis of globules, are presented and clearly show the extreme contrast in composition of the two phases. Fig. 4.40 illustrates globules of high silica glass in an Apollo 11 low-K rock. Such a process produces the long sought "lunar granites." Possibly some of the "granitic glass" compositions in the soils (Table 3.4) result from segregation of this material by impact. The process is not quantitatively important, for the amount of "granite" produced in this fashion is minute (see section 3.7).

### 4.19   FRACTIONAL CRYSTALLIZATION

There is much evidence from the petrological and mineralogical studies that internal element fractionation of great diversity occur during the crystallization of the basaltic lavas[31, 125]. How much has this affected the bulk compositions? The observed trends resemble those familiar on the earth during the crystallization of basaltic magmas, but the overall effect is much less. In many of the rocks, as noted (e.g., Apollo 12 and 15

**Table 4.13**   Chemical Analysis (Normalized to 100 percent) of High- and Low-Silica Glasses Resulting from Silicate Liquid Immiscibility[145].

| Type | $SiO_2$ | $Al_2O_3$ | FeO | MgO | CaO | $Na_2O$ | $K_2O$ | $TiO_2$ | Total |
|------|------|------|------|------|------|------|------|------|------|
| High-silica | 76.2 | 11.6 | 2.6 | 0.3 | 1.8 | 0.4 | 6.6 | 0.5 | 100.0 |
| Low-silica | 46.4 | 3.1 | 32.3 | 2.2 | 11.3 | 0.1 | 0.3 | 4.3 | 100.0 |

Data given in weight percent.

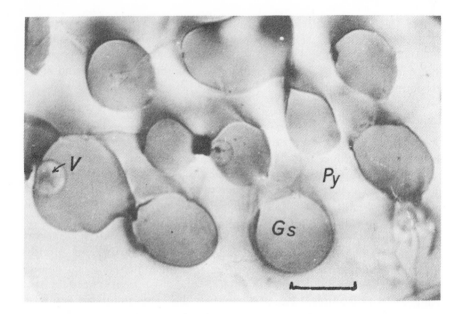

**Fig. 4.40**  Photomicrograph[145] of late interstitial crystal of pyroxferroite (Py), containing blebs of clear, high-silica glass (Gs). V, vapor (shrinkage bubble or gas). Scale bar = 10 $\mu$m. Plane transmitted light. Low-K Apollo 11 basalt 10003. (Courtesy E. Roedder.)

samples), there is good evidence for removal of olivine and some clinopyroxene, but the changes in bulk composition are small and do not produce the extremely fractionated rocks typical of terrestrial basalts. Thus, there are no lunar equivalents of the basalt differentiation sequences of Hawaii or the Skaergaard intrusion. It is difficult to find a lunar whole rock with more than 48 percent $SiO_2$.

Several different lines of petrographic and geochemical evidence bear on this problem.

(a) In terrestrial lavas, the appearance of large crystals (phenocrysts) in a matrix of small crystals or glass indicates that crystallization began well before eruption and was interrupted by rapid chilling following extrusion. Separation of early phases is possible under these conditions. Some of the lunar lavas (e.g., Apollo 12 and 15 pyroxene-porphyritic quartz-normative basalts) have textures that have been interpreted as indicating a two-stage crystallization.

For example, the chemical trends in the lunar pyroxenes could be correlated with the sequence of crystallization, the bulk composition of the rock, and the oxygen fugacity [30, 147]. In basalts with high Ti (Apollo 11 and 17), the pyroxenes show continuous chemical variation from augite to pyroxferroite. In the quartz-normative Apollo 12 and 15 basalts, with lower Ti/Al ratios, a break occurs in the pyroxene compositions apparently due to the crystallization of plagioclase. The detailed history of the cooling of the magmas is recorded in the pyroxene compositions.

Two models were presented to account for the break in clinopyroxene compositions and the crystallization of plagioclase. The first, involving initial crystallization at depth, followed by surface extrusion was narrowly favored over *in situ* crystallization of all phases, with delayed nucleation of plagioclase [30, 133, 147]. More recent experimental studies on cooling history have resolved the problem [148]. The porphyritic textures characteristic of the Apollo 12 and 15 quartz-normative basalts were reproduced during single-stage monotonic cooling, at rates on the order of 10°C per hour.

(*b*) Chromium is an element that is rapidly depleted during fractional crystallization. Its concentration decreases dramatically in terrestrial basaltic lavas when opportunity for removal of early phases, which Cr enters, is present. This is because $Cr^{3+}$ has a high crystal field site preference energy, like $Ni^{2+}$, and enters the earliest available sixfold coordination sites. On the moon, some $Cr^{2+}$ is present [83]. This has a geochemical behavior similar to $Co^{2+}$, and is not so rapidly depleted as $Ni^{2+}$.

Most of the lunar chromium is trivalent. It is present at high levels (<300 km) in the moon, unlike $Ni^{2+}$, because the principal phases at depths below 300 km are probably olivine and orthopyroxene, which exclude the trivalent ion. Partial melting of clinopyroxene contributes Cr to the melt. This is retained in the surface lavas, where high levels (typically 1,000–3,000 ppm Cr) are present. Even moderate degrees of fractional crystallization and removal of chromite or early pyroxenes would deplete the magma in Cr in the manner of terrestrial sequences.

One sample (15597), which has been studied in detail [149] is distinctive in having very chromium-rich spinels (with 55 percent $Cr_2O_3$), which apparently crystallized before the pyroxene. This particular sample appears to have had no local differentiation or separation of phases, providing evidence for the general lack of near-surface fractional crystallization before the lavas were extruded.

(*c*) As discussed earlier, strong depletion of the rare earth element, europium, is characteristic of the lunar rocks, and would be consistent with removal of plagioclase feldspar, which is the chief host for this trace element. Various workers calculate that removal of between 50 and 90 percent of the feldspar would be needed to account for the observed depletion.

In most lunar basalts, plagioclase is not a liquidus phase[150], so that near-surface crystallization and removal of the phase is not a possible explanation for the Eu anomaly. In the class of aluminous maria basalts[16], where plagioclase appears on the liquidus, the Eu anomaly is not well developed (Fig. 4.22).

(d) There is much evidence of intense melt-mineral fractionation at the microscopic level. The overall uniformity in composition of the rocks is in marked contrast, since separation of the complex minerals would produce a heterogeneous rock suite. Many of the minerals present (ilmenite, sulfides, and metallic iron, for example) are much denser than the melt, and would readily separate, depleting the melt, in titanium, for example. The failure of the dense phases to separate indicates either very rapid crystallization or late appearance of the phases and, in any event, little fractionation.

(e) It has been suggested that the high titanium content of the Apollo 11 and 17 rocks might be a consequence of accumulation of crystals of ilmenite[71]. However, there is no evidence from the rock fabric to indicate "cumulate" textures resulting from selective accumulation of crystals during cooling of silicate melts[134]. The textural and experimental evidence indicates that for much of the period of crystallization, the three main rock-forming minerals—ilmenite, pyroxene, and plagioclase— were precipitating together.

In summary, the evidence is decisively against large-scale near-surface fractionation. After considering all the petrological and chemical evidence outlined in this chapter, the apparent consensus is that the maria basalts are derived from the lunar interior by partial melting, with only minor near surface fractionation. The source region itself has undergone at least one previous stage of element fractionation, following accretion of the moon.

## REFERENCES AND NOTES

1. Wilson, A. T. (1962) Nature. 196: 11.
2. Gold, T. (1955) Mon. Not. Roy. Ast. Soc. 115: 585.
3. Gilvarry, J. J. (1968) Nature. 218: 336.
4. A last-ditch defense of the sedimentary hypothesis was offered by J. J. Gilvarry (1970, Radio Sci. 5: 322) following the Apollo 11 sample return.

5. Baldwin, R. B. (1949) *The Face of the Moon*, Chicago.
6. Kuiper, G. (1954) *Proc. U.S. Nat. Acad. Sci.* 40: 1096.
7. Fielder, G. (1963) *Nature*, 198: 1256.
8. LSPET (1969) *Science.* 165: 1211.
9. Murase, T., and McBirney, A. R. (1970) *Science.* 167: 1491.
10. Hartmann, W. K. (1965) *Icarus.* 4: 164.
11. Hartmann, W. K. (1966) *Icarus.* 5: 406.
12. Gault, D. E. (1970) *Radio Sci.* 5: 289.
13. LSPET (1970) *Science.* 167: 1325.
14. LSPET (1972) *Science.* 175: 363.
15. LSPET (1973) *Science.* 182: 659.
16. Reid, A. M., and Jakeš, P. (1974) *LS V*: 627.
17. On this occasion, 12 $km^3$ of lava were extruded from the 25-km-long Laki fissure and covered an area of 565 $km^2$.
18. James, O. B., and Jackson, E. D. (1970) *JGR.* 75: 5793.
19. James, O. B., and Wright, T. L. (1972) *Bull. GSA* 83: 2357.
20. Warner, J. (1971) *PLC 2*: 469.
21. Brown, G. M., et al. (1971) *PLC 2*: 583.
22. Gancarz, A. J., et al. (1971) *EPSL.* 12: 1.
23. Albee, A. L., et al. (1972) *EPSL.* 13: 353.
24. Brown, G. M., et al. (1972) Apollo 15: 40.
25. Dowty, E., et al. (1973) *PLC 4*: 423.
26. Rhodes, J. M., and Hubbard, N. J. (1973) *PLC 4*: 1127.
27. Ridley, W. I., et al. (1973) *PEPI.* 7: 133.
28. Ridley, W. I. (1973) *EOS.* 54: 611.
29. Bence, A. E. (1973) *EOS.* 54: 580.
30. Brown, G. M., et al. (1973) *LS V*: 89.
31. Bence, A. E., and Papike, J. J. (1972) *PLC 3*: 431.
32. Haggerty, S. E. (1973) *Proc. Int. Conf. Kimberlites*, University of Cape Town, Abstracts, 147.
33. Levinson, A. A., and Taylor, S. R. (1971) *Moon Rocks and Minerals*, Pergamon Press.
34. Frondel, J. W., and Frondel, C. (1974) *Lunar Mineralogy*, Wiley.
35. Frondel, J. W. (1973) *A Glossary of Lunar Minerals*, Department of Geological Sciences, Harvard University.
36. Wellman, T. R. (1970) *Nature.* 225: 716.
37. Sato, M. (1973) *PLC 4*: 1074.
38. Ibid., 1061.
39. Brett, R., et al. (1971) *PLC 2*: 301; Reid, A. M., et al. (1970) *EPSL.* 9: 1.
40. O'Hara, M., et al. (1970) *PLC 1*: 695; Brown, G. M., and Peckett, A. (1971) *Nature.* 234: 262.
41. Philpotts, J. A. et al. (1973) *PLC 4*: 1427.
42. Haggerty, S. E. (1970) *PLC 1*: 513; Burns, R. G. (1973) *EOS.* 54: 618.
43. Huneke, J. C., et al. (1973) *LS IV*: 404.
44. Huneke, J. C., et al. (1974) *LS V*: 377.
45. Rhodes, J. M. (1973) *EOS.* 54: 609.
46. Jovanovic, S., et al. (1973) *EOS.* 54: 595.
47. Gibson, E. K., and Moore, G. (1973) *EOS.* 54: 589.
48. Vaughan, D. J., and Burns, R. G. (1973) *EOS.* 54: 618.

49. Mao, H. K., et al. (1973) *EOS.* 54: 598.
50. Schaeffer, O. A., and Hussain, L. (1973) *EOS.* 54: 613.
51. Tatsumoto, M. (1973) *EOS.* 54: 615.
52. Roedder, E., and Weiblen, P. W. (1973) *EOS.* 54: 612.
53. Prinz, M., et al. (1973) *EOS.* 54: 605.
54. Heiken, G., et al. (1974) *GCA. 38*: 1703; McKay, D. S., et al. (1973) *EOS.* 54: 599.
55. Reid, A. M., et al. (1973) *EOS.* 54: 606.
56. The terms *siderophile, chalcophile,* and *lithophile* elements were introduced by Goldschmidt to describe the distribution of elements among *metallic, sulfide,* and *silicate* phases; the classification stems from the observed distribution of elements among metallic, troilite (FeS), and silicate phases in meteorites. The behavior of an element is dependent on local conditions of temperature, pressure, oxidizing or reducing conditions, and so on, but the classification remains a useful first approximation to indicate the geochemical behavior of the elements. For an excellent recent review, see Grossman, L., and Larimer, J. W. (1974) *Rev. Geophys. Space Phys.* 12: 71.
57. Trzcienski, W. E., and Kulik, C. G. (1972) *PLC 3*: 591.
58. Gibson, E. K., and Hubbard, N. J. (1972) *PLC 3*: 2003. See section 3.16.
59. Volatile elements are those that condense below 1,300°K at a solar nebula pressure of $10^{-3}$ atm. Refractory or involatile elements condense above this temperature. Grossman, L., and Larimer, J. W. (1974) *Rev. Geophys. Space Phys.* 12: 71.
60. Data for H and L chondrites from Mason, B. H. (1970) *Elemental Abundances in Meteorites,* Gordon and Breech.
61. The element europium occurs at that point in the sequence of the 14 rare earth elements when the 4 f electron subshell is half-filled (with 7 electrons) and the outer shell (6 s) has 2 electrons. Accordingly, it loses these two electrons readily and a third with more difficulty. It is trivalent only under oxidizing conditions (e.g., in the outer regions of the earth), when its behavior is similar to that of the other trivalent REE. In such cases, the REE patterns, relative to those of chondrites, show a smooth variation with ionic radius (or atomic number).
62. Weill, D. F., and Drake, M. J. (1973) *Science.* 180: 1059; Sun, C., et al. (1974) *GCA.* In press.
63. Philpotts, J. A. (1970) *EPSL.* 9: 257.
64. Nguyen-Long-Den, and Yokoyama, Y. (1970) *Meteoritics.* 5: 214.
65. Schnetzler, C. C., and Philpotts, J. A. (1971), *PLC 2*: 1101.
66. O'Hara, M. J., and Biggar, G. M. (1970) *Geol. Soc. Amer. Abstracts.* 2: 639.
67. See also sections 3.16 and 4.5.
68. Gast, P. W., et al. (1970) *PLC 1*: 1143; Gast, P. W., and Hubbard, N. J. (1970) *EPSL.* 10: 94.
69. Ringwood, A. E., and Essene, E. (1970) *PLC 1*: 796.
70. Green, D. H., et al. (1971) *PLC 2*: 601.
71. O'Hara, M. J., et al. (1970) *PLC 1*: 695.
72. Biggar, G. M., et al. (1971) *PLC 2*: 617.
73. Graham, A., and Ringwood, A. E. (1972) *EPSL.* 13: 105.
74. Compston, W. (1974) *LS V*: 135.
75. Weill, D. F. (1974) *LS V*: 842.
76. Schnetzler, C. C., and Philpotts, J. A. (1971) *PLC 2*: 1116.
77. Ringwood, A. E. (1974) *LS V*: 635.
78. Peckett, A., Phillips, R., and Brown, G. M. (1972) *Nature.* 236: 215.

79. Eldridge, J. S. (1973) *PLC 4*: 2115.
80. Taylor, S. R. (1973) *Nature.* 245: 203.
81. Duncan, A. R., et al. (1973) *PLC 4*: 1097.
82. Duncan, A. R. (1974) *LS V*: 187.
83. Jakeš, P., and Reid, A. M. (1974) *LS V*: 381.
84. Brett, R. (1973) *GCA.* 37: 165.
85. See sections 3.16 and 4.5.
86. Schmitt, R., and Laul, J. C. (1973) *Moon.* 8: 182.
87. Kaplan, I. R., and Petrowski, C. (1971) *PLC 2*: 1402. The $^{34}S/^{32}S$ values are expressed as deviations from a standard sample, as follows:

$$\delta\,^{34}S\,\permil = \left(\frac{^{34}S/^{32}S\ \text{sample} - \,^{34}S/^{32}S\ \text{std.}}{^{34}S/^{32}S\ \text{std.}}\right)1{,}000.$$

Std. = FeS (troilite) from Canyon Diablo meteorite.
88. Gibson, E. K., and Moore, G. W. (1974) *LS V*: 267.
89. Rees, C. E., et al. (1974) *LS V*: 621.
90. See section on reduced nature of lunar basalts.
91. Anders, E., et al. (1971) *PLC 2*: 1021.
92. De Wys, J. N. (1968) *JGR.* 73: 6915; (1968) NASA SP 173: 187.
93. Anders, E. (1973) *Moon.* 8: 6.
94. Ganapathy, R., et al. (1970) *PLC 1*: 1117.
95. Johnson, T. V., and Fanale, F. P. (1972) *EOS.* 53: 1037.
96. The $^{18}O/^{16}O$ data are customarily expressed as deviations from a standard sample, in parts per 1,000:

$$\delta\,^{18}O = \left(\frac{(^{18}O/^{16}O)\ \text{sample}}{(^{18}O/^{16}O)\ \text{std. ocean water}} - 1\right)1{,}000.$$

97. Taylor, H. P., and Epstein, S. (1973) *PLC 4*: 1657.
98. Clayton, R. N., et al. (1973) *PLC 4*: 1535.
99. LSPET (1973) *Science.* 182: 659; Moore, C. B., et al. (1971) *PLC 2*: 1343 and (1973) *PLC 4*: 1613; Epstein, S., and Taylor, H. P. (1971) *PLC 2*: 1421. For nitrogen abundances, see Müller, O. (1973) *PLC 4*: 1625.
100. The variation in $^{13}C/^{12}C$ data are given as:

$$\delta\,^{13}C\permil = \left(\frac{^{13}C/^{12}C\ \text{sample} - \,^{13}C/^{12}C\ \text{std. limestone}}{^{13}C/^{12}C\ \text{std. limestone}}\right)1{,}000.$$

101. Papanastassiou, D. A., and Wasserburg, G. J. (1971) *EPSL.* 12: 36.
102. Turner, G. (1973) *PLC 4*: 1907.
103. Tatsumoto, M., et al. (1973) *EOS.* 54: 614.
104. Murthy, V. R., et al. (1973) *EOS.* 54: 587.
105. Schaeffer, O., and Hussain, L. (1973) *EOS.* 54: 614.
106. Turner, G. (1970) *PLC 1*: 1665.
107. Panastassiou, D. A., and Wasserburg, G. J. (1971) *EPSL.* 11: 37.
108. Turner, G. (1971) *EPSL.* 11: 183.
109. Huneke, J. C., et al. (1972) *EPSL.* 13: 375.
110. Papanastassiou, D. A., and Wasserburg, G. J. (1972) *EPSL.* 13: 368.
111. Ibid. (1973) 17: 324.
112. Podosek, F. A., et al. (1972) *Science.* 175: 423.

113. $^{40}$Ar-$^{39}$Ar ages[106] as old as 3.92 aeons have been measured for Apollo 11 low-K 10003. Eberhardt, P., et al. (1971, *EPSL*. 11: 245) obtain a $^{40}$Ar-$^{39}$Ar age of 3.82 aeons for a feldspar concentrate from 10003. The low-K Apollo 11 samples may thus be the oldest post-Imbrium and post-Orientale basalts sampled. Stettler, A., et al. (1974, *LS V*: 738) find an age of 3.92 aeons for 10003 confirming the ancient nature of this rock.

114. The method is based on the decay of $^{40}$K to $^{40}$Ar with a half-life of $12.1 \times 10^9$ years.

115. The $^{39}$Ar-$^{40}$Ar method is an important modification of the K-Ar technique. The method depends on converting some of the $^{39}$K in the sample to $^{39}$Ar by neutron activation. The sample is then heated to release this $^{39}$Ar together with the $^{40}$Ar produced by decay of $^{40}$K. Thus both potassium and argon are effectively measured by the same analytical technique. In a sample that has quantitatively retained argon, both $^{39}$Ar and $^{40}$Ar will be in the same lattice sites and will be released in fixed proportions, and an age can be calculated. If argon has migrated within the rock, or if it has been lost or gained, variable $^{39}$Ar/$^{40}$Ar ratios will result. During heating of the sample to release the argon, that from the more readily outgassed sites is released first, and the $^{40}$Ar/$^{39}$Ar ratio will decrease as the more retentive sites release argon. The argon released at higher temperatures comes from the potassium lattice sites, and the age calculated from the ratios approaches the true age. Eventually a plateau of $^{40}$Ar/$^{39}$Ar ratios is reached, indicating a maximum age.

116. Hussain, L., et al. (1972) *PLC 3*: 1557.

117. $^{87}$Rb decays to $^{87}$Sr by $\beta$ decay with a half-life given as $4.88 \times 10^9$ years. Rb-Sr dating techniques have many advantages. These include a simple decay scheme of parent to daughter involving weak $\beta$ decay without lattice disruption, nongaseous daughter product, and ready retention of daughter isotope in the parent crystal lattice site, due to generally similar geochemical behavior of the two elements, as pointed out in a prescient paper by Ahrens (1948, *Bull. GSA*. 60: 217).

118. Tera, F., et al. (1974) *LS V*: 792.

119. Those readers with a classical bent will recall that a fifth element or "quintessence" was the material making up the heavenly bodies in Greek cosmology. The familiar four elements, earth, air, fire and water, sufficed for terrestrial geochemistry.

120. Other low T BABI ages are 10020 (4.29 AE), 15379 (4.21 AE), and 15499 (4.23 AE).

121. Taylor, S. R., and Jakeš P. (1974) *LS V*: 786.

122. Wetherill, G. W. (1968) *Science*. 160: 1256.

123. See chapter 6.

124. Opik, E. J. (1969) *Ann. Rev. Astron. Astrophys*. 7: 473.

125. Smith, J. V., et al. (1969) *PLC 1*: 897.

126. Urey, H. C. (1951) *The Planets*, Yale University Press.

127. Birck, J. L., et al. (1974) *LS V*: 64.

128. See chapter 2.

129. The history of these hypotheses is given at some length to illustrate in part the nature of scientific inquiry and to remind the reader that what is revealed truth to one observer is irrelevant detail to another.

130. Dence, M. R., et al. (1974) *Meteoritics*. In press.

131. See chapter 6.

132. Chappell, B. W., and Green, D. H. (1973) *EPSL*. 18: 237.

133. Grove, T. L., et al. (1973) *PLC 4*: 995.

134. Walker, D., et al. (1974) *LS V*: 814.

135. The pressure at the center of the moon, at a depth of 1,738 km, is 47 kilobars. (One

bar $= 10^6$ dynes/cm$^2 = 0.987$ atm.) This pressure is equivalent to that reached at a depth of 200 km in the earth.

136. Grove, T., et al. (1973) *PLC 4*; 995.
137. See section 4.15.
138. A summary of the long-standing controversy between the Canberra and Edinburgh experimental petrology groups is given in ref. 136, 1005–1009. See also[134].
139. Jessberger, E. K., et al. (1974) *Nature*. 248: 202; Papanastassiou, D. A., et al. (1970) *EPSL*. 8: 1.
140. Papanastassiou, D. A., and Wasserburg, G. J. (1973) *EPSL*. 17: 336.
141. O'Hara, M. J., and Biggar, G. M. (1972) *EPSL*. 16: 388.
142. De Hon, R. A. (1974, *LS V*: 163) indicates that the maximum depth in Mare Tranquillitatis is about 2 km.
143. Chappell, B. W., and Green, D. H. (1973) *EPSL*. 18: 237.
144. Compston, W., et al. (1971) *PLC 2*: 1474.
145. Roedder, E., and Weiblen, P. W. (1970) *PLC 1*: 801.
146. Weiblen, P. W., and Roedder, E. (1973) *PLC 4*: 681.
147. Bence, A. E., et al. (1970) *EPSL*. 8: 393; Bence, A. E., et al. (1971) *PLC 2*: 559.
148. Lofgren, G. E., et al. (1974) *LS V*: 458.
149. Weigand, P. W., and Hollister, L. S. (1973) *EPSL*. 19: 61.
150. The interpretation by the Edinburgh group[70, 71] that plagioclase was a liquidus phase is based partly on the more aluminous nature of the maria soils, compared to the basalts sampled. We have also seen that the aluminous maria basalts[16], represented by 12038, 14053, and other samples may be contributing plagioclase to the maria soils, as well as, of course, the plagioclase-rich components, derived by impacts from the highlands.

# CHAPTER 5

# The Highlands

As the moon either is without atmosphere or has one of extreme tenuity, the mechanical effect of this bombardment may be important, for the average velocity of the meteors is from fifty to one hundred times as great as that with which the swiftest ball leaves the cannon...

G. K. Gilbert (1893)

## 5.1 THE HIGHLAND CRUST

The highlands form the oldest exposed areas on the surface of the moon (Figs. 2.4, 2.5) and are chemically distinct both from the maria and the whole moon. The meteoritic bombardment of this surface has drawn a curtain across the landscape through which we peer dimly to discern the earlier history. The oldest landscape is saturated with large craters and probably with giant ringed basins (Figs. 2.14, 5.1). Thus, the earlier structure of the lunar crust is obliterated, and there is "no vestige of a beginning"[1]. All the samples returned from the highlands are, in general, intensely brecciated, so that simple stratigraphic or chemical relationships are obscured.

The study of the highlands rocks is one of the most interesting and fascinating areas of lunar science. Terrestrial analogies are few, and fresh approaches are demanded by the pulverized nature of the material. It is not surprising that scientific controversies, matching the complexities of the samples themselves, swirl around the highland rocks.

The extreme positions adopted are: (a) that the highland crust is a chemically distinct refractory layer, accreted or condensed during the last stages of formation of the planet; (b) the aluminous rich crustal material

206

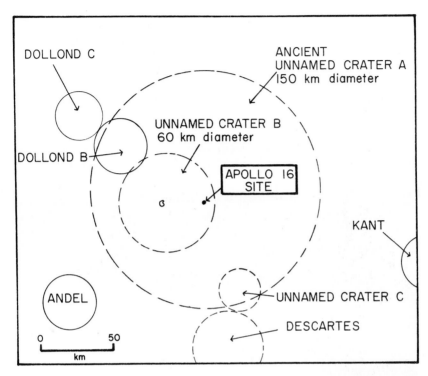

**Fig. 5.1**  The overlapping sequence of old craters at the Apollo 16 Descartes site[9]. (Courtesy J. W. Head.) (Cf. Fig. 2.10.)

is derived by differentiation from the bulk moon during extensive melting early in lunar history. The discussion of these alternatives and various intermediate possibilities will be considered in the section dealing with the geochemical evolution of the moon. The questions raised by the highlands bear heavily on the fundamental questions of homogeneous versus heterogeneous accretion of the planet and the presence or absence of a lunar core. It will appear later that some resolution of these problems may be possible.

The first direct information on lunar highland composition was obtained from the Luna 10 orbiting gamma-ray experiment[2]. This experiment indicated that the potassium content over the highlands was apparently lower than over the maria, contrary to expectations that the highlands might be "granitic."

The next data, from the soft-landing Surveyor 7 on the ejecta blanket at

Tycho revealed high aluminum and low iron compositions[3]. Extensive searches were made in the maria soils returned by the Apollo 11 and 12 missions, since it was apparent that part of the regolith would be derived as impact ejecta from highland regions. This study led to the recognition of an anorthositic component of nonmare origin[4] and of a nonmare basalt (KREEP) enriched in potassium, rare earths, and associated elements[5]. Similar material was collected from the first direct sampling of the highlands by the Apollo 14 mission to the Fra Mauro formation. This was interpreted as an ejecta blanket, produced by the Imbrium collision (Fig. 2.9). A wide variety of breccias was returned (Fig. 5.2).

**Fig. 5.2** "Contact rock" near the south end of the white rock boulder field at Cone Crater, Fra Mauro Apollo 14 site. The boulder is 3 m long and shows a well-developed irregular contact between white and grey breccias. Note the resemblance to a wombatlike creature.

**Fig. 5.3** The "black and white" breccia, 15455, from the Apennine Front (Apollo 15 site). The black portion is low-K Fra Mauro basalt; the white portion is anorthositic gabbro (highland basalt). (NASA S-71-43891.)

The Apollo 15 mission to the Hadley-Apennine region (Figs. 2.7, 4.1) sampled the base of the Apennine Front. Although the stratigraphic position of the samples collected cannot be related directly to depth beneath the pre-Imbrium surface (because of slumping, later cratering, etc.) the possibility remains that material from deep within the crust was sampled. It is also possible that much of the front material was from the Serenitatis basin impact. Fig. 5.3 shows one of the breccias.

The Russian Luna 20 mission returned samples from the Apollonius highlands, between Mare Crisium and Mare Fecunditatis. This area is dominated by ejecta from the impacts forming these two basins.

The Apollo 16 mission to the Descartes region (Fig. 2.10), collected the first highland material remote from the maria basins. Two of the units established by photogeological mapping techniques were sampled. These were the Cayley formation, the major plains-forming unit of the highlands, and the associated hilly Descartes formation. No volcanic rocks were found, and the brecciated samples returned showed the typical evidence of exposure to the intense highland impact cratering. The Apollo 17 mission sampled three distinct highland sites, in a complex area where ejecta from the Serenitatis, Tranquillitatis, Crisium, and Imbrium basins may be present (Fig. 4.1).

Both the Apollo 15 and 16 missions carried out orbital XRF and gamma-ray remote sensing experiments[6,7] providing detailed information on the distribution of Si, Al, Mg, and the radioactive elements. The orbiting XRF data confirm that the highlands in general are alumina-rich and that they are broadly uniform in composition, although areal differences exist with Al/Si ratios varying from 0.51 to 0.71, and Mg/Si ratios from 0.16 to 0.28. Ground truth for these observations is well established.

Several problems beset geochemists and petrologists in studying highlands samples.

(a) Is there any primitive crust?

(b) Can samples of a primary crust be obtained?

(c) How has the intense bombardments of the highlands affected the chemistry, mineralogy, petrology, and age of the samples?

Seismic data[8] show that the crust is brecciated to a depth of 10 km

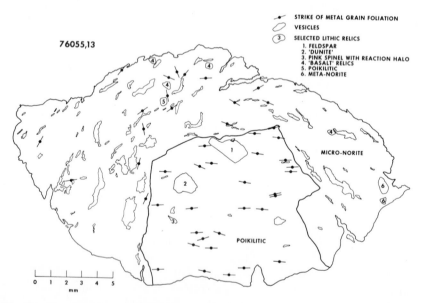

**Fig. 5.4** Drawing of an impact-melted rock 76055, showing many inclusions of other highland rock types. (NASA S-73-771.)

and fractured to a depth of 25 km. The upper 10 km at least is thoroughly stirred and mixed. This is a consequence of the early intense bombardment, which perhaps overlapped the process of crustal formation itself. Toward the close of this period, but perhaps extending much earlier, occurred the series of large impact events that excavated the ringed basins. The effect of this cratering was to destroy any primitive highland crust (Fig. 5.1).

The formation of the ringed basins overturned vast sectors of the already heavily cratered highland crust. Shock and impact metamorphism attended all these events. Melting and glass production (Fig. 5.4) occurs to some extent in all impacts: the question of how much occurs during large-basin-forming impacts is unsettled. The great bulk of the mare basalt lavas filling the basins came up to several hundred million years later, but the hummocky terrain seen in parts of the Orientale basin, in particular dammed against the second scarp, and in the floors of some large craters (e.g., Tycho) may be true impact melts.

It is clear from the preceding discussion and from the observations in chapter 2 that any primary structure or layering in the crust has been destroyed, and that the textures and mineralogy of the rocks collected will be dominated by the metamorphic processes and brecciation occurring during the impacts.

## 5.2   BRECCIAS

With the exception of the soils and four crystalline rocks (14053, 14072, 14073, and the famous 14310), the samples returned from the first highland site, Fra Mauro, consisted of breccias (Fig. 5.2). Most of these were compound, containing breccias within breccias, indicating a complex history. Two generations of breccia were present in many samples, and up to four generations were recognized. The crystalline rocks were similar to clasts or fragments observed in the breccias. Sample 14310 has been interpreted as an impact melt, and no evidence of primary unbrecciated samples was obtained from the site.

Much debate arose over classification and origin of these breccias. Although the Fra Mauro formation was accepted by most as an ejecta blanket from the Imbrium event, an ingenious alternative holds that it was a thick regolith developed on Fra Mauro basalts[10]. Further debate arose over how much brecciation was due to the Imbrium basin-forming collision, and how much was due to previous events, how hot the ejecta blanket became, and how much chemical alteration and resetting of the age clocks occurred.

A major advance was the establishment of a working classification of the breccias[11–13]. The scheme adopted here is based on textural and mineralogical criteria, and these proved much more useful in dealing with the breccias, which were rather uniform in chemical composition, than similar textural attempts to classify the maria basalts, where differences in chemistry were more important. The criteria are set out in Tables 5.1 and 5.2. They are based on recognition of eight groups, subjected to increasing temperatures, so that characteristics based on progressive metamorphism can be recognized. Thus with increasing temperature, glass clasts and spherules are devitrified[14] and disappear. Minerals such as pyroxene and feldspar recrystallize, developing greater perfection of external form.

Many other changes occur in this sequence. As the temperature increases, the noble gases He, Ne, Ar, Kr, and Xe are progressively lost (Table 5.1). Also, the carbon content decreases, particle track densities decrease, due to annealing, and an increasing number of vugs and vesicles appear. In many of the latter, crystals of pyroxene, feldspar, ilmenite, whitlockite, iron, and troilite grown by vapor deposition appear. Their perfection of form recalls the comment that the beauty of crystals lies in the planeness of their faces (Figs. 5.9, 5.10). The highest grades also show some loss of K and Rb relative to Ba as the melting temperature is approached[16, 17]. Loss of alkalis is not a very efficient process, for the feldspars become more sodium- and potassium-rich as the higher grades are reached. This produces small areas of high potassium ("pegmatitic") residual patches, although this process does not create more than trivial amounts of such "acidic" residuum. A correlation with a proposed temperature scale is given in Table 5.2. Williams[15] estimates that the temperatures reached at least 1,100°C in the base layer, capped by a layer with temperatures less than 500°C. The breccias may have been heated above 700°C, since even the least coherent breccias possess stable remnant magnetization.

It has been noted that the highest grade material[12], with most vugs[18], came from the deeply excavated material of Cone Crater. While there is a correlation[12] between the stratigraphic position and degree of metamorphism, the picture is complicated by previous generations of breccias, caught up once again in the cataclysm, and by the variation in degree of metamorphism with distance from the center of the impact. How much of these effects are due to shock rather than to thermal metamorphism is a moot question.

Table 5.1 Classification of Apollo 14 Breccias[11,15].

| Grade | Warner group | Glass content | Plagioclase composition | Matrix texture | Process | Carbon content | $^{22}$Ne $10^{-6}$ cm$^3$/g stp. | Sample nos. 14- |
|---|---|---|---|---|---|---|---|---|
| Low | 1 | High | | | | 130–230 | 73.4 | 042, 047, 055, 307, 313 |
| | 2 | Intermediate | | Detrital | Devitrification | | 71.6 | 049, 301 |
| Medium | 3 | Low | | | Pyroxene becomes equant | 80 | 1.40 | 063, 082, 315, 318 |
| High | 5 | None | | Equant | Plag. becomes euhedral | 40 | | 311 |
| | 6 | | An$_{83}$Or$_1$ | | | 30 | 0.062 | 006, 171, 303, 304, 305, 306, 320, 321 |
| | 7 | | An$_{76}$Or$_2$ | Euhedral | | | 0.72 | 066, 270, 312, 314, 319 |
| | 8 | | An$_{73}$Or$_7$ | Sheath-like | Matrix melts | 35˙ | | 068 |

**Table 5.2**  Metamorphic Grade, Temperature and Processes in Apollo 14 Breccias[11, 15].

| Grade | Group | °C | Process |
|---|---|---|---|
| Low | Soil | 600 | Neon loss |
| | | | No sintering ($t = 10^{11}$ sec) |
| | 0 | 700 | Tracks annealed |
| | 1 | 800 | Curie point (Fe) |
| | | | Ar loss devitrification |
| | 2 | 900 | Carbon species lost |
| | | | Rb loss |
| | | | K loss |
| | | | Kr loss |
| | | | Sintering ($t = 10^0$ sec) |
| Medium | 3 | | FeS melt, K-granite melt |
| High | 5 | 1,000 | Ne and Ar (cosmogenic) loss |
| | 6 | | |
| | 7 | 1,100 | Na loss, Xe loss |
| | | | Mare basalt solidus |
| | 8 | | Fra Mauro basalt solidus |

**Clasts in Fra Mauro Breccias**

A wide variety of clasts was reported. Wilshire and Jackson[12] subdivide the clasts into class A, glass; class B, minerals; class C, "igneous" rocks; and class D, "metamorphic" rocks. Class A glasses are divided into yellow-brown and colorless glasses, which are probably shocked plagioclase. Among class B clasts, plagioclase is dominant, but representatives of almost all lunar minerals appear to be present. The class C "igneous" clasts mostly resemble 14310, which was almost certainly a clast. In thin section, the maximum clast sizes observed were about 6–7 mm, but much larger ones are known (e.g., 14310 was 18 cm long). The most common clasts were class $D$, thermally metamorphosed fine-grained rocks in which plagioclase is the dominant mineral phase. A few clasts of aluminous maria basalts (section 4.2) were present, indicating that maria basaltic activity preceded the Imbrium collision.

## The Apollo 16 and 17 Breccias

The wide variety of breccias returned from the Descartes region by the Apollo 16 mission effectively refuted the hypothesis that the Cayley and Descartes formations were of volcanic constructional origin. In turn, the samples provided petrologists with an interesting and complex suite. Various schemes of classification based on textural relationships, mineralogy, and chemistry have been proposed. Several petrogenetic schemes have been proposed, but none have met with complete acceptance. This is not surprising. The suite of rocks, probably typical of the highlands as a whole, have been subjected to a multiple-impact history. What has survived? Possibly the chemical composition, but certainly not the original textures or mineralogy.

Many representatives of the suite of rocks described as anorthosites, gabbroic anorthosites, highland basalts, and the Fra Mauro basalts were recovered. Table 5.3 gives a listing of the various names and alternatives in use. A common acronym, ANT[19], for anorthosite-norite-troctolite (Fig. 5.5) has crept into use to describe the overall lithologic and chemical characteristics of the rocks other than the Fra Mauro basalts.

**Table 5.3** Terminology for Highland Rock Types.

| Commonly used name | Alternative equivalent names | $Al_2O_3$ (%) |
|---|---|---|
| Anorthosite | — | 33–36 |
| Gabbroic anorthosite | Noritic and troctolitic anorthosites | 28–33 |
| Anorthositic gabbro or highland basalt | Anorthositic norite and troctolite | 24–28 |
| Troctolite | Spinel troctolite | 20–25 |
| Low-K Fra Mauro basalt | High-Al basalt Low-K KREEP | 17–23 |
| Medium-K Fra Mauro basalt | KREEP KREEP basalt Norite | 15–20 |
| High-K Fra-Mauro basalt | Nonmare basalt | |

The samples were classified into several types. Among the more important[20] of these are the

(*a*) light matrix breccias,
(*b*) dark matrix breccias,
(*c*) feldspathic intersertal igneous rocks,
(*d*) pyroxene poikiloblastic breccias.

The chemical composition of these, given in Table 5.4 shows a strong correlation with the rock compositions proposed by the soil survey. The light matrix breccias are close to anorthosites, the dark matrix breccias to gabbroic anorthosites, the pyroxene poikiloblastic breccias equivalent to the Fra Mauro low- and medium-K rocks, and the feldspathic igneous rocks to the highland basalts[21] (Table 5.3).

The light matrix breccias appear to come from a deeper zone at the

**Table 5.4** Chemical Composition of Four Major Lithologic Types Found in the Descartes Region.

| (wt %) | 1 | 2 | 3 | 4 |
|---|---|---|---|---|
| $SiO_2$ | 43.6 | 43.9 | 45.2 | 45.6 |
| $TiO_2$ | 0.1 | 0.5 | 0.8 | 1.3 |
| $Al_2O_3$ | 34.0 | 28.8 | 23.4 | 17.2 |
| FeO | 1.5 | 4.9 | 6.1 | 10.5 |
| MnO | — | 0.1 | 0.1 | 0.1 |
| MgO | 1.3 | 5.7 | 10.8 | 13.2 |
| CaO | 19 | 15.6 | 12.7 | 10.4 |
| $Na_2O$ | 0.5 | 0.5 | 0.5 | 0.6 |
| $K_2O$ | — | 0.1 | 0.2 | 0.4 |
| $P_2O_5$ | — | — | — | — |
| S | — | — | — | — |
| $Cr_2O_3$ | — | 0.2 | 0.2 | — |
| Σ | 100.0 | 100.3 | 100.0 | 99.3 |

Major elements expressed as oxides in weight percent.
1. "Light Matrix Breccia."
2. "Dark Matrix Breccia."
3. "Feldspathic intersertal igneous rocks."
4. "Pyroxene poikiloblastic breccias."
Data from Delano, J. W., et al. (1973) *PLC 4*: 537.

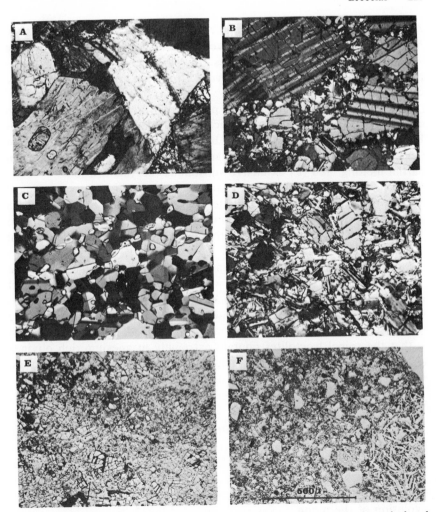

**Fig. 5.5**  Photomicrographs of Apollo 16 rocks. All are to the same scale, shown in f. a–d (photographed with partially crossed polarizers) represent the range of textures observed. (a) A coarse-grained, shocked, but unrecrystallized anorthositic norite. (b) A cataclastic anorthosite, which has been preceptibly recrystallized. (c) An anorthosite with a granulitic texture, the product of prolonged high temperature, subsolidus annealing. All gradations exist between the textures shown in a-c. (d) A noritic anorthosite that has been partially melted, as indicated by the euhedral plagioclase laths in the groundmass. (e) A light-matrix breccia, taken in unpolarized light. Clasts of plagioclase, olivine, and pyroxene are surrounded by a much finer-grained, but not glassy groundmass. (f) A light-matrix breccia somewhat more annealed than e. Note the clast of fine-grained feldspathic basalt on the right. (From Fig. 1, Ref. 28.)

Apollo 16 site. They are common at the North Ray Crater, where they may have been excavated by that event. The light matrix breccias include samples with old highland ages (4.1–4.25 aeons). Possibly these plagioclase-rich rocks are survivors from an original feldspathic crust[22].

The origin of the poikiloblastic or poikilitic[23] rocks has aroused much controversy. These rocks are chemically equivalent to low-K or medium-K Fra Mauro basalts. Three origins have been debated[24–30]. These are (a) crystallization from an impact melt, (b) metamorphism resulting in partial melting, and (c) extensive subsolidus recrystallization.

Much of the debate results from our lack of adequate petrological criteria to decide between these alternatives. The lunar highlands rocks present us with materials for which we have few terrestrial or meteoritic analogues, and much basic descriptive work remains before the textural evidence can yield up its secrets.

Several rocks have been classed as impact melts[31], analogous to the Apollo 14 "igneous" rock 14310, which is almost certainly an impact melt[32] (Fig. 5.6). The presence of iron-nickel blebs and the near-ubiquitous presence of schreibersite $(Fe\,Ni)_3P$ (except in the poikilitic rocks) perhaps indicates an impact melt origin[26]. A further observation is that the spinel troctolites contain extremely magnesium-rich olivines $(Fo_{84-95})$. These are the most Mg-rich olivines yet found on the moon, and it is of extreme interest that they occur in the highlands[26].

### Dunite

Fragments of a highly crushed dunite[33], composed mainly of large ($\sim 10$ mm) pale green crystals of olivine, in a crushed olivine matrix were collected at the Apollo 17 site (72415). The olivine is Mg-rich $(Fo_{86-89})$. The rock yields an age of 4.60 aeons. The significance of this important sample for lunar evolution is discussed in section 7.6 on geochemical evolution of the moon.

### 5.3  IMPACT-INDUCED MELTING

During the great collisions that produced the large craters, such as Copernicus, Tycho, and the giant ringed basins, melting due to the impact process will occur[34]. The basic questions are the amount of melting, the relative proportions of partial or complete melting, and whether this is a significant petrogenetic process.

Evidence of temperatures up to and exceeding melting are observed in

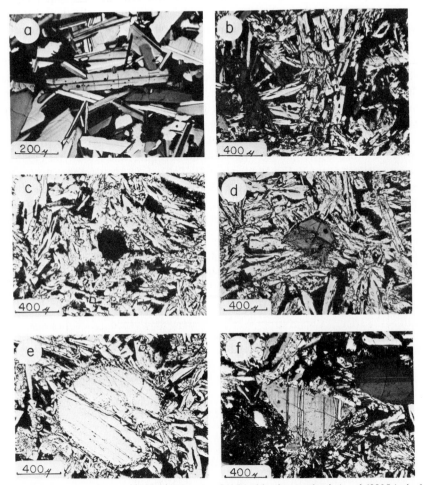

**Fig. 5.6** Textures observed in highland rocks 68415 (gabbroic anorthosite) and 62295 (spinel troctolite). (a) Plagioclase lath with Fe-Ni-Co spherules in 68415: crossed polarizers. (b) Hollow, diamond-shaped olivine crystals intergrown with hollow plagioclase laths in 62295: crossed polarizers. (c–f) Xenocryst assemblage in 62295. (c) Fe-Ni-Co metal. Note abundant clear spinel octahedra: plain light. (d) Pink spinel fragment: plain light. (e) Olivine xenocryst with reaction rim filled with clear spinel and glass inclusions: plain light. (f) Twinned plagioclase xenocrysts with spinels in rim: crossed polarizers. (From Fig. 3, Ref. 70.)

the breccias. For example, some quartz-alkali feldspar intergrowths are partially melted (e.g., 14318). These effects are erratic, with fused clasts and no fused material occurring alongside one another. It is thus difficult to tell when the *partial* melting occurred, whether before or after the consolidation of the breccia. Some of this quartzo-feldspathic material has devitrified, producing material that closely resembles the well-known Apollo 12 sample 12013. The degree of melting and the effects of melting during impact are both uncertain. If substantial amounts of *partial* melting can occur, then there is a possibility that fractionation might occur in the melts and produce a new series of highland igneous rocks.

Such *partial* melting may take place on a small scale [35] and produce, from an anorthositic gabbro (highland basalt) parent, a rock type close in composition to low-K Fra Mauro basalt (Table 5.5). How important is this process on a large scale? A major problem lies in concentrating the trace elements (REE, Zr, Hf, Th, U, Ba, etc.), as well as in segregating the melt.

The basic question is whether *partial* melting is an important pet-

**Table 5.5**  Composition of Highland Basalt 64455, Glass Coating and 1-mm-wide Zone of Partial Melt.

| (wt %) | 1 | 2 | 3 |
|---|---|---|---|
| $SiO_2$ | 47.2 | 45.2 | 48.6 |
| $TiO_2$ | 0.60 | 0.39 | 0.67 |
| $Al_2O_3$ | 25.0 | 24.8 | 17.5 |
| FeO | 5.28 | 6.40 | 6.53 |
| MnO | 0.06 | 0.04 | 0.07 |
| MgO | 7.76 | 8.34 | 14.0 |
| CaO | 13.54 | 14.4 | 11.3 |
| $Na_2O$ | 0.28 | 0.44 | 0.84 |
| $K_2O$ | 0.21 | 0.05 | 0.26 |
| $P_2O_5$ | — | — | — |
| S | — | — | — |
| $Cr_2O_3$ | 0.13 | 0.15 | 0.25 |
| $\Sigma$ | 100.1 | 100.2 | 100.0 |

Major elements expressed as oxides in weight percent.
  1. Whole rock 64455.
  2. Glass coating average.
  3. Partial melt zone.
From Grieve, R. A. F., and Plant, A. G. (1973) *PLC 4*: 674.

rogenetic process. Contrary views exist, with some workers favoring extreme thermal metamorphism (Sanidinite facies)[24] or *partial* melting[27] as major petrogenetic processes on the moon. Relevant evidence comes from large terrestrial impact craters, such as Lake Mistastin, Labrador, and West Clearwater Lake, Quebec, where thicknesses of impact melt of more than 100 m are known[35]. From a study of these, and smaller examples (e.g., Ries Crater suevite deposits), it appears that *partial* melting is a minor phenomenon, as it is at smaller craters such as Henbury. Experience at such terrestrial impact craters indicates either no change in composition or some mixing of original rock compositions. Changes in composition by vapor fractionation are trivial. The major process is total melting and mixing of this material with less strongly shocked rocks[35].

Further support for these ideas comes from the comparison of the impact glasses from the Lonar meteorite crater, India. More than 90 percent of the impact glasses closely resemble the composition of the country rock basalt[36]. Texturally, many of the breccias resemble the lunar breccias, except that evidence of induration or recrystallization is lacking. In the lunar breccias, these effects are caused by multiple impact events.

In summary, the production of *substantial* bodies of rock types by partial melting during impact is judged a remote possibility. "Lunar examples of partial melting processes have been noted in rock 64455—but appear to be relatively as rare on the moon as they are on earth"[35].

A different question is whether large enough volumes of impact melt may be produced to allow the processes of conventional crystal fractionation to operate during cooling. This process is judged to be inherently more effective in producing differentiated rocks than partial melting during impact. Extrapolation from the terrestrial examples noted above suggest that substantial amounts of impact-produced melt should occur, particularly during the ringed basin impacts[34]. The cumulative effect of the 43 presently known events of this magnitude (together with the probability of older basins, now obliterated) could make this process of major petrological importance in the evolution of the rock types forming the highland crust. This process remains one of the more enigmatic and frustrating problems of lunar petrology, which might have been solved by a further Apollo mission to Copernicus or Orientale. The ultimate resolution of this question probably awaits the resumption of manned lunar landings. Unmanned landers, even with sample return to earth, do not possess the sampling capability to resolve this problem.

## 5.4   ELEMENT MIGRATION IN BRECCIAS

Element redistribution during the large impact events is part of the larger question of the thermal history of the ejecta blankets. An excellent review of this topic has been given by Williams[15]. Much confusion arose initially over the question of temperatures in thick ejecta blankets such as the Fra Mauro formation. The debate over whether the ejecta blankets were cool or hot was partly a matter of sampling, since all gradations were observed from essentially unmetamorphosed material, up to rocks such as 14310, which were impact-generated melts.

The debate is analogous to that over the stratigraphic position and origin of the plains-forming units in the highlands. So long as the mechanism of formation was not understood, confusion resulted from apparently contradictory evidence. Such was the case with the breccias. The scale and extent of the highland cratering, producing a surface saturated with craters up to 100 km in diameter, followed by the giant-basin-forming impacts, has produced every variety of brecciation, lithification, shock effects, metamorphism, and melting.

Table 5.2 shows a correlation of metamorphic grade with the temperature scale[11, 15]. The highest temperatures correspond to melting, producing rocks such as 14310. A variation in temperature exists with depth in the breccia blankets. Thus, the deeply excavated samples from Cone Crater were of higher metamorphic grade than the surficial samples at the Fra Mauro site. Williams[15] presents a model for the Fra Mauro formation in which the bottom layer is at 1,100–1,300°C, overlain by a cooler (less than 500°C) layer. These would correspond to the laminar and turbulent layers of terrestrial ash flows. Cooling takes place in minutes from 1,200°C to 900°C, while the middle layers cool to 800°C in several days. This produces a zone-refining effect with the volatiles driven upward. The lower portions are rapidly sintered. Gases may be driven out completely (rare gases) or trapped in the upper porous layers (CO, $CO_2$, etc.), producing an enrichment of carbon compounds in the lower metamorphic grades. Possibly iron migrates as well since the higher grade breccias contain less iron[37] than the lower grades.

Experimental work shed much light on these processes. Gibson and co-workers[16, 17] found that Rb was lost relative to K, and K relative to Ba, in a series of heating experiments. They were able to reproduce the observed K/Rb and K/Ba ratios in Apollo 14 rocks. Thus in Fig. 5.7, 14163 has normal K/Rb (325) and K/Ba (6) lunar ratios. Progressive loss of K and Rb is shown in 14006 and 14161,35. Such losses are duplicated by heating as shown by the experimental data in Fig. 5.7.

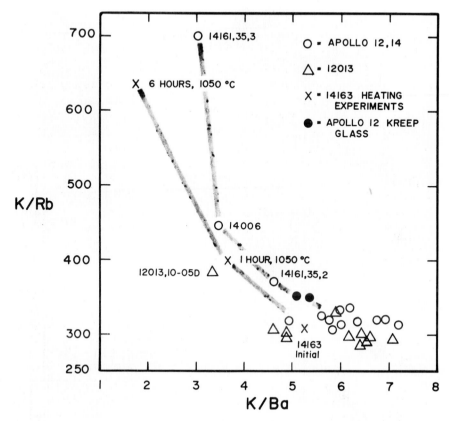

**Fig. 5.7** Natural changes and experimentally produced changes in the K/Rb versus K/Ba ratios. Note the heating experiments on sample 14163 causes the K/Ba ratio to decrease while the K/Rb ratio increases. Both of these changes are similar to the ratios observed in certain lunar samples that have undergone thermal alteration[16]. (Courtesy E. K. Gibson.)

McKay and co-workers[38] have shown in a series of excellent scanning electron microscope photographs that growth of crystals has taken place in vugs in the highest breccia grades (Figs. 5.8–5.10). Vapor deposition is most likely in the vugs within the breccias, since many of these cavities are totally enclosed, so that no drainway exists for liquids[39]. The net result will be much local redistribution of volatile elements such as Rb and Pb at medium metamorphic grades, coupled with losses of the very volatile elements, during cooling of the ejecta blankets. Thus, highly metamorphosed breccias may have suffered loss of these elements, and soils and lower grade breccias will become enriched in

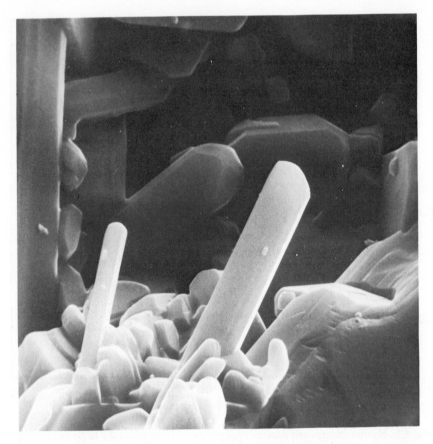

**Fig. 5.8**   Scanning electron microscope (SEM) photograph of a vuggy recrystallized lunar breccia. Euhedral crystals of apatite, pyroxene, and plagioclase form an open network of free-standing crystals. The large crystal in the foreground is 8 $\mu$m long. (NASA S-73-30445.) (Courtesy D. S. McKay.)

"parentless" lead (since the involatile U and Th are not affected). Conversely, $^{87}$Sr will be retained and $^{87}$Rb lost from the higher grades. Thus, the higher grade breccias should give young Rb-Sr ages and soils and low grade breccias give old Rb-Sr ages.

### Vapor Fractionation

Impact-produced melts, formed during the intensive bombardment of the highlands, might lose some elements by vaporization in the hard lunar vacuum. The evidence for some loss of very volatile elements, on a minor scale, has been discussed in relation to redistribution of minor amounts of Pb, Rb, etc. in the soil (section 3.16). The process has also been invoked to explain the low Na and K contents in the maria basalts (section 4.5). The consensus is that it is not a major process. In the highlands, the process also seems to be minor. Some glasses appear to have lost volatile components[40], but rocks that are demonstrably impact melts (14310, 68415)[41] have not undergone any significant change in chemistry.

**Fig. 5.9**    SEM photograph of a doubly terminated apatite crystal 17 $\mu$m long in an Apollo 14 breccia vug. First- and second-order prisms; first-, second-, and third-order hexagonal dipyramids: and basal pinacoid faces are present on many of the lunar apatite crystals. (NASA S-73-30448.) (Courtesy D. S. McKay.)

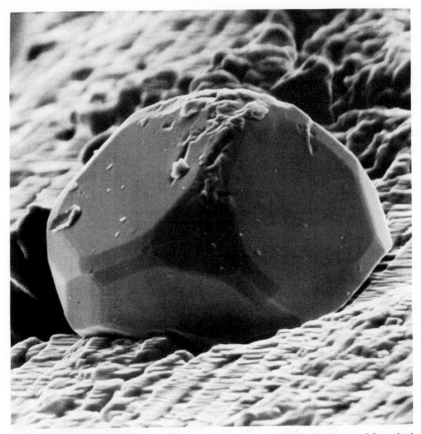

**Fig. 5.10**   SEM photograph of an iron crystal 2 $\mu$m across; the dominant crystal form is the cube, the trapezohedron and tetrahexahedron faces are smaller. The substrate is a pyroxene fragment; the bunched growth lines form 150A growth steps (15402). (NASA S-72-53208.) (Courtesy D. S. McKay.)

Positive evidence of vapor fractionation is limited. A fragment of anorthositic gabbro from the Luna 20 site in the Apollonius highlands appears to have lost 2–6 percent $SiO_2$ by such a process [42]. The rarity of such samples indicates that the process of vapor fractionation is not an important modifying influence on lunar highland compositions.

### Lunar "Chondrules"

The origin of chondrules in meteorites has long been studied without much progress beyond the observation of Sorby in 1877 that they had been "molten drops in a fiery rain." Origins by impact on planetary or asteroid surfaces, or by volcanism have often been proposed. Thus it was of considerable interest when several workers[43–45] reported the discovery of chondrulelike forms from the Apollo 14 breccias (Fig. 5.11). The first question was whether or not these were trapped meteoritic chondrules. They showed typical lunar compositions, far removed from those of the meteoritic chondrules. Table 5.6 gives typical compositions. Chondrules appear in the fine-grained breccia matrix, sometimes up to 10 percent by volume. The average diameters are 20–500 $\mu$m. Most of the lunar highland compositions are recognized among the chondrules, but basaltic compositions are rare.

Various questions are raised by these observations. The chondrules are not simply devitrified glass spherules. Indeed, glass spheres are often contained in the same breccias. There is no doubt that the resemblance to meteoritic chondrules, except for composition, is very close. The available experimental evidence[45] suggests that the typical chondrules form by spontaneous rapid crystallization of super-cooled droplets. The

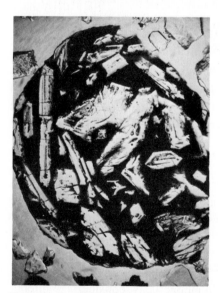 

**Fig. 5.11** Porphyritic lunar chondrule (0.9 mm) from Apollo 16 sample no. 64811. Skeletal olivines, all with ~16 percent FeO except for a narrow rim with high iron content, are imbedded in a cryptocrystalline matrix with high FeO (~32 percent), $Al_2O_3$ (~16 percent), $TiO_2$ (~1 percent) and low MgO (~2 percent). *Left*, transmitted light, olivine white; *right*, reflected light, olivine light gray, sulfides white. (Courtesy K. Fredriksson.)

**Table 5.6** Bulk Compositions of Chondrules in Breccia 14318,4 as Obtained by Broad-Beam Electron Microprobe Techniques.

|  | Anorthosite | Gabbroic anorthosite | Fra Mauro basalt (KREEP) | High-K basalt |
|---|---|---|---|---|
| $SiO_2$ | 45.4 | 47.2 | 49.0 | 45.2 |
| $TiO_2$ | 0.05 | 0.30 | 0.97 | 3.4 |
| $Al_2O_3$ | 34.1 | 24.8 | 17.9 | 12.1 |
| $Cr_2O_3$ | <0.02 | 0.15 | 0.20 | 0.37 |
| FeO | 0.25 | 6.0 | 7.9 | 17.3 |
| MnO | 0.01 | 0.09 | 0.15 | 0.31 |
| MgO | 0.34 | 5.7 | 9.7 | 9.3 |
| CaO | 18.4 | 14.9 | 12.0 | 11.4 |
| $Na_2O$ | 1.19 | 0.51 | 0.36 | 0.34 |
| $K_2O$ | 0.11 | 0.17 | 0.73 | 0.41 |
| $P_2O_5$ | 0.04 | 0.11 | 0.22 | 0.10 |
| Total | 99.89 | 99.93 | 98.98 | 100.23 |
| No. samples | 1 | 17 | 6 | 1 |

Adapted from Kurat, et al., 1972, *Proc. 3rd Lunar Sci. Conf.*, Table 1, p. 713.
Data in weight percent.

mechanism is undoubtedly provided by the major meteoritic impacts. Thus, few chondrules, but abundant glass spherules, characterized the maria soils and breccias. This must be attributed to the difference in scale of the impact events. In small-scale impacts, most molten drops will cool rapidly and solidify to form glass spheres. In the larger events, cooling rates may be low enough in the hot ejecta blankets to allow for nucleation and hence crystallization.

In general, chondrules may be expected in the highland samples but only rarely in those from the maria, except in the case of large impacts on the maria. Conditions for chondrule formation are likely to be present in large, thick ejecta blankets, such as the Fra Mauro formation. The observations indicate that meteoritic chondrules may form in ejecta blankets on planetary or asteroidal surfaces.

### Rusty Rock 66095 and Lunar Water

Water is effectively absent from the moon. Thus, considerable interest was generated in the unique sample of "rusty" rock 66095, returned from station 6, close to South Ray Crater, at the Descartes site (Fig. 5.12). The rock is a partly shock-melted breccia of complex composition, mainly anorthosite, but with troctolite (plagioclase-olivine) portions. There are no vugs or cavities but many veins of shock-melted glass, crowded with metallic spherules, having Ni and Co contents in the meteoritic range. The most noteworthy feature is a pervasive red-brown rusty stain, comprised of goethite (FeO OH).

There are two distinct occurrences of goethite ($a$) associated with the meteoritic Fe/Ni spherules and ($b$) occurring with troilite (FeS), sphalerite (ZnS), and chlorine bearing Zn and Fe sulphates. The sample is also high in lead, with local concentrations up to 4,000 ppm at troilite-goethite

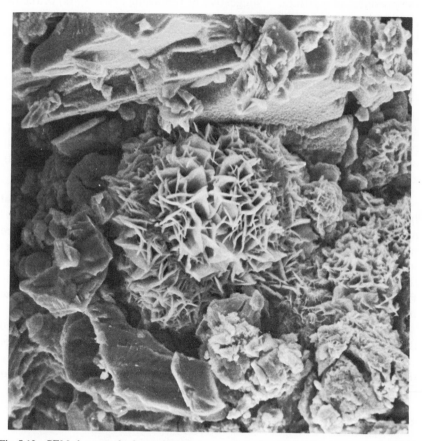

**Fig. 5.12**    SEM photograph of one of the three morphologies of "rust" on lunar sample 66095. Compositionally the rosettes contain iron, chlorine, and occasionally up to 5 percent Ni. The "rust" appears to be both goethite and lepidocrocite based on petrographic studies. The central rosette is 7 $\mu$m in diameter. (NASA S-73-17705.) (Courtesy D. S. McKay.)

boundaries. Many suggestions have been made to explain these occurrences:

(*a*) The rust is caused by the dissociation of the meteorite mineral lawrencite ($FeCl_3$), due to exposure to terrestrial water vapor, during and after the sample return[46].

(*b*) The water, Cl, Zn, etc., are derived from the impact of a comet or carbonaceous chondrite[47].

(*c*) The high abundances of Br, Cd, Ge, Sb, Tl, and Zn, coupled with the presence of goethite, is suggestive of fumarolic activity[48] or the impact of a comet or carbonaceous chondrite. Some of the element ratios (e.g., Cd/Zn) do not appear characteristically meteoritic[48]. Other workers[47] dispute this claim, noting that there is much variation in the ratios.

Can we distinguish between these various possibilities? The shock evidence favors a meteoritic addition, but the many Fe/Ni spherules indicate perhaps an iron, rather than a chondritic, meteorite. A most significant observation is that the lead isotope composition is highly radiogenic[49]. The $\mu$ ($^{238}U/^{204}Pb$) ratio inferred for the source is 570, about intermediate between that for the source of maria basalts (100–300) and highland anorthosites (600–1,000).

Although a cometary impact has many attractive features and cannot be ruled out entirely, the most likely origin seems to be that "fumarolic" activity impregnated and coated the breccia with chloride vapor enriched in volatile trace elements. Even the proponents of cometary impact invoke this process to account for the lead[47]. The latter workers note that reaction rims are very small, indicating a short-lived phenomenon. Possibly a cometary impact provided some of the components and triggered fumarolic activity.

The isotopic evidence, however, indicates that the $^{18}O/^{16}O$ ratios and the deuterium/hydrogen ratios are indisputably terrestrial[50]. The water component found in rusty rock 66095 appears to be terrestrial contamination, on the basis of these isotopic data, as is all other water so far reported in lunar samples[50, 51].

### 5.5  SAMPLING OF THE HIGHLAND CRUST

Sampling of the highland crust has proceeded in three ways:

(*a*) collection of individual rock specimens;
(*b*) collection of soil samples;
(*c*) overall sampling by orbital gamma-ray and XRF measurements.

What information has been gathered from such sampling? The individual rocks are in general complex breccias. Because of the long continued history of impact events, they may contain fragments of most of the components of the highland crust. Thus, all samples are likely to be random. Any crystalline rocks (e.g., 14310, 68415) are likely to be products of shock or impact melting, rather than representing a primary igneous origin. Since the impacts are large, pools of impact melt, as indicated earlier, may be generated. On a hand specimen scale, it may be very difficult to establish textural or petrological evidence indicative of primary melt or impact origins.

All samples will be inherently random with respect to past position on the lunar crust. Is there any way in which the components of an original primary crust may be identified? It is clear that only a large-scale statistical sampling can adequately overcome these problems. Surface sampling is necessarily restricted to a few sites, and the rocks collected cannot be a representative sample in a statistical sense. Orbital measurements fall at the other extreme, are influenced by the upper layers of the soil, and are restricted to a few elements.

A useful and promising approach to these problems has been adopted by the Apollo Soil Survey [52–57] and other investigators. The soils collected at each site contain a wide variety of rock fragments, mineral fragments, and glasses produced by the meteoritic bombardment. Of these several components, the glasses possess useful properties:

(*a*) They are abundant.

(*b*) The individual fragments, spherules, etc., are usually homogeneous, enabling rapid major element analyses to be obtained by electron microprobe techniques.

(*c*) Glass formation during impact is essentially a random nonselective process, so that the frequency of compositions encountered is likely to be a good statistical sample of the rock types encountered by the colliding objects.

When a large enough number of analyses is available, preferred compositional groupings appear (Table 5.7). Cluster analysis techniques establish the various groupings. These groups appear on two component plots (e.g., $CaO$-$Al_2O_3$) but are more clearly and less ambiguously demonstrated by a nine component computer program [53].

What is the significance of these groupings? Are they representative of the original rock types in the highland crust, or are they artifacts produced during impact and metamorphism? Direct answers to such questions are inherently difficult to obtain. However, the Apollo Soil Survey

Table 5.7  Common Glass Compositions in Highlands Soils[52].

| (wt%) | 1 | 2 | 3 | 4 | 5 | 6 | 7 | 8 |
|---|---|---|---|---|---|---|---|---|
| $SiO_2$ | 44.3 | 44.5 | 44.5 | 45.4 | 46.6 | 46.1 | 48.0 | 49.6 |
| $TiO_2$ | 0.06 | 0.35 | 0.39 | 0.43 | 1.25 | 0.79 | 2.1 | 1.43 |
| $Al_2O_3$ | 35.1 | 31.0 | 26.0 | 27.6 | 18.8 | 20.1 | 17.0 | 17.6 |
| FeO | 0.67 | 3.46 | 5.77 | 4.62 | 9.37 | 9.36 | 10.9 | 9.52 |
| MgO | 0.80 | — | 8.05 | 6.13 | 11.04 | 10.3 | 8.70 | 8.94 |
| CaO | 18.7 | 17.3 | 14.9 | 15.6 | 11.6 | 12.6 | 10.7 | 10.8 |
| $Na_2O$ | 0.80 | 0.12 | 0.25 | 0.42 | 0.37 | 0.37 | 0.70 | 0.74 |
| $K_2O$ | 0.04 | 0.01 | 0.04 | 0.05 | 0.12 | 0.08 | 0.54 | 0.47 |
| $Cr_2O_3$ | 0.02 | 0.04 | 0.11 | 0.07 | 0.20 | 0.19 | — | 0.17 |
| | | | | | | | | |
| Number | 22 | 30 | 176 | 111 | 82 | 44 | 224 | 90 |
| Rock type | Anorthosite | Gabbroic anorthosite | Anorthositic gabbro | Anorthositic gabbro | Low-K Fra Mauro | Low-K Fra Mauro | Med-K Fra Mauro | Med-K Fra Mauro |
| Mission | L-20 | A-16 | L-20 | A-16 | A-15 | L-20 | A-14 | A-15 |

Major elements expressed as oxides in weight percent.

workers [54] raise the following four points in support of the conclusion that original or primary rock types are represented by the glass compositional clusters. They note that "(1) with the exception of the feldspathic glasses, there are no monomineralic glasses (2) the same glass groupings can be recognized in soils of different bulk compositions and from different selenographic locations (3) there is a good correspondence between glass compositional groupings and lithic fragments from soils and breccias and (4) large rocks equivalent in composition to the major highland glass groups have been returned from the moon. For these reasons we use rock names, based on selenographic location or on normative mineralogy, for the glass groups" [54].

Further evidence is available from terrestrial experience. Glasses resulting from fusion of country rocks by meteorite impact have been extensively studied. In such cases, both the parent rock and the glass formed from it are available for study. A general conclusion is that the major element chemistry survives essentially unchanged. Loss of the very volatile components ($H_2O$, $CO_2$, etc.) occurs, but otherwise the glass composition mirrors that of the parental rock [58].

Is it valid to extrapolate this conclusion to impact conditions on the moon? The answer is probably yes since the pressure and temperature conditions of glass formation from silicate melts formed by impact are most likely to be similar. The loss of volatile components at terrestrial sites is more likely to affect the composition by removing other elements entrained with them. While the vacuum conditions on the moon might aid loss, it is probable that this is offset by more rapid temperature drop. Accordingly, it is concluded that the glass compositions reflect those of the parental rocks [58], and that the groupings revealed by the cluster analysis represent the most frequent rock types in the primary highland crust.

## 5.6  HIGHLAND ROCK TYPES

The work of the Apollo Soil Survey has established several principal compositional groupings. These are listed in Table 5.7 in order of decreasing $Al_2O_3$ content. Major element compositions [52] are given in Table 5.8. This approach has been extended to the trace element data [59]. The state of the art for trace element analyses results in data for tens rather than hundreds of samples. The eventual development of ion probes may in future match the multianalytical capabilities of electron probes, but at present the statistical approach employed so usefully by the Apollo

Soil Survey for major elements is not possible with the trace element data.

However an alternative approach is possible. Among the many breccia clasts and glasses that have been analyzed, it is possible to identify samples whose major element composition corresponds with one of the major element groupings identified by the Soil Survey. The trace element data [59–69] for such samples may then be used as diagnostic for the rock type. Data based on this approach are given in Tables 5.9 to 5.12.

The various rock compositions in the highlands are discussed in the approximate order of their abundance and importance, with the various names that have been attached to them, in the following pages.

(a) *Anorthositic gabbro, highland basalt, anorthositic norite, anorthositic troctolite:* From the glass abundances, this appears as a common constituent in the highlands. It is not far removed from the overall average highland compositions. Typical examples appear to be 15418 and the white portion of the "black and white" breccia 15455 (Fig. 5.3), which resemble the glass composition major element data closely. The normative mineral content is 70 percent plagioclase, 20 percent orthopyroxene, 9 percent olivine, and 1 percent ilmenite. The $Al_2O_3$ content is 26 percent.

(b) *Low-K Fra Mauro basalt, high-alumina basalt:* This composition

**Table 5.8** Major Elements Expressed as Oxides in Weight Percent in Highland Rock Types [52, 60].

| (wt%) | Anorthosite | Gabbroic anorthosite | Anorthositic gabbro | Troctolite | Low-K Fra Mauro basalt | Medium-K Fra Mauro basalt |
|---|---|---|---|---|---|---|
| $SiO_2$ | 44.3 | 44.5 | 44.5 | 43.7 | 46.6 | 48.0 |
| $TiO_2$ | 0.06 | 0.35 | 0.39 | 0.17 | 1.25 | 2.1 |
| $Al_2O_3$ | 35.1 | 31.0 | 26.0 | 22.7 | 18.8 | 17.6 |
| FeO | 0.67 | 3.46 | 5.77 | 4.9 | 9.7 | 10.9 |
| MnO | — | — | — | 0.07 | — | — |
| MgO | 0.80 | 3.38 | 8.05 | 14.7 | 11.0 | 8.70 |
| CaO | 18.7 | 17.3 | 14.9 | 13.1 | 11.6 | 10.7 |
| $Na_2O$ | 0.80 | 0.12 | 0.25 | 0.39 | 0.37 | 0.70 |
| $K_2O$ | — | — | — | — | 0.12 | 0.54 |
| $Cr_2O_3$ | 0.02 | 0.04 | 0.06 | 0.09 | 0.26 | 0.18 |
| Σ | 100.5 | 100.2 | 99.9 | 99.9 | 99.6 | 99.4 |

Data expressed as oxides in weight percent.

**Table 5.9**  Abundance of Large Cations in Highland Rock Types[59, 61–69].

| | Anorthosite | Gabbroic anorthosite | Anorthositic gabbro | Troctolite | Low-K Fra Mauro basalt | Medium-K Fra Mauro basalt |
|---|---|---|---|---|---|---|
| $Cs^+$ | — | — | — | — | 0.16 | 1.0 |
| $Rb^+$ | 0.2 | — | 0.5 | — | 2.7 | 15 |
| $K^+\%$ | — | — | — | — | 0.10 | 0.45 |
| $Ba^{2+}$ | 15 | 69 | 42 | 100 | 370 | 730 |
| $Pb^{2+}$ | 0.6 | 0.8 | 1.0 | 1.2 | 3.0 | 7 |
| $Sr^{2+}$ | 170 | 180 | 220 | — | 140 | 210 |
| $Ca^{2+}\%$ | 13.4 | 12.4 | 10.6 | 9.36 | 8.29 | 7.65 |
| $Na^+\%$ | 0.59 | 0.09 | 0.19 | 0.29 | 0.27 | 0.52 |

Data expressed as parts per million except where indicated in weight percent.

**Table 5.10**  Abundance of Rare Earth Elements in Highland Rock Types[59, 61–69].

| | Anorthosite | Gabbroic anorthosite | Anorthositic gabbro | Troctolite | Low-K Fra Mauro basalt | Medium-K Fra Mauro basalt |
|---|---|---|---|---|---|---|
| $La^{3+}$ | 0.46 | 4.52 | 3.0 | 5.31 | 32 | 80 |
| $Ce^{3+}$ | 0.72 | 12.1 | 6.7 | 13.3 | 81 | 214 |
| $Pr^{3+}$ | 0.07 | 1.54 | 0.95 | 1.76 | 11.5 | 26 |
| $Nd^{3+}$ | 0.32 | 6.25 | 3.73 | 7.33 | 47 | 102 |
| $Sm^{3+}$ | 0.11 | 1.82 | 0.88 | 2.17 | 12.8 | 28 |
| $Eu$ | 0.80 | 1.00 | 1.67 | 0.79 | 1.82 | 2.60 |
| $Gd^{3+}$ | 0.10 | 2.42 | 0.95 | 2.73 | 15.5 | 31 |
| $Tb^{3+}$ | — | 0.37 | 0.14 | 0.48 | 2.41 | 4.7 |
| $Dy^{3+}$ | — | 2.51 | 0.84 | 2.97 | 16 | 33 |
| $Ho^{3+}$ | 0.02 | 0.59 | 0.17 | 0.67 | 3.76 | 8.0 |
| $Er^{3+}$ | 0.06 | 1.66 | 0.46 | 1.85 | 10.7 | 19 |
| $Tm^{3+}$ | — | 0.26 | 0.06 | 0.28 | 1.6 | 3.3 |
| $Yb^{3+}$ | 0.06 | 1.60 | 0.36 | 1.72 | 9.8 | 19 |
| $Lu^{3+}$ | — | 0.25 | 0.06 | 0.27 | 1.5 | 3.0 |
| $\Sigma$ REE | ~2.9 | 36.9 | 20 | 41.6 | 247 | 574 |
| $Y^{3+}$ | — | 15 | 4.8 | 18 | 93 | 191 |
| $\Sigma$ REE + Y | — | 51.9 | 24.8 | 59.6 | 340 | 765 |

Data in parts per million.

**Table 5.11**   Abundance of Large High-Valency Cations in Highland Samples[59, 61–69].

|  | Anorthosite | Gabbroic anorthosite | Anorthositic gabbro | Troctolite | Low-K Fra Mauro basalt | Medium-K Fra Mauro basalt |
|---|---|---|---|---|---|---|
| $Th^{4+}$ | — | 0.73 | 0.23 | 1.0 | 5.3 | 12 |
| $U^{4+}$ | — | 0.17 | 0.05 | 0.27 | 1.37 | 3.2 |
| $Zr^{4+}$ | 0.5 | 48 | 11 | 85 | 480 | 930 |
| $Hf^{4+}$ | — | 1.36 | 0.17 | 1.53 | 9.8 | 17 |
| $Nb^{5+}$ | 0.15 | 4.12 | 0.95 | 5.2 | 33 | 67 |
| $Ti^{4+}\%$ | 0.04 | 0.21 | 0.23 | 0.10 | 0.75 | 1.26 |

Data expressed in parts per million except for Ti in weight percent.

appears to be the second most abundant in the highlands. It is much lower in $Al_2O_3$ (19 percent). The normative mineralogy contains 53 percent plagioclase, 30 percent orthopyroxene, 10 percent olivine, 7 percent clinopyroxene, 2.5 percent ilmenite, and < 1 percent orthoclase. It is very similar in major element chemistry to the other Fra Mauro basalts but is very much lower in the so-called KREEP component (K, REE, P, U, Th, Zr, Hf, Nb, etc.). A typical example is the black component of the black and white breccia 15455 (Fig. 5.3).

  (c) *Anorthosite:* It is effectively monomineralic plagioclase, with the

**Table 5.12**   Abundance of Ferromagnesian Elements in Highland Rock Types[59, 61–69].

|  | Anorthosite | Gabbroic anorthosite | Anorthositic gabbro | Troctolite | Low-K Fra Mauro basalt | Medium-K Fra Mauro basalt |
|---|---|---|---|---|---|---|
| $Cr^{3+}$ | 17 | 270 | 440 | 600 | 1800 | 1220 |
| $V^{3+}$ | 7 | 23 | 16 | 33 | 39 | 43 |
| $Sc^{3+}$ | — | 10 | — | 5 | 13 | 23 |
| $Ni^{2+}$ | — | 110 | 12 | 28 | 184 | 370 |
| $Co^{2+}$ | — | 15 | 10 | 17 | 22 | 34 |
| $Cu^{2+}$ | — | 3 | 1.3 | 1 | 3.3 | — |
| $Fe^{2+}\%$ | 0.52 | 2.69 | 4.49 | 3.81 | 7.54 | 8.47 |
| $Mn^{2+}$ | — | — | — | 540 | — | 1100 |
| $Mg^{2+}\%$ | 0.48 | 1.23 | 4.86 | 8.87 | 6.63 | 5.23 |
| $Ga^{3+}$ | — | — | 2.6 | — | 3.3 | 4.1 |
| $Al^{3+}\%$ | 18.6 | 16.4 | 13.8 | 12.0 | 9.95 | 9.3 |
| $Si^{4+}\%$ | 20.7 | 20.8 | 20.8 | 20.4 | 21.8 | 22.4 |

Data in parts per million except where indicated in weight percent.

anorthite component usually in the range 90–98 percent. A typical example is 15415, the so-called "genesis rock." The abundance of minor and trace elements varies widely, depending on the purity of the analyzed samples.

(*d*) *Gabbroic anorthosite, noritic anorthosite, troctolitic anorthosite:* This is a less abundant composition, intermediate (30 percent $Al_2O_3$) between anorthosite and highland basalt. Typical samples are 68415 and 64435.

(*e*) *Medium-K Fra Mauro basalt, KREEP, KREEP basalt, norite, nonmare basalt:* This component has much the same major element composition as the low-K Fra Mauro basalt but is distinguished by a high (for lunar rocks) K content (~0.5 percent) and extremely high abundances of Cs, Rb, Ba, REE, Th, U, Zr, Hf, and Nb. Typical samples are 14047 and crystalline 14310 from the Fra Mauro site. The average composition at Fra Mauro is close to that of the medium-K Fra Mauro type. 14310 is the only large crystalline rock of this type with "basaltic" texture.

(*f*) *High-K Fra Mauro basalt:* This is an extreme variant of the KREEP composition. It has more than 1 percent K and appropriate amounts of the REE and other elements at up to 500 times the chondritic abundances. The dark portions of the famous 12013 are perhaps the best examples of this composition, which the Soil Survey work[52] shows to be rather rare.

(*g*) *Troctolite, spinel troctolite:* The importance of these rather rare components is difficult to assess. A typical example is 62295 from Apollo 16, the white portion of 73235, and the troctolitic clast from 14321 breccia. It appears only as a rare component in the Soil Survey statistical analysis, but it forms an important link in many petrogenetic schemes[60, 70].

(*h*) *The ANT suite* of rocks as originally conceived encompassed anorthosite (>90 percent plagioclase), noritic and troctolitic anorthosite (plagioclase 77.5–90 percent) (= gabbroic anorthosite), anorthositic norite and troctolite (plagioclase 60–77.5 percent) (= highland basalt), and spinel troctolite.

The range in $Al_2O_3$ content was from 23 to 35 percent. The use of the acronym ANT has been somewhat modified from the original definitions. Thus, many workers exclude the spinel troctolites and use ANT as a term for the gabbroic anorthosites and anorthosites[71], restricting the range of $Al_2O_3$ content to 28–35 percent.

(*i*) *Very high alumina (VHA) basalt:* This is a recently proposed rock type[72]. It falls close to the low-K Fra Mauro or high-Al basalt compositions and to the spinel troctolites. It does not appear as a major grouping from the Apollo Soil Survey work, and its status as a primary highland composition is in doubt. It has recently been reinterpreted as a mixture of other rock types[73], and this view is probably correct.

(*j*) *Meteoritic component:* This is discussed in detail in section 5.11, comprises all chondritic, iron meteoritic, and cometary material, and provides much important genetic information on highland history. For example, if the smooth highland plains (e.g., Cayley formation) were the result of late volcanic constructional processes (section 2.8), then the meteoritic component should be similar to that in the maria soils. If this material is derived from preexisting highlands, then a high meteoritic component, derived from the intense cratering episodes, should be present.

(*k*) Other components present in very small amounts include high K ($\sim 5$ percent) low Mg ($< 1$ percent) granitic fragments, identified mainly among the soil constituents. They are a minor constituent and do not represent an abundant rock composition in the lunar highlands. Most probably they are derived from sources such as the granitic portions of rock 12013 and the glassy residual phases in the maria basalts, transported to the highlands by impact events.

## 5.7   EXPERIMENTAL PETROLOGY AND THE SOURCE OF THE HIGHLAND ROCK TYPES

These studies have proved more difficult than similar experiments on the maria basalts. The latter were directly comparable in mineralogy, texture, and cooling history to terrestrial analogues. The wealth of experimental expertise with these systems led rapidly, although not without controversy, to an understanding of the sources of the maria basalts.

The complexity of the highland breccias has precluded such solutions. Only very recently has an understanding of the basic rock types been reached. Although the major rock types have been tentatively identified[74], petrogenetic schemes that might link them are less clear. Three geochemical components, which are not usually closely associated on earth are present. These are a high Mg content reflected by olivine and orthopyroxene (and dunite), high Ca and Al abundances (in plagioclase), and a high content of rare earth elements and other trace elements, more typical of terrestrial pegmatites. Possible origins for these associations are discussed in section 7.6 on geochemical evolution of the moon. It is clear that the ultimate question of the petrogenesis of the highland rocks is intimately bound up with the origin of the crust itself. Was this chemically distinct crust a product of large-scale melting and differentiation of the moon, or was it a chemically distinct late addition, applied to the outside like a coat of plaster on a wall? While geochemists have debated these problems, experimental petrologists have made several significant contributions.

An important first conclusion is that the rocks are not partial melts from the same source regions as the maria basalts[70, 75]. The highland anorthositic rocks and the maria lavas come from very different source materials. Crystalline rocks such as 68415 and 14310 have their origins as near-surface impact melts[70]. The plagioclase-rich anorthosites are generally agreed to represent magmatic feldspathic cumulates, although the nature of the primary magma from which they crystallized is argued. The presence of the other plagioclase-rich rocks suggests a genetic connection, and the notion has arisen that the whole suite, excluding the spinel troctolites and the Fra Mauro basalts, is genetically related by such processes[60, 70, 75].

Experimental work carried out on this basis has been profitable. Fig. 5.13 shows various highland compositions (see figure legend for details) plotted on a now standard silica-olivine-anorthite diagram[70]. From experimental studies on the spinel-bearing species, it has been shown that they are of near-surface origin. It is possible to relate the major rock compositions to partial melting of two parents, of cumulate origin.

This scheme, shown in Table 5.13, indicates how the low-K and medium-K Fra Mauro basalts might be derived from the more feldspathic rocks by varying degrees of partial melting. A very small amount of partial melting will be required for the medium-K Fra Mauro basalts, with their high trace element contents. They are not very common rocks in comparison with the low-K Fra Mauro basalt, which may make up 20 percent of the highland crust (section 5.10). These schemes, which are backed by experimental data[70], need to be evaluated with respect to the trace element data.

## 5.8  THE ORBITAL CHEMICAL DATA

Measurements of the chemical composition of the lunar surface were made on the Apollo 15 and 16 missions. Two experiments were carried out. One measured the secondary X-rays produced at the lunar surface by the primary solar X-rays. Data for Si, Al, and Mg were obtained.

A second experiment measured the natural radioactivity of the surface.

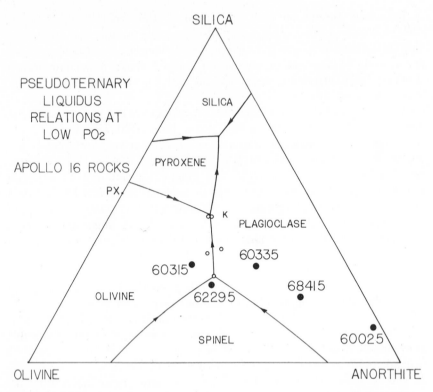

**Fig. 5.13** Results of crystallization experiments at low $PO_2$ on Apollo 16 samples presented as a pseudo-ternary liquidus section in the system $SiO_2$-$CaAl_2Si_2O_8$-$Fe_2SiO_4$-$Mg_2SiO_4$ at a molar $Fe/Fe + Mg$ of ~0.3. Boundary curves in the top portion of the diagram are from D. Walker, et al. (1972, *PLC 3* : 797), and those in the lower portion of the diagram are constructed on the basis of microprobe analyses of the experimental glasses. Open circles show those analyses used to locate or bracket the curves [70]. The rock types, corresponding to those given in Table 5.8 are: 60025, anorthosite; 68415, gabbroic anorthosite; 62295, spinel troctolite; 60315, medium-K Fra Mauro basalt; 60335 is close to the average composition of the highland crust (Table 5.15). (Courtesy J. F. Hays.)

After suitable corrections for background, information on the absolute abundance of thorium has been obtained. The area of the moon covered was limited to the track of the command vehicle. This was at a high inclination for the Apollo 15 mission, but approximately equatorial (9° inclination) for the Apollo 16 flight. The agreement, where overlap occurred, between data from the two missions, was generally within 10 percent. Ground truth was established when the Command Module

**Table 5.13**  Possible Relationships among Lunar Highland Rock Types.

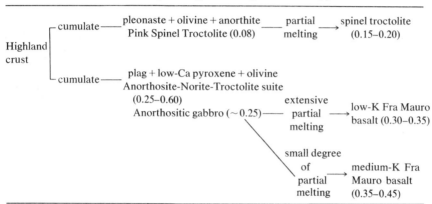

Adapted from Walker et al.[70].

(Numbers in parentheses are Fe/Fe + Mg.) The cumulate sources result from large-scale melting of at least the outer few hundred kilometers of the moon.

passed over the landing sites. Full details of the analytical methods and the experimental details are given by Adler[76] and Arnold[77].

The depth of sampling of the XRF experiment is about 10 $\mu$m, the "very surface" layer (see section 3.1), and the data collection is of course limited to those areas in sunlight. The gamma-ray experiment, in contrast, samples somewhat deeper, on the order of a few tens of centimeters. Both of these experiments provided exceedingly valuable geochemical data. Although the data base of 3–4 elements might be thought sparse, it will be shown later that it is possible to extrapolate from these numbers to provide nearly complete trace and major element information about the areas surveyed.

The gamma-ray data[78, 79] are shown in Fig. 5.14. The Al/Si data[80, 81] are shown in Fig. 5.15, while Fig. 5.16 shows the variation in Al/Si ratios with lunar longitude. The spatial resolution of the data is about 50 km for the XRF data and about 70 km for the gamma-ray values. Both values are better than anticipated and open the prospect of rather detailed geochemical mapping of the moon by remote orbital spacecraft.

The first-order observation from the gamma-ray data is that the distribution is exceedingly inhomogeneous, with large values in the western maria regions, around Mare Imbrium. Since rocks and soils high in K, U, and Th have been found in abundance at the Fra Mauro site, it is natural to correlate such occurrences with the gamma-ray counts.

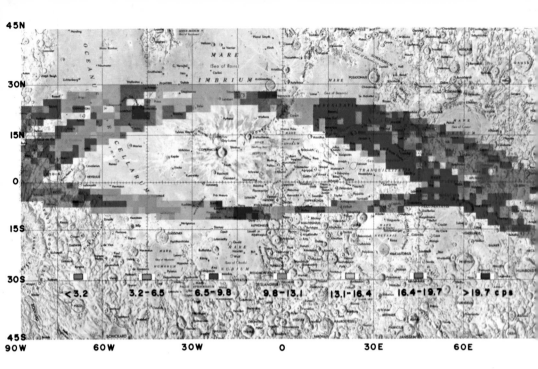

**Fig. 5.14** A relief map of the radioactivity of regions of the moon overflown by the Apollo 15 and 16 Command Modules. Analysis has shown that differences in the integrated counting rate in the energy range 0.55 to 2.75 Mev are chiefly due to differences in the concentration of the radioactive elements Th, U, and K. These data are the net count rates in this energy band after (a) correction for altitude, (b) removal of the celestial cosmic gamma-ray flux and the background due to cosmic ray interactions with the spacecraft, and (c) subtraction of a

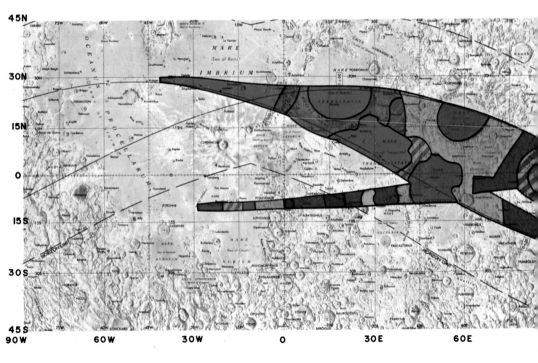

**Fig. 5.15** Aluminum-silicon concentration ratios for specific areas along the Apollo 15 and 16 ground track [81].

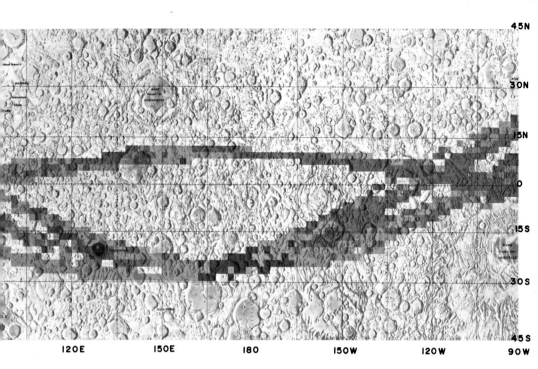

fixed-rate including to a first approximation both continuum processes and cosmic-ray-induced radioactivities in the lunar surface. The data are averaged over $2° \times 2°$ areas. The net counting rates range from <1 counts per second to 21.5 counts per second. The maximum 1 $\sigma$ value, ±1.9 counts per second, is based on the minimum data period of 25 sec accepted for plotting while the typical 1 $\sigma$ value is ±0.6 counts per second[80].

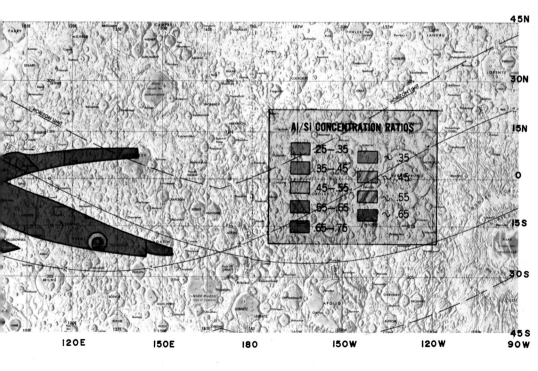

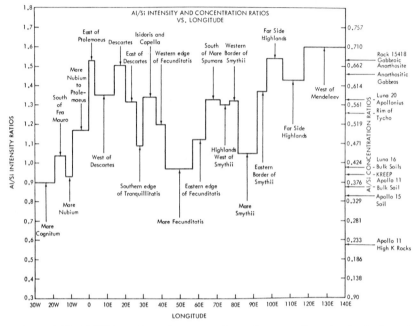

**Fig. 5.16** Orbital Al/Si intensity and concentration ratios versus lunar longitude along the orbital tracks[81].

This striking evidence for the lateral heterogeneity of the distribution of thorium across the lunar surface exceeds that predicted from the first-order highlands-maria dichotomy. The absolute abundance of thorium in the highlands is also a matter of great consequence for geochemical theories of lunar evolution, as discussed later.

The Al/Si values from the XRF orbital experiment have been discussed frequently throughout this text. The first-order observation is that the ratio is higher in the highlands than in the maria (Figs. 5.15, 5.16), consistent with the more aluminous nature of the highlands, reflected by the high content of plagioclase feldspar.

The sharpness of the boundaries between maria and highlands is instructive. The Al/Si values in both highlands and maria reflect rather closely the values in the bedrock samples from these areas. Thus this primary difference in composition persists to the "very surface." This observation places severe constraints on the lateral movement of fine-grained material from the highlands to the maria by dust transfer mechanisms.

A further consequence of the data has been remarked with reference to the problem of the origin of the smooth highlands plains of Cayley formation type. The lack of correlation between the gamma-ray data and the areas mapped as Cayley formation precludes their derivation as a uniform ejecta blanket from a single source, such as Mare Orientale. The lateral variations in composition indicate that the cratering and ringed basin formation has not homogenized the highlands rocks. It appears to indicate that mixing by cratering is not a very efficient process. A first-order observation is that most of the highlands samples are heterogeneous at all scales down to a few millimeters. Thus the belief that the intense cratering might produce an exceedingly uniform highland crustal composition appears unfounded [82].

## 5.9    INTER-ELEMENT CORRELATIONS

The first analytical data for the Apollo 11 samples revealed a strong Th/U coherence, with values for the ratio of 3.5–4.0, in line with those found in meteoritic and many terrestrial samples. The good K/U and K/Th correlations [83] were less expected, particularly since there was an observed strong depletion of volatile (K) and enrichment of involatile (Th) elements relative to their primordial abundances. The increasing amount of analytical data of high quality for samples from subsequent missions revealed a host of further correlations [84–90], often unexpected on the basis of terrestrial geochemical experience. Values for well-established element ratios in lunar samples are given in Table 5.14.

These correlations are significant for several reasons. First the geochemical correlations such as K/Rb give evidence about partial melting and fractional crystallization processes on the moon. The ratios of volatile/involatile elements provide us with information on condensation processes, while other ratios in the highland samples provide an index of mixing processes. Ratios that appear to be moon-wide provide useful comparisons between the moon, earth, meteorites, and inferred primordial solar system compositions. The compositions of these bodies, for example, are clearly separated by the K/U plot (Fig. 4.24).

Three distinct reasons appear for the correlations:

(*a*) Similarity between elements of ionic radius, valency, and bond type leading to conventional geochemical coherence. Good examples are Th/U, Zr/Hf, REE (except Eu), K/Rb, Ba/Rb, Rb/Cs, (Fig. 5.17), and $Fe^{2+}/Mn^{2+}$ (Fig. 4.25). The closeness of these correlations is due to the

**Table 5.14** Lunar Element Ratios.

(A) Geochemically Associated Elements

|  |  | Reference |
|---|---|---|
| K/Ba | 6.10 | 84 |
| Rb/Cs | 23 | 88 |
| K/Tl | $2 \times 10^5$ | 88 |
| Th/U | 3.8 | 87 |
| Tl/Cs | $4 \times 10^{-2}$ | 88 highlands |
|  | $1.2 \times 10^{-2}$ | 88 maria |
| $Sr^{2+}/Eu^{2+}$ | 100 | 89 |
| Cr/V | 28 | 89 |
| Zr/Hf | 45 | 90 highlands |
|  | 35 | 90 maria |
| Cr/Sc | 70 | 89 |
| FeO/Sc | 5400 | 86 |
| Ba/Rb | 60 | 89 |
| FeO/MnO | 80 | 86 |

(B) Volatile/Involatile Element Ratios

|  |  | Reference |
|---|---|---|
| K/Zr | 4.23 | 84 |
| K/Nb | 67 | 84 |
| K/La | 70 | 85 |
| Cs/U | 0.23 | 88 |
| K/Hf | 210 | 84, 90 |
| K/Th | 500 | 87 |
| K/U | 1500 | 87 highlands |
|  | 2500 | 87 maria |

(C) Involatile Elements

|  |  | Reference |
|---|---|---|
| Ba/Zr | 0.69 | 84 |
| Zr/Ba | 1.44 | 84 |
| Zr/Nb | 14 | 84 |

similarity in radius, valency, and bond type between the two cations. In this context, the lack of water and other volatiles in the moon produces simple crystal chemical relationships. None of the ions will be hydrated, for example, and simple Goldschmidtian crystal chemical principles will hold.

(*b*) Concentration of elements of diverse chemistry in residual melts

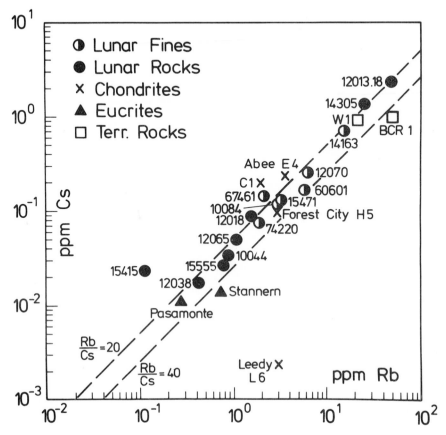

**Fig. 5.17**   The close association between rubidium and cesium in lunar and terrestrial rocks and meteorites. (Courtesy H. Wänke.)

during fractional crystallization due to their inability to enter the major rock-forming minerals. For the same reasons, these elements may be concentrated in initial melts during partial melting (e.g., K/U, Zr/Nb, Cs/U, K/Zr, K/La).

The Zr/Nb ratio is a good example (Fig. 5.18). Excellent analytical data, often obtained for both elements from the same laboratory[84], are available. The ratio value is 14, and these elements show, in lunar samples, a coherence of the same order as that seen on earth between such closely associated elements as K and Rb. The Zr/Nb correlation arises since both elements do not enter the main rock-forming minerals. It

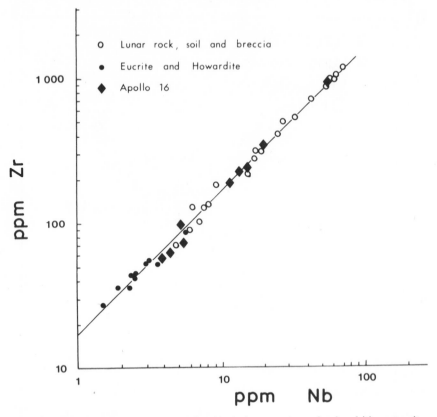

**Fig. 5.18**  The zirconium-niobium relationship in lunar rocks and achondritic meteorites (eucrites and howardites)[84].

is the closeness of the correlation that is so significant, for the elements have been involved in severe geochemical fractionation episodes.

Other examples are the K/Zr and K/La (Fig. 4.23) ratios. These have the following properties. (1) The analytical data are good for the three elements; (2) K is volatile while Zr and La are both involatile; (3) the K/Zr and K/La ratios are the same in both mare and highland samples. The preservation of element ratios in the highlands, if these were formed by a *single stage* event early in lunar history, is readily understood. Less easy to understand is the preservation of these ratios in the source material of the maria basalts for several hundred million years, followed by partial melting processes and fractional crystallization during extrusion of the lavas.

The geochemical association of elements of such widely differing valency, radius, bond type, and volatility as $K^+$, $La^{3+}$, and $Zr^{4+}$ through multistage processes is indeed striking. One immediate consequence may be noted. The similarity of those volatile/involatile element ratios places severe constraints on heterogeneous accretion models invoking volatility differences to explain the highland chemistry.

(c) Correlations produced by mixing of different rock types during intense cratering of the highlands. This is a further process that will contribute to the observed close inter-element ratios in highland samples. Since the chemistry of the highland samples appears to be dominated by two major rock types (highland basalt or anorthositic gabbro, and low-K Fra Mauro or high-Al basalt), many of the highland breccias will show element abundances dominated by two component mixtures and hence exhibit simple element correlations.

## 5.10   THE CHEMICAL COMPOSITION OF THE HIGHLANDS

The observed inter-element ratios greatly facilitate the study of overall highland chemistry. The various ratios form an interlocking system so that, provided some are known, the rest may be calculated. The orbital XRF and gamma-ray data provide information on Al/Si and Mg/Si ratios and Th values across wide regions of the highlands [77–81].

These data form a base on which to build up a multi-element compositional table, by using established inter-element relationships. Average Al/Si and Mg/Si values are 0.62 ($\pm$0.10) and 0.24 ($\pm$0.05), respectively. $SiO_2$ concentrations are relatively uniform at 45 percent in highlands samples, yielding values of 24.6 percent $Al_2O_3$ and 8.6 percent MgO. A value of 6.6 percent FeO is obtained from the MgO/FeO relationship observed in the highland soils and breccias. From the Fe/Cr relationship [69], a figure of 0.10 percent $Cr_2O_3$ results. No estimates are made for Ni and Co because of the random meteoritic component. Allowing a typical lunar $Na_2O$ abundance of 0.45 percent, the remaining major constituent is CaO, which yields, by difference, a value of 14.2 percent. This value is consistent with that observed in samples of this approximate composition and with the Ca/Al relationship.

The thorium average for much of the highlands is in the range 1.0–2.0 ppm [78]. Adopting 1.5 ppm Th as an average, and using the well-established Th/U ratio of 3.6 [87], the U abundance is 0.4 ppm. From the K/U value of 1,500 (Table 5.14), the K value may be calculated as 600 ppm or 0.075 percent $K_2O$. From K/Rb = 350, Rb = 1.7 ppm, and from Rb/Cs = 23, Cs = 0.07 ppm.

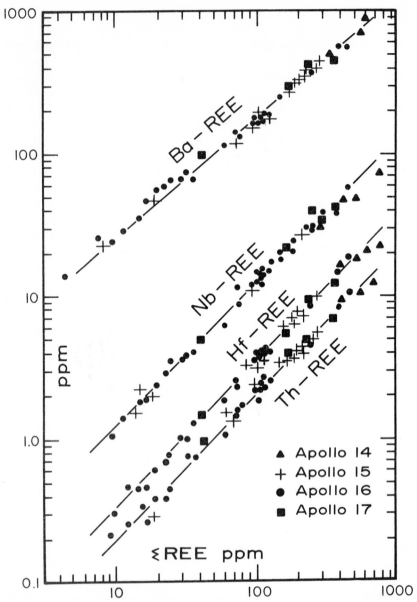

**Fig. 5.19** The close correlation observed between many involatile elements in the highlands samples. In this diagram, the abundances of Ba, Nb, Hf, and Th are plotted against total REE abundances. Correlations with individual REE would be similar. Many other similar correlations exist. These shown here are selected to emphasize the correlations between elements of dissimilar geochemical behavior [89].

Further abundances can be calculated by utilizing the inter-element relations shown in Fig. 5.19. Thus, for a thorium value of 1.5 ppm, $\Sigma REE = 65$ ppm, and hence $Hf = 2.3$ ppm, $Nb = 7.5$ ppm, and $Ba = 110$ ppm, from the relationships in Table 5.14. The Zr/Nb ratio of 14 is firmly established [84], yielding 105 ppm Zr from the Nb value. Individual values for the rare earths (with $\Sigma REE = 65$ ppm) can be obtained by reference to Fig. 5.20, which shows the chondrite-normalized REE patterns. Assuming that the La/Yb ratio is the same (3.1) as in nearly all the Apollo 16 samples (so that the patterns remain parallel), individual rare earth element abundances are obtained. On this basis, La = 8.8 ppm, with appropriate values for the others (see Table 5.15).

A consequence of the REE abundance patterns is that the average highland composition has a positive Eu anomaly. The consequences of a positive Eu anomaly in the highland rocks are profound. It is a reasonable assumption that the total REE patterns in the moon parallel those of chondrites, although the overall concentration levels are perhaps 5–6

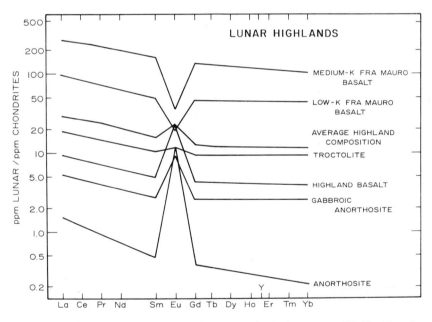

**Fig. 5.20** Rare earth element (REE) abundances in highland rock types [89, 92]. Note that the average highland composition has a positive Eu anomaly. The slopes of the patterns are nearly parallel. The La/Yb ratio is close to 3.1 for most patterns, except for the plagioclase-rich samples, where the La/Yb ratio rises.

Table 5.15   Average Composition of the Highlands[92].

| | (wt.%) | (wt.%) | | (ppm) | | (ppm) |
|---|---|---|---|---|---|---|
| $SiO_2$ | 45.0 | 45.5* | Rb | 1.7 | La | 8.8 |
| $TiO_2$ | 0.56 | 0.6 | Cs | 0.07 | Ce | 21.6 |
| $Al_2O_3$ | 24.6 | 24.0 | Ba | 110 | Pr | 3.06 |
| FeO | 6.6 | 5.9 | | | Nd | 12.4 |
| | | | Sr | 200 | Sm | 3.26 |
| MgO | 8.6 | 7.5 | Th | 1.5 | Eu | 1.70 |
| CaO | 14.2 | 15.9 | U | 0.4 | Gd | 3.86 |
| $Na_2O$ | 0.45 | 0.6 | Zr | 105 | Tb | 0.59 |
| $K_2O$ | 0.075 | — | Hf | 2.3 | Dy | 3.87 |
| | | | Nb | 7.5 | Ho | 0.89 |
| | | | Cr | 710 | Er | 2.51 |
| $Cr_2O_3$ | 0.10 | — | Sc | 7.6 | Tm | 0.37 |
| | | | V | 21 | Yb | 2.25 |
| Σ | 99.3 | 100.0 | Tl ppb | 4 | Lu | 0.35 |
| | | | | | ΣREE | 66 |
| | | | | | Y | 22.4 |

*Data from reference 91.

times those in the primitive type I carbonaceous chondrites. Further, it is generally held that the highland crust developed by differentiation from the interior, following homogeneous accretion.

It is of interest to test this proposed composition by independent comparisons. One such test is to use mixing program studies to see if the values obtained by this empirical technique are realistic in terms of the various individual highland crustal rock types. By testing against the four components (anorthosite—highland basalt—low-K Fra Mauro basalt—medium-K Fra Mauro basalt), the closest match was obtained from a 2-component mixture of 80 percent highland basalt (anorthositic gabbro) and 20 percent low-K Fra Mauro basalt. The important role of these two rock types in highland composition has already been noted. Neither medium-K Fra Mauro basalt nor anorthosite are required as separate components.

On the basis of a homogeneously accreted moon, with a REE abundance pattern parallel to that of chondrites, the interior should display a pattern complementary to that of the crust. Thus the source regions of the maria basalts could reasonably be expected to possess an inbuilt negative europium anomaly, removing many problems.

A value of 22.4 ppm Y is obtained from the observed relationship that chondrite-normalized yttrium values are similar to those for the heavy REE (notably Ho, which has the same ionic radius). The Cr/V ratio of 28 yields a value of 21 ppm V. The Cr/Sc ratio yields 7.6 ppm Sc. A Tl value of 4 ppb results from the K/Tl ratio of $2 \times 10^5$.

The overall highland composition so derived is given in Table 5.15. This is specifically based on orbital Al/Si ratios of 0.62 and a Th value of 1.5 ppm. Compositions for individual highland areas can be obtained from this same approach if the Al/Si and Th values are specified. These data place a premium on the acquisition of further values from both XRF and gamma-ray orbital experiments.

The lateral variations in composition of the highland crust (Figs. 5.14–5.16) have been noted. Are there significant variations in depth? Do the abundances derived in Table 5.15 refer only to a superficial layer, or are they representative of the 60-km-thick highland crust indicated by the geophysical data (section 6.4)? This is a question vital to geochemical models of total lunar composition.

The large craters have overturned crustal segments down to at least 10 km. The depth of excavation and overturning by the ringed basin collisions is much less certain with wide variations [93]. It seems likely that adequate deep excavation has occurred. If this has not done a very good job of homogenization, at least extensive overturning has occurred, and any primary crustal zonation has been destroyed. Accordingly the composition of the crust is probably not grossly different at depth.

### Comparison With Maria Compositions

The abundances of the chemical constituents in the highlands crust are distinctly different from those in the maria basalts, Al, Ca, and Ni being enriched, and Fe, Ti, Cr, V, Sc, Co, and Cu depleted in the highlands relative to the maria basalts. Overlaps in composition occur for the other chemical elements. Despite the differences in chemistry, the maria and the highlands share many distinctive lunar geochemical characteristics. These include the many similar element ratios (Fe/Mn, Ba/Rb, K/La, K/Zr). Such similarities of ratios of volatile and involatile elements between the maria and the highlands samples are a major piece of evidence refuting the hypothesis that the highlands were separately accreted or condensed from more refractory material than the source regions of the maria basalts.

## Comparison With Primitive Solar-Nebula Abundances

Various workers have suggested that the highland material was directly accreted and represents the last stage of accumulation of a heterogeneous moon. In order to establish the degree of chemical fractionation, the element concentrations for the highland components are compared with those in Type I carbonaceous chondrites.

In Tables 5.16 and 5.17 the chondritic abundances are compared with those for anorthositic gabbro (highland basalt) and low-K Fra Mauro basalt. In each case there is a first-order difference based on volatility and siderophile character. This is the same type of relationship common to all lunar samples first observed in the initial examination[94] and attributed to depletion at or before accretion[95].

When the *involatile* elements are looked at in more detail, a second relationship, illustrated in Fig. 5.21, emerges. In this diagram the elements are arranged in order of ionic radius and valency. The assumption is made that there is no relative fractionation of the *involatile* elements between the moon and the primitive abundances. For example, they are assumed to have the same relative abundances for the rare earth elements. Evidence for this comes from the similarity in REE patterns (excluding Eu) between the most primitive maria basalts and the chondritic patterns, although the former are enriched by 3–5 times over the chondritic abundances.

If this assumption is correct, then the involatile elements in the highlands components have been fractionated to a degree that depends on the differences in ionic radii and/or valency from those of $Fe^{2+}$ and $Mg^{2+}$.

**Table 5.16**   Comparison of Anorthositic Gabbro, or Highland Basalt, with that of Type I Carbonaceous Chondrites.

| | Concentration relative to chondrites | Element |
|---|---|---|
| Enriched | >20 | Eu Sr |
| | 10–20 | Ba Al La |
| | 2–10 | REE (—La, Eu) Th U Zr |
| | 1–2 | Si Hf Nb |
| Depleted | 0.5–1 | Mg |
| | 0.1–0.5 | Cr V Fe Ga |
| | <0.1 | Ni Co Cu |

**Table 5.17**  Comparison of Low-K Fra Mauro Basalt with
that of Type I Carbonaceous Chondrites.

|  | Concentration relative to chondrites | Element |
|---|---|---|
| Enrichment | 100–150 | Ba La Th U |
|  | 50–100 | REE (—La, Eu) Zr Hf Nb |
|  | 20–50 | Al |
|  | 3–20 | Ca Sc |
|  | 1–3 | Rb K Pb Si |
| Depletion | 0.5–1 | Na Cr V Mg |
|  | 0.1–0.5 | Sr Fe Ga |
|  | <0.1 | Ni Co Cu |

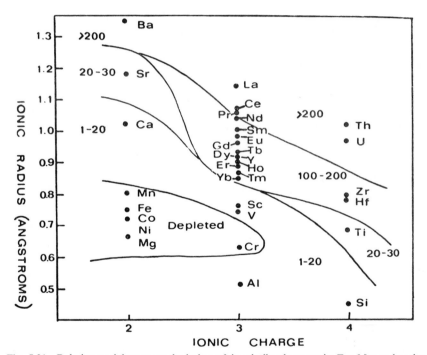

**Fig. 5.21**  Relative enrichment or depletion of involatile elements in Fra Mauro basalts
relative to abundances in Type I carbonaceous chondrites, based on ionic radius and
valency. Contour lines separate areas of differing degrees of enrichment. Note the
progressive enrichment as radius and valency differ from those of Mg and Fe. Similar
patterns appear when other highland components are plotted in this manner[97].

Similar observations have been interpreted[96] as evidence for fractionation based on crystal-liquid equilibria, and hence imply large-scale partial
melting in the outer layers of the moon. The type and levels of enrichment
are analogous to those observed in terrestrial crustal rocks and show no
dependence on volatility (e.g., fractionation is observed within the REE
group). From this evidence it is concluded that the chemically distinct
rock types in the highlands are derived by partial melting in postaccretion
processes. Preaccretion processes are responsible for loss of volatile, and
probably the siderophile, elements. Postaccretive processes of melting
and fractionation are responsible for the production of the surface rocks.

One fact that has been cited as evidence for a relative enrichment of
refractory elements in the highlands is the K/U ratio. This is lower
($\sim 1,500$) in highland samples than in mare basalts ($\sim 2,500$). This enrichment of U relative to K could be due to accretion of more refractory
material. But it may also be a consequence of crystal-liquid fractionation.
It can be seen from Fig. 5.21 that U (and Th) are the most highly enriched
elements in the highlands and are thus concentrated upwards to a greater
extent than potassium. Additional evidence of crystal-chemical rather
than volatility dependence comes from the much more uniform values
observed for Rb/U ratios, although Rb is more volatile than K. Furthermore, elements that are more refractory than U (such as Zr) do not show
such variations with K between mare and highlands samples.

### Chromium-Nickel Ratios in the Highlands

Important constraints on lunar origin and composition arise from the
abundances of Cr and Ni (and other siderophile elements) in the lunar
highlands. The highland compositions are characterized by three unusual
geochemical element associations. These are (*a*) high Mg and Cr, (*b*) Ca-
Al-Sr-Eu, and (*c*) high REE, etc.

In the geochemical model developed later in the book, these three
element associations are derived from different sources. The high Mg and
Cr (and related elements) abundances are thought to be derived from the
initial chilled or frozen surface layer. The composition of this zone is
essentially that of the accreted material. If this is a valid deduction, the
material forming the moon was depleted in siderophile elements before
accretion took place. The evidence for this comment comes from the
Cr/Ni ratios.

In the primitive solar nebula composition (as represented by the Type I
carbonaceous chondrite abundances) the Cr/Ni ratio is about 0.25. In

contrast, in the lunar highlands Cr/Ni is about 5. (Chromium averages about 500–600 ppm, while Ni is rarely more than 100 ppm.) Thus, Ni is depleted relative to Cr by at least an order of magnitude. The initial depletion must have been much greater, for much of the Ni (and other siderophile elements) presently in the highland rocks is derived from the later meteoritic bombardment. Hence, if our original assumption is correct, Ni (and the other siderophiles) were strongly depleted in the primordial lunar composition.

This has further consequences. One reason for postulating the existence of a lunar core is that it provides a useful and convenient sink to deplete siderophile elements from the surface lunar samples. If these elements were never accreted, then this reason for the existence of a core disappears.

### Enrichment of Volatile Elements in Highland Samples

The moon is in general greatly depleted in volatile elements, so it is of great interest that some highland anorthositic rocks contain excess amounts of the volatile elements[88]. Tl, Br, Cd, Sb, Zr, and Ge were all enriched in some highland samples. Their occurrence is sporadic and not related to brecciation. Some minor examples occur at the Apennine Front (Apollo 15), but the best examples are in the Apollo 16 Descartes breccias. The most notable examples are the "rusty rock" (66095), and 60016, which contains 131 ppb Tl, over two orders of magnitude greater than the average. Enrichments up to $10^4$ times are known.

Fig. 5.22 shows the normal Tl/Cs and Tl/U correlations. In Fig. 5.23 the dispersion of Tl relative both to Cs and to U are shown[88]. What is the cause of this variability in the ratios? It is clear that the volatile enrichment occurs after the brecciation, for the lead is easily leached.

The major effects are confined to the anorthosites, and thus there may be a mineralogical control by plagioclase. $Tl^+$ is nearly the same radius as $Rb^+$. However, Rb does not fractionate from Cs in the anorthosites, and thus explanations based on crystal chemistry face difficulties, although they cannot be ruled out.

Since other volatile elements, such as Pb and Bi, correlate with thallium, the enrichment is most likely a consequence of volatility. A wide variety of explanations have been offered. Comets are popular sources, since they provide volatiles (although usually not in the right ratios), water, and impact energy. Perhaps the most telling evidence against the direct involvement of a comet is that the lead enrichments are lunar, not

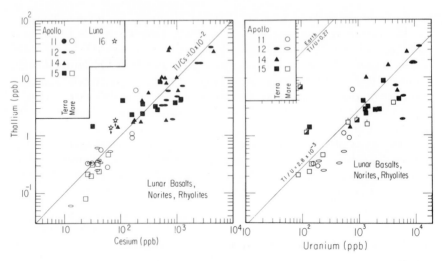

**Fig. 5.22**  Thallium correlates well with cesium and uranium. Luna 16 points are soils that contain a meteoritic Tl contribution and therefore lie too high. Half-filled symbols belong to the green glass breccia 15426[88]. (Courtesy E. Anders.)

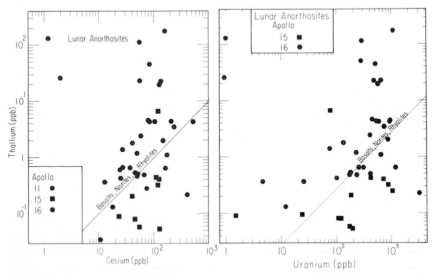

**Fig. 5.23**  Tl-Cs and Tl-U correlation fails in most lunar anorthosites (rocks and soil separates). Apparently Tl was redistributed by volatilization[88]. (Courtesy E. Anders.)

meteoritic [49], and such water as is present is terrestrial contamination [50]. Enrichment of volatiles through vaporization in a hot
ejecta blanket is attractive, particularly since euhedral crystals, deposited
from the vapor state, are observed in vugs and cavities, most notably at
Apollo 14 (Figs. 5.8–5.10). One problem here is the degree of enrichment.
To obtain 2–4 orders of magnitude concentration, Tl must be baked out of
$10^2$–$10^4$ volumes of rock. Such large amounts of Tl-poor rocks do not seem
common. The subject seems to be a fertile field for further research,
correlating impact and regolith formation studies with the chemistry of the
volatile elements.

## 5.11  THE ANCIENT METEORITIC COMPONENT

Three types of meteoritic debris exist on the lunar surface. These are
($a$) the micrometeoritic component in the regolith, ($b$) the debris from the
large-crater-producing bodies, and ($c$) the material added during the
intense early bombardment.

The identification of the first component has been aided by the extreme
depletion of both siderophile and volatile elements in the lunar rocks [98].
This fortunate circumstance has established the major meteoritic component in the soils as Type I carbonaceous chondritic debris, although the
identification in highland soils is complicated by the ancient component [99] (Fig. 5.24). As noted earlier, about 1.5 percent of the lunar soil is
composed of this material. Whether this is of cometary or asteroidal
origin remains a question of debate, with the latter origin currently in
favor.

The identification of the projectiles responsible for the large craters has
proved more elusive. It will probably remain so until extended sampling is
possible around a large lunar crater, if terrestrial experience at impact
sites is a guide. The highland rocks contain abundant evidence of the
intense cratering episodes, which are so clearly displayed in the highland
topography. Both highland rocks and soils contain abundant metallic
fragments. The nickel content of breccias is typically 100–400 ppm,
almost all of this being derived from the meteoritic material. Only a few
highland samples are free from this component. These include the
anorthosite 15415 and similar plagioclase-rich samples. Rocks that have
been through an impact melt stage or have recrystallized under equilibrium conditions may exclude the meteoritic components. This may not be
an efficient process, as the high meteoritic metal content of the crystalline
rock 14310 shows [32].

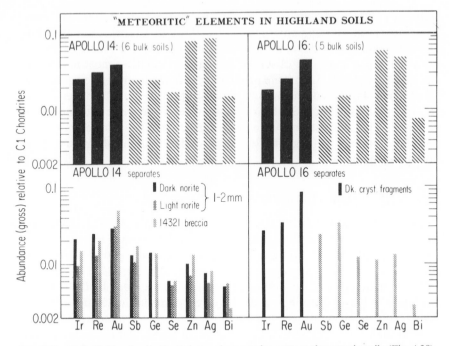

**Fig. 5.24** Bulk highland soils (top) show a less regular pattern than maria soils (Fig. 4.28), largely due to an "ancient" meteoritic component. This component is seen most clearly in breccias and coarse soil separates, which contain no recent micrometeorite contribution (bottom). It has a distinctly fractionated pattern, with volatiles less abundant than siderophiles. In contrast to the mare data in Fig. 4.28 the highland data have not been corrected for an indigenous contribution[99]. (Courtesy E. Anders.)

The use of trace element ratios has enabled six classes of ancient meteoritic components to be identified. Fig. 5.25, based on subdivision by Au, Ir, and Ge content, shows these. Figs. 5.26 and 5.27 (with the same co-ordinates as Fig. 5.25) show that the six lunar classes avoid both presently known iron meteorite groups and the chondritic classes[99–102].

Thus, the ancient component does not resemble that of any known meteorite class, iron or chondritic. Although the Ni and Co contents match those of some meteorites[103], the other trace elements clearly indicate the uniqueness of the ancient components. The old component is intimately associated with the rocks: in contrast, the recent meteoritic additions to the soils contain easily leached materials. The enrichment of siderophiles is generally $10^2$–$10^3$ times the indigenous levels in the highlands rocks.

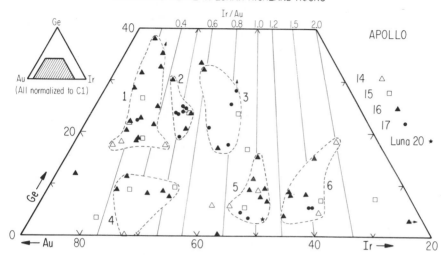

**Fig. 5.25**  The six groupings of the ancient meteorite components in the highlands, separated by differing Au, Ir, and Ge contents. (Courtesy E. Anders.)

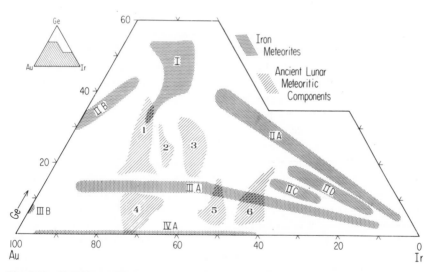

**Fig. 5.26**  The six ancient lunar meteorite groups, compared with known iron meteorites. The lunar groups avoid the presently known meteorite compositions[102]. (Courtesy E. Anders.)

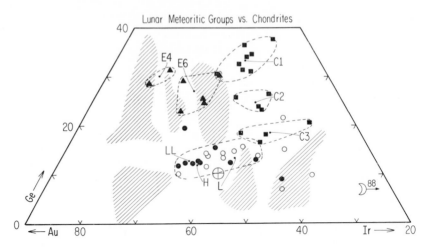

**Fig. 5.27** Comparison of the ancient lunar meteorite groups with known chondritic meteorite classes[102]. As in the case of the iron meteorites, the match is very poor. (Courtesy E. Anders.)

What is the origin of the material? A particular highland breccia only contains one type of ancient meteoritic debris[99–102]. Thus we are looking, not at a micrometeorite flux, but the debris resulting from large projectiles. It is not clear whether the ringed basin projectiles differ from those responsible for the smaller (<100 km diameter) craters. However, since the surface structure is dominated by ringed basin impacts, most of the meteoritic material we now observe in the highlands samples is probably derived from these large projectiles, or 'planetesimals"[100].

Attempts are currently being made to detect the compositions of the projectiles responsible for the latest impacts, notably the Imbrium projectile. This is a complex task, since, for example, the ejecta from the Imbrium collision sampled at Fra Mauro probably contains a large amount of Serenitatis ejecta, as well as possible megaregolith from the Imbrium area. Tentative assignments to various basin collisions have been made. Of the groups shown in Fig. 5.24, 1 appears to be from the Imbrium collision; 2 is assigned to Serenitatis since it is abundant at the Apollo 17 site; 3 is possibly from Crisium; the origin of 4 is uncertain; 5 is potentially from Nectaris; while 6 is old, possibly from Humorum or Nubium[102]. The final results of this fascinating piece of selenodetection remain to be uncovered.

As a result of much painstaking work, the following characteristics of those ancient meteoritic components seem well established. They had a high content of siderophile elements, about in the solar nebula ratios. Thus, they were not from bodies that had separated a core. They cannot, accordingly, be pieces of earth mantle spun off after core formation[104] or any sort of residual material from the accretion of the earth. They are depleted in volatile components, indicating analogies with the eucrites, the earth and the moon.

It is suggested[100] that the most probable origin is planetesimals in earth-crossing orbits. It is notable that most of the "planetesimals" appear to be depleted in Ir relative to Au, contrary to the case for the moon. Thus they are not leftover pieces of the primordial lunar building blocks, but "the complement of such building blocks"[101], "a fact of profound if obscure significance"[100].

Alternative explanations that the siderophiles in the highlands samples are not meteoritic but are hydrothermal in origin[105] have not received support. They predict, for example, the reverse of the observed strong Ir/Au and weak Tl/Au correlations.

## 5.12 AGES OF THE HIGHLAND ROCKS

Revolutions still more remote appeared in the distance of this extraordinary perspective. The mind seemed to grow giddy by looking so far into the abyss of time

John Playfair (1802)

The evidence for an ancient lunar crust appears dimly through the destruction caused by the intense bombardment. This cratering activity can be expected to have reset the radiometric clocks to varying degrees. Thus it would be unduly optimistic to expect a clear and simple age picture to emerge from the highly shocked and brecciated samples, and primary age data indicative of the crystallization of the crust will be difficult to find. However, many clues to these processes can be gained. We have seen in the section on the geochemistry of the elements that the evidence for a primitive lunar crust is strong. When did this form? The stratigraphic evidence indicates that a crust of considerable thickness was in existence well before the main ringed-basin-forming impacts occurred.

The very low content of Rb in many of the highland samples, and the ease with which the Rb-Sr clock is reset, means that the Rb-Sr method is not easy to apply. The U-Th-Pb method is even more model dependent. Perhaps the technique likely to yield most information is the $^{40}$Ar/$^{39}$Ar modification of the K-Ar method. This provides some evidence of the previous thermal history of the samples. In practice, all of the methods provide evidence of value, sometimes interlocking, in unraveling the history of the highlands.

Most of the highlands ages cluster around 3.9–4.0 aeons. This is partly a sampling effect and in part due to the massive or cataclysmic resetting of

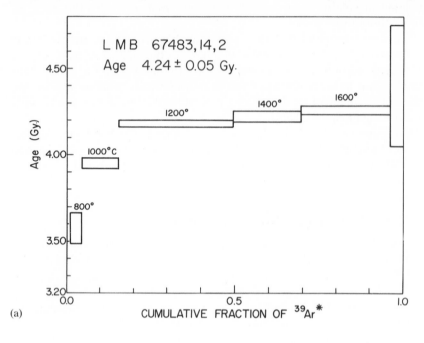

(a)

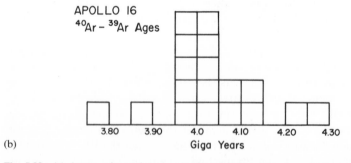

(b)

**Fig. 5.28**   (a) Argon release data for Apollo 16 light matrix breccia fragments 67483,14,2, one of the oldest lunar samples dated so far. (b) Histogram of $^{40}$Ar-$^{39}$Ar ages for Apollo 16 samples (Schaeffer, O. A., et al., 1973, *PLC 4*: Figs. 8 and 9).

many age clocks by the late ringed-basin-forming events. There is a current debate whether there was a "cataclysm"[106] or a "terminal cataclysm"[107, 108] at 3.9–4.0 aeons, or whether the collisional processes extended back toward 4.6 aeons[109]. The trend is toward the second view.

There are few samples with ages older than 4 billion years. A few dates extend to 4.05 aeons, and some samples give $^{39}Ar/^{40}Ar$ dates of 4.2 aeons (Fig. 5.28). There is some suggestion of a 4.3 aeon event. Most interpretations of the rubidium and lead isotopic systematics place the formation of the crust somewhat earlier, perhaps very close to the accretion date of 4.6 aeons. An early date for the crust is desirable largely because of the many events that have to be fitted in between the formation of the moon and the commencement of mare volcanism at 3.9 aeons. Recently the first unequivocal example of a crystalline rock with an internal mineral Rb-Sr isochron yielding an age of 4.6 aeons has been reported[110] (Fig. 5.29).

## The Imbrium Ages

Both Apollo 14 samples from the Imbrium ejecta blanket at Fra Mauro and Apollo 15 samples from the base of the Apennine Front could be expected to be dominated by the Imbrium event. The ages for all methods peak at 3.9–4.0 aeons[111–118]. An alternative explanation of the Fra Mauro dates has been attempted[10]. This depends heavily on the stratigraphic interpretation of the position of the Fra Mauro formation. Similar ages from the Apennine Front[119–122] serve to strengthen the consensus that Fra Mauro is Imbrium throwout. In particular, the large anorthosite 15415 from the Apennine Front gave $^{40}Ar/^{39}Ar$ ages of 4.1 aeons[119, 120], slightly older than the Rb-Sr ages of 3.90 aeons[121].

## Age of the Imbrium Collision

The date of this event can be closely set. It must be older than the oldest mappable mare basalt, since these cover the thrown-out debris of the collision. $^{40}Ar/^{39}Ar$ dating suggests 3.8 aeons for the Apollo 11 and 17 basalts. These are younger than the Imbrium event. The Fra Mauro formation samples can provide direct age evidence, if it is composed of outthrown material produced during the cratering event. As noted above, the Fra Mauro breccias yield ages in the range 3.9–4.0 aeons. These dates indicate only the last resetting of the Rb-Sr clock and are not "primary" in any sense. Sample 14310, one of the few crystalline rocks from Fra

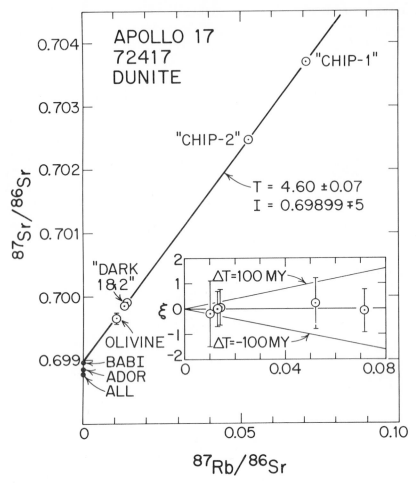

**Fig. 5.29** The oldest lunar rock. Rb-Sr evolution diagram for dunite 72417. Insert indicates the effect on age of uncertainties (in parts in $10^4$) of $^{87}Sr/^{86}Sr$. Sample enriched in symplectic intergrowths has the low Rb/Sr. Initial Sr is equal to BABI and distinctly higher than ADOR (Angra dos Reis) and ALL (Allende). (Courtesy G. J. Wasserburg.)

Mauro, was produced by impact melting[32]. Its age is 3.88 aeons. This gives an upper age to the Imbrium collision. Of course, 14310 may have crystallized from an earlier puddle of impact melt, but the age is similar to that of other Fra Mauro ages.

**The Descartes Ages**

The Descartes site, well removed from the maria basalt floods, should be least difficult to interpret, and much of the evidence of the older ages comes from this area. Following the discussion of the geology of the site (section 2.8), it is concluded that most of the Apollo 16 material is local to the site, and the amount of Imbrium or Orientale primary debris is very small.

The significance of this interpretation for the age data is that the old highland crust at Descartes is not much affected by the great lunar cataclysm at Imbrium, at about 3.9 aeons. Thus the Descartes site is critical to the evaluation of the age data, with respect to the evolution of the highland crust. Fragments of old material are to be expected. A range of $^{40}Ar/^{39}Ar$ ages up to 4.24 aeons is found, the oldest total rock age being from a light matrix breccia[123] (Sample 67483,14,2).

Other evidence of old events comes from plagioclase crystals. Sample 65015, a breccia, contains relict plagioclase, which gives ages of 4.42 aeons and 4.49 aeons, by $^{40}Ar/^{39}Ar$ dating[106] (Fig. 5.30). Further work on this sample has revealed relict ages of 4.5 aeons in the cores of plagioclase crystals, using the $^{40}Ar-^{39}Ar$ technique[124] (Fig. 5.30). These crystals seem not to have been isotopically or chemically equilibrated with the rest of the breccia and denote possible ages of primary crystallization. The plagioclases in the lunar breccias are particularly-retentive of argon[123]. Other evidence is less equivocal, but it is worth noting that 68415, a crystalline "igneous" rock, which is an impact melt, while giving Rb-Sr internal isochron ages and $^{40}Ar/^{39}Ar$ ages of 3.9 aeons, has a final (8 percent) high temperature argon release from the plagioclase indicating an age of 4.5 aeons[125]. The $^{40}Ar/^{39}Ar$ dates thus look back to the crystallization of the original highland crust, through the immense cratering and basin-forming events culminating in the formation of the Imbrium and Orientale basins at 3.9 aeons.

**Apollonius Highlands**

The small samples returned from the Russian Luna 20 mission to the Apollonius highlands, just north of Mare Crisium, were dated[125] at 3.90 aeons by $^{40}Ar/^{39}Ar$. This age is in remarkable agreement with the Imbrium ages, but this is probably coincidental. The samples are too far away (1,600 km) to be reset by thermal events. Some throwout from Imbrium will have reached the site but has probably been either gardened or overlain by throwout from nearby younger impact craters (e.g., Ap-

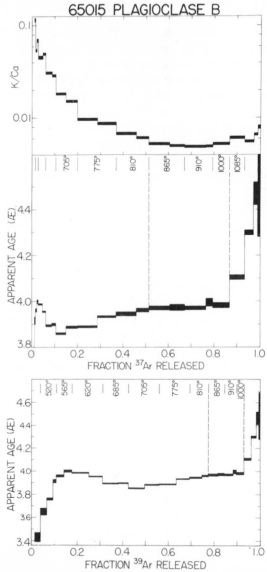

**Fig. 5.30**  Relict highland ages of 4.5 aeons in cores of plagioclase crystals. Apparent age and K/Ca vs $^{37}$Ar release (top) and apparent age vs $^{39}$Ar release (bottom) from 65015 plagioclase B. Low temperature releases from high K, low Ca contaminant phases dominate the $^{39}$Ar plot. A plateau at 3.98 AE and the subsequent rise to higher ages, which is associated with retentive relict plagioclase, includes a significant portion of $^{37}$Ar release[125, 132]. (Courtesy G. J. Wasserburg.)

ollonius C). Thus, the ages probably reflect local rather than distant events and are expected to be dominated by the Crisium ejecta. Crisium is the next oldest basin to Imbrium in most lunar basin chronologies, although some workers[126] consider it to be much older (see Table 2.6 for the relative basin chronology).

An alternative age, based on samples from the Apollo 17 site, of 4.13 aeons has been suggested for the Crisium event[109]. It will take much detailed sampling and evaluation of data to decide which rocks are recording a particular ringed basin excavation. Integration with the search for the ancient meteorite components should prove fruitful.

An attempt to provide an absolute basin chronology has been made by Schaeffer, et al.[109]. They provide the following age scale:

Orientale    3.85 aeons
Imbrium    4.0 aeons
Crisium    4.13 aeons
Humorum    4.13–4.20 aeons
Nectaris    4.20 aeons

This scale uses the older Crisium age. The relative chronology is in accord with the morphological evidence (Table 2.6) based on basin rim degradation by cratering. It is still too early, however, to pass final judgment on the absolute chronology of the ringed basin events. An excellent review of this topic has been given by Turner[112].

### Highland Soils

The highland soils all show model ages clustering around 4.6 aeons[127], as was the case with the maria soils. Figs. 3.3 and 3.4 show the model age data for the lunar soils from all missions. This is a remarkable regularity since the soils are complex mixtures. The best fit to the data yields an age of 4.35 aeons with $I = 0.69921$. The range in model "ages" is from 4.1 to 4.9 aeons. The reasons for this have been discussed in section 3.5, where it has been concluded that the surface impact processes have perturbed both the Rb/Sr ratios and the Rb-Sr model ages[128] (Fig. 3.5).

### Lead Data

The volatile nature of lead has caused much redistribution of this element during soil-forming processes so that the great potential of this method for dating[129] is not always realized. Silver[130] has given a description of the possible complexities of the lead isotope redistribution in lunar surface processes, regarding the movement as local rather than moon-wide [107]. Added to this problem are the assumptions underlying the lead model age calculations. Where the model age is close to 4.6 aeons, a single stage for lead evolution may be assumed. Where the age is greater or less than this, multi-stage models involving fractionation of U, Th, and Pb are involved.

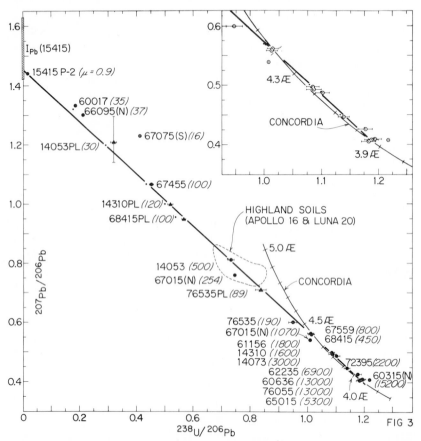

**Fig. 5.31** U-Pb evolution diagram showing all available data on possible lunar highland rocks and including plagioclase separates (PL). These results form a remarkable linear array and are compatible with the model of a terminal lunar cataclysm at ~3.9 aeons, which redistributed lead from a crust with an "age" of ~4.43 aeons. Note in particular the troctolite 76535 total rock and plagioclase. The reference isochron is for 14310. The upper intersection with concordia at 4.43 aeons is well below the presumed age of the moon. The value of $\mu \equiv {}^{238}U/{}^{204}Pb$ is given in parentheses after the sample number. Note the systematic trend from $\mu \sim 1$ near the upper end of the isochron [107]. (Courtesy G. J. Wasserburg.)

There are indications from the lead data of crustal formation at 4.47 aeons[131] or 4.43 aeons[107], followed by much redistribution of lead at 3.9–4.0 aeons (Fig. 5.31). The resolution of some of the problems associated with the lunar lead data appears to be close[107, 131], but it would be premature at this stage to consider them solved.

### The Age of the Highland Crust

The overall geological, geochemical, and geochronological evidence combine to indicate that the formation of the highland crust was an early event in lunar history. Since the time of the last collisions producing the ringed basins ($\sim 3.9$ aeons), the highland crust of the moon (Fig. 2.5) has not changed. Fainter evidence persists from earlier epochs, just as the face of an ancient dowager may retain vestiges of youthful beauty.

The relict plagioclase cores[109, 123, 132] contain evidence of ages approaching 4.5 aeons. The dunite[110] Rb-Sr age of 4.6 aeons has survived. This rock sample is interpreted in chapter 7 as a relict of a primordial frozen crust, predating the highland anorthosites.

The Rb-Sr isotopic studies point to low initial ratios, equivalent to those of basaltic achondrites (BABI) or perhaps lower. A value as low as 0.69885 has been suggested[133]. Whatever the precise value of the initial ratio, there is a consensus among the isotope workers that large-scale melting and differentiation occurred at or shortly after the accretion of the moon.

Independent evidence from all three age clocks, Rb-Sr, K-Ar, and Pb-U-Th, combines to suggest extensive melting, fractionation, and formation of the highland crust at a time close to the condensation of the solar system at 4.6 aeons[134]. Can this estimate be refined? This depends on interpretations of Rb-Sr and Pb-U-Th systematics[95, 107, 133], which are heavily model dependent, but the indications are that perhaps half the crust formed in the first 100 million years (4.6–4.5 aeons) and that crustal differentiation processes producing fractionated rock types continued for another 200 million years to 4.3 aeons[128].

## REFERENCES AND NOTES

1. Hutton, J. (1788) *Trans. Roy. Soc. Edin.* 1: 209.
2. Vinogradov, A. P., et al. (1966) *Geochemistry.* 3: 707.
3. Turkevich, A. L., et al. (1968) *Science.* 162: 117.
4. Wood, J. A., et al. (1970) *PLC 1*: 965; Marvin, U., et al. (1971) *PLC 2*: 679.
5. Meyer, C., et al. (1971) *PLC 2*: 393.

6. Adler, I., et al. (1973) *PLC 4*: 2783.
7. Trombka, J. I., et al. (1973) *PLC 4*: 2847.
8. See section 6.4.
9. Head, J. W. (1973) *Moon*. In press.
10. Schonfeld, E., and Meyer, C. (1973) *PLC 4*: 125.
11. Warner, J. (1972) *LS III*: 788; (1972) *PLC 3*: 623.
12. Jackson, E. D., and Wilshire, H. G. (1972) *LS III*: 418; Wilshire H. G., and Jackson, E. D. (1972) USGS Prof. Paper, 785.
13. Chao, E. C. T., et al. (1972) *PLC 3*: 645.
14. See section 5.4 on lunar "chondrules."
15. Williams, R. J. (1972) *EPSL*. 16: 250.
16. Gibson, E. K., and Hubbard, N. J. (1972) *PLC 3*: 2003.
17. Gibson, E. K., et al. (1973) *PLC 4*: 1263.
18. McKay, D. S., et al. (1972) *PLC 3*: 739.
19. The moon is rapidly becoming populated with acronyms. A partial list includes:

| ANT, | Anorthosite-norite-troctolite; |
|---|---|
| ANTIC, | A variation on ANT; |
| FETI, | Iron-titanium rich; |
| FIIR, | Feldspathic intersertal igneous rocks; |
| KREEP, | Potassium-rare earth elements-phosphorus; |
| KREZP, | KREEP with zirconium; |
| KREPZBAU, | KREEP with barium and uranium; |
| KREEPUTH, | KREEP with uranium and thorium; |
| META-ANT, | Metamorphosed ANT; |
| VHA, | Very high alumina. |

Acronyms offer a deceptively easy path through the complexities of the lunar highland rocks. In reality, their unrestricted use will further entangle us in the thickets of terminology. Scientists from other disciplines, already baffled by the complex jargon of petrology, are unlikely to gain much insight from them. Future workers will rightly scold us for entering these semantic swamps.

20. Delano, J. W., et al. (1973) *PLC 4*: 537.
21. See section 5.6.
22. Hussain, L., and Schaeffer, O. A. (1973) *LS IV*: 406.
23. Further textural jargon:
    (*a*) Poikilitic or poikiloblastic (large host crystals enclosing many smaller crystals of other phases. Poikilitic textures are igneous, poikiloblastic are metamorphic).
    (*b*) Oikocryst: A term for the host crystal (usually orthopyroxene or pigeonite).
    (*c*) Chadacryst: A term for the included crystals (usually plagioclase and olivine).
24. Albee, A. L., et al. (1973) *LS IV*: 24.
25. Bence, A. E., et al. (1973) *PLC 4*: 597.
26. Brown, G. M., et al. (1973) *PLC 4*: 505.
27. Simonds, C. H., et al. (1973) *PLC 4*: 613.
28. Taylor, G. J., et al. (1973) *PLC 4*: 553.
29. Steele, I. M., and Smith, J. V. (1973) *PLC 4*: 519.
30. Warner, J. L., et al. (1973) *PLC 4*: 481.
31. 60215—Meyer, H. O., and McCallister, R. H. (1973) *PLC 4*: 661; 67955—Hollister, L. S. (1973) *PLC 4*: 633; 68415—Helz, R. T., and Appleman, D. E. (1973) *PLC 4*: 643.

32. For a very detailed description of 14310, see James, O. B. (1973) U.S. Geol. Survey Prof. Paper, 841.
33. Albee, A., et al. (1973) *LS V*: 3.
34. Head, J. W. (1974) *Moon*. In press.
35. Grieve, R. A. F., and Plant, A. G. (1973) *PLC 4*: 661; Grieve, R. A. F., et al. (1974) *LS V*: 290.
36. Fredriksson, K., et al. (1974) *LS V*: 245.
37. Gose, W., et al. (1972) *PLC 3*: 2389.
38. McKay, D. S., et al. (1972) *PLC 3*: 739.
39. Skinner, B. J., and Winchell, H. (1972) *PLC 3*: 243.
40. Glass, B. P. (1973) *GCA*. 37: 841.
41. Gancarz, A. J., et al. (1972) *EPSL*. 16: 307.
42. Dowty, E., et al. (1973) *EPSL*. 21: 91.
43. King, E. A., et al. (1972) *PLC 3*: 673.
44. Kurat, G., et al. (1972) *PLC 3*: 707.
45. Nelen, J., et al. (1972) *PLC 3*: 723.
46. Taylor, L. A., et al. (1973) *LS IV*: 715.
47. El Goresy, A., et al. (1973) *EPSL*. 18: 411.
48. Krähenbühl, U., et al. (1973) *PLC 4*: 1325.
49. Tatsumoto, M. (1973) *EOS*. 54: 615; Nunes, P. D., and Tatsumoto, M. (1973) *Science*. 182: 916.
50. Epstein, S., and Taylor, H. P. (1974) *LS V*: 212.
51. Epstein, S., and Taylor, H. P. (1973) *PLC 4*: 1559; and (1972) *PLC 3*: 1442.
52. Reid, A. M. (1974) *Moon*. 9: 141.
53. Reid, A. M., et al. (1972) *PLC 3*: 363.
54. Ridley, W. I., et al. (1973) *PLC 4*: 316.
55. Reid, A. M., et al. (1972) *Meteoritics*. 7: 395.
56. Apollo Soil Survey (1971) *EPSL*. 12: 49.
57. Warner, J., et al. (1973) *EPSL*. 17: 7.
58. Fredriksson, K., et al. (1974) *LS V*: 245.
59. Taylor, S. R. (1973) *Moon*. 7: 181; (1974) *LS V*: 791.
60. Prinz, M., et al. (1973) *GCA*. 37: 979.
61. Bansal, B. M., et al. (1973) *LS IV*: 49.
62. Haskin, L. A., et al. (1973) *PLC 4*: 1275.
63. Church, S. E., et al. (1972) Apollo 15: 212.
64. Wänke, H., et al. (1973) *PLC 4*: 1461.
65. Hubbard, N., et al. (1972) *LS III*: 406; (1974) *EPSL* 13: 71–75.
66. Tatsumoto, M., et al. (1972) Apollo 15: 394.
67. Tera, F., et al. (1973) *LS IV*: 724.
68. Philpotts, J. A., et al. (1973) *LS IV*: 593; *PLC 4*: 1427.
69. Laul, J. C., and Schmitt, R. A. (1973) *The Moon*. 8: 183–184; (1972) Apollo 15: 223; *PLC 4*: 1349.
70. Walker, D., et al. (1973) *PLC 4*: 1013; and (1973) *EPSL*. 20: 325.
71. Drake, M. J., et al. (1974) *LS V*: 180.
72. Hubbard, N. J., et al. (1973) *Science*. 181: 339.
73. Dowty, E., et al. (1974) *Science*. 183: 1214. Other proposed types, (e.g., LKAS Suite, Hubbard, N. J., et al., 1974, *LS V*: 366) meet with similar objections.
74. Perhaps the most hopeful sign is that the debate has shifted from the nature of the rock

types to the nomenclature of the proposed species. If terrestrial experience is a guide, many years of acrimonious debate lie ahead.

75. Hodges, F. N., and Kushiro, I. (1973) *PLC 4*: 1033.
76. Adler, I., et al. (1972) NASA SP 289, 17-1; (1972) NASA SP-315, 19-1.
77. Arnold, J. R., et al. (1972) NASA SP-289, 16-1; (1972) NASA SP-315, 18-1.
78. Metzger, A. E., et al. (1974) *LS V*: 501.
79. Trombka, J. I., et al. (1973) *PLC 4*: 2847.
80. Adler, I., et al. (1973) *PLC 4*: 2783.
81. Podwysocki, M. H., et al. (1974) *LS V*: 611.
82. Hörz, F. (1974) *LS V*: 357.
83. O'Kelley, G. D., et al. (1970) *PLC 1*: 1407.
84. Duncan, A. R., et al. (1973) *PLC 4*: 1108.
85. Wänke, H., et al. (1973) *PLC 4*: 1461.
86. Laul, J. C., and Schmitt, R. A. (1973) *PLC 4*: 1349.
87. Eldridge, J. S., et al. (1973) *PLC 4*: 2115.
88. Krähenbühl, U., et al. (1973) *PLC 4*: 1325.
89. Taylor, S. R., et al. (1973) *GCA.* 37: 2665.
90. Chyi, L. D., and Ehmann, W. D. (1974) *LS V*: 118.
91. Turkevich, A. L. (1973) *PLC 4*: 1165.
92. Taylor, S. R., et al. (1974) *PLC 5.* In press.
93. See section 2.7.
94. LSPET (1969) *Science.* 165: 1211.
95. Wetherill, G. (1971) *Science.* 173: 383.
96. Taylor, S. R., et al. (1972) *PLC 3*: 1246; (1973) *Nature.* 245: 203.
97. Taylor, S. R. (1973) *Moon.* 7: 181.
98. Krähenbühl, U., et al. (1973) *PLC 4*: 1325.
99. Anders, E., et al. (1973) *Moon.* 8: 3.
100. Anders, E., et al. (1971) *PLC 1*: 1021.
101. Ganapathy, R., et al. (1973) *PLC 4*: 1239.
102. Morgan, J., et al. (1974) *PLC 5.* In press; *LS V*: 526.
103. Goldstein, J. I., et al. (1972) *PLC 3*: 1037.
104. O'Keefe, J. A. (1970) *JGR.* 75: 6565.
105. Hughes, T. C., et al. (1973) *LS IV*: 400.
106. Tera, F., et al. (1973) *LS IV*: 723.
107. Tera, F., et al. (1974) *LS V*: 792.
108. Kirsten, T., et al. (1973) *EPSL.* 20: 125.
109. Schaeffer, O. A., et al. (1974) *LS V*: 663.
110. Albee, A., et al. (1974) *LS V*: 3.
111. Papanastassiou, D. A., and Wasserburg, G. J. (1971) *EPSL.* 12: 36.
112. Turner, G., et al. (1972) *PLC 3*: 1589.
113. Compston, W., et al. (1972) *PLC 3*: 1487.
114. Hussain, L., et al. (1972) *Science.* 173: 1235; *PLC 3*: 1557.
115. Nyquist, L. E., et al. (1972) *PLC 3*: 1515.
116. Murthy, V. R., et al. (1972) *PLC 3*: 1503.
117. Tatsumoto, M., et al. (1972) *PLC 3*: 1531.
118. Pepin, R. O., et al. (1972) *PLC 3*: 1569.
119. Hussain, L., et al. (1972) *Science.* 175: 428; Apollo 15, 374.

120. Turner, G. (1972) *EPSL.* 14: 169. See Turner, G. (1973, *PLC 4*: 1889) for an excellent review of argon selenochronology. $^{40}Ar/^{39}Ar$ ages on plagioclase are the most reliable. In general, whole rock mineral isochron Rb-Sr ages have agreed with plagioclase $^{40}Ar/^{39}Ar$ ages. This happy situation does not always hold. 68415, for example[125], shows higher ages of 4.09 aeons compared with the Rb-Sr age of 3.84 aeons.

121. Nyquist, L. E., et al. (1973) Apollo 15, 380.

122. Tera, F., et al. (1972) Apollo 15, 396.

123. Hussain, L., and Schaeffer, O. A. (1973) *LS IV*: 406.

124. Huneke, J. C., et al. (1974) *LS V*: 375.

125. Huneke, J. C., et al. (1973) *LS IV*: 403.

126. Hartmann, W. K., and Wood, C. A. (1971) *Moon.* 3: 3.

127. Compston, W., et al. (1973) *LS IV*: 158.

128. Nyquist, L. E., et al. (1973) *PLC 4*: 1823.

129. $^{232}Th$ decays to $^{208}Pb$, emitting $6\alpha$ and $4\beta$ particles, with a half-life of 14.0 billion years. $^{235}U$, which is composed of 0.72 percent natural uranium, decays to $^{207}Pb$ emitting $7\alpha$ and $4\beta$ particles, with a half-life of 0.70 billion years. $^{238}U$, the principal isotope of uranium, composed of 99.28 percent of the element, decays to $^{206}Pb$, emitting $8\alpha$ and $6\beta$ particles, with a half-life of 4.46 billion years, close to the accepted age of the moon meteorites and the earth[134]. The remaining lead isotope, $^{204}Pb$ is nonradiogenic and serves as an index of the amount of common lead present.

130. Silver, L. T. (1972) *LS III*: 704.

131. Nunes, P. D., et al. (1973) *PLC 4*: 1797.

132. Jessberger, E. K., et al. (1974) *Nature.* 248: 199.

133. Nunes, P. D., et al. (1974) *LS V*: 559.

134. Tatsumoto, M. (1973) *Science.* 180: 1279; Oversby, V. (1974) *Nature.* 248: 132.

CHAPTER 6

# The Interior of the Moon

> The moon must be enormously cavernous with an atmosphere within, and at the centre of its caverns a sea. One knew that the moon had a lower specific gravity than the earth; one knew that it had little air or water outside; one knew, too, that it was sister planet to the earth and that it was unaccountable that it should be different in composition. The inference that it was hollowed out was as clear as day.
>
> H. G. Wells (1901)

Great advances in our knowledge of the interior of the moon have occurred as a result of the Apollo missions. By their very nature, most geophysical problems require the acquisition of large amounts of data over long periods of time. Thus, months of recording seismic signals were required to reveal the existence of a partially molten zone in the interior. Extensive magnetic measurements, including two subsatellite magnetometer experiments have provided much insight into the intensity and distribution of the localized lunar magnetic fields.

Two measurements of lunar heat flow are available. These are effectively equal, although they come from different sites. They indicate that the heat-producing elements must be concentrated near the lunar surface. The temperature of the lunar interior is constrained by these measurements, the lunar electrical conductivity data, and by the seismic observations that a partially molten shell exists at a depth of 1,000 km. All these data make it possible to establish a consistent model of the moon that fits the presently known geochemical values as well. In this chapter, the emphasis is on geophysical properties. Internal composition, thermal history, and other inferences drawn from these data are discussed in the sections in chapter 7 on the geochemical evolution of the moon.

276

## 6.1  RADIUS, DENSITY, AND MOMENT OF INERTIA

The mean lunar radius is 1,738 km and the mean density is 3.34 g/cm³. The density of the highland rocks lies within the range 2.75–3.0 g/cm³ with a mean value[1] of 2.95 g/cm³. The maria basalts have higher densities (3.3–3.4 g/cm³), about equal to the bulk density of the moon. The density of the lower crust[2] (25–60 km) is probably about 3.0–3.1 g/cm³. Assuming that the crustal average density is 2.95 g/cm³, the bulk density of the interior of the moon below the crust[1] will be 3.39 g/cm³.

The coefficient of moment of inertia ($I/MR^2$) is critical for understanding the density distribution in the lunar interior. The latest value[1, 3, 4] is $0.395 \pm 0.005$. Early values as high as 0.6, implying a hollow moon, have been refuted. Kaula[5] proposed a value of 0.402, very close to the value for a homogeneous sphere. Subsequent work[6] reduced the value to below 0.40. This removes some of the difficulties created by the earlier value, since the density of the lower mantle for a value of 0.402 needed to be about 5 percent less than that of the upper mantle to satisfy the moment of inertia criterion[2].

The new value allows a modest increase in density with depth. The moment of inertia value of 0.395 does not rule out the possibility of a core. The data permit the existence of an iron core of radius 450 km, for which there is no seismic evidence, or of a Fe-FeS core of radius 700 km, which corresponds to the $S$ wave seismic discontinuity.

## 6.2  LUNAR GRAVITY AND THE MASCONS

Mascons are the near-surface gravity anomalies of large magnitude characteristic of most of the circular maria (but not the irregular maria). First reported[7] in 1968 they have caused much speculation and an enhanced interest in the lunar gravity field. On the moon, the gravity field on the front side, near the equator, has become well defined as a result of the "$S$-band transponder experiments" carried out on Apollo 14 through 17 missions. These high precision measurements of the changes in velocity of the spacecraft (CSM, LM, and subsatellite for Apollo 15 and 16) enable the variations in the lunar gravity field to be mapped[8]. The following picture (Fig. 6.1) emerges:

(*a*) Unfilled lunar craters have negative anomalies, a consequence both of the mass defect and of the low-density material partially filling craters.

(*b*) Filled craters and maria with diameters greater than about 200 km have positive gravity anomalies, or mascons. The smallest example is

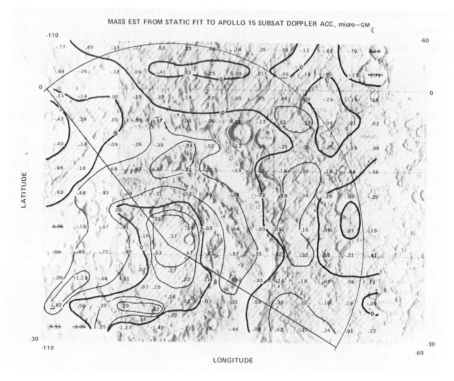

**Fig. 6.1** Mass contour map of region from Grimaldi to Mare Orientale. The heavy contours separate areas of mass excess and deficiency per 3° square units (about 8,000 km²). The values are given as "micromoons" ($10^{-6}$ mass of the moon). Note the excess mass in the center of Orientale, with a mass-deficient belt further out. Areas of mass excess are cross-hatched. (1974, Sjogren, W. L., *Moon.* 9: 115.) (Courtesy W. L. Sjogren.)

Grimaldi (150 km diameter). The positive gravity anomaly over the mare basin Grimaldi (+60 mgal) is just the reverse of the −60 mgal anomaly over the crater Copernicus. The largest anomalies are 220 mgal, under Mare Imbrium and Mare Serenitatis[10]. Smaller positive anomalies exist under the following circular maria: Crisium, Nectaris, Humorum, Humboltianum, Orientale, Smythii, and under Sinus Aestuum and Grimaldi, and some other minor features. Frequently, the anomalies possess a ringlike structure, matching the topography excellently as shown by Mare Orientale. In this example the positive anomaly of +150 mgal is confined to the central, basalt filling[8]. Commonly, negative anomaly rings surround the mascons.

It is now clear that the mascons are near-surface features rather than deep seated. They are most closely simulated by surface disk-shaped bodies rather than deep-buried spherical bodies and show a good correlation between surface area of the mare basalt fill and the size of the mascon[11]. For example, the outer limit of the anomaly in Mare Serenitatis closely matches the main concentric wrinkle ridge system (Fig. 4.1).

(c) Filled craters less than about 200 km in diameter have negative gravity anomalies. Sinus Iridum, the Bay of Rainbows on the coast of the Sea of Rains (Mare Imbrium), possesses a negative anomaly of − 90 mgal.

(d) The lunar highlands are in isostatic equilibrium.

(e) Large mountain ridges, such as the Apennines, have small positive anomalies. This great feature, standing 7 km above Mare Imbrium, has a small positive gravity anomaly of + 85 mgal. If the mass of the Apennines were totally uncompensated, a positive anomaly of + 300 mgal would result, so that some isostatic readjustment has occurred.

These data have wide implications for early lunar history. The lunar crust was hot enough to allow the Apennine ridge to sink to nearly isostatic equilibrium. The other ringed basins are also not seriously out of isostatic adjustment. The Outer Cordillera Mountain ring has a positive anomaly of + 50 mgal, while the small amount of lava in the center of the basin is associated with an anomaly of + 150 mgal. Thus the mountain rings show minor anomalies, while the mascons, occupying the basins show major uncompensated positive anomalies. Hence the mascons must be associated with the later filling of the basins and not with their excavation, for otherwise, isostatic adjustment would have removed them. The Marius Hills, widely interpreted as volcanic domes, superimposed on the basaltic maria, show a positive anomaly of + 65 mgal, indicating again that virtually no late isostatic adjustment has occurred in the mare flooding stage.

Many ingenious suggestions have been made about the origin of the mascons. Central to the problem is the strength of the outer regions of the moon. The seismic data currently reveal a solid stable lithosphere to a depth of about 1,000 km (section 6.4). Since the mascons are clearly associated with the basaltic basin filling, they have existed at least since 3.7–3.2 aeons, so that the outer portions of the moon have been capable of supporting these gravity anomalies for that time.

The moon's crust must therefore have been weak enough at the time of the excavation of the ringed basins to allow some adjustment, but it must have cooled down in the next few hundred million years to support the mascons, and the later volcanism. The lunar crust was cold and rigid at the time of the maria flooding[12]. The partial melting of the lunar interior, which produced the lavas and the mascons, thus took place well beneath the crust, which was not affected structurally by these events. The melting was too deep to allow isostatic compensation to occur. Similarly, some of the last volcanic episodes, the building of the lava domes at the Marius Hills, took place on a crust thick and cold enough to support their mass.

The theories of origin of the mascons form two main groups:

(*a*) External origin. One suggestion is that the mascons are the remnants of the colliding objects (large meteorites, asteroids, or primitive earth satellites), which produced the great maria basins by impact. This is now rendered unlikely by the observation[13] that the mascons are due to flat disk-shaped surface bodies, simulating the maria fill, rather than deeply buried (~ 100 km depth) spherical bodies.

(*b*) Internal origins. The best correlation of mascon masses is with the volume of mare basalt in each basin[14], and the consensus is that the flooding of the ringed basins with basaltic lavas produces the positive gravity anomaly. This involves a net lateral transfer of mass. Objections have been raised to volcanic explanations for mascons on the grounds that excess mass per unit area cannot result simply from transfer upwards of material. However, with only small degrees of partial melting in the interior, it is possible to segregate the lavas from wider areas than their surface outcrop.

There are two reasons for the concentration of lavas initially at the sites of the circular maria. Firstly, the basins are low lying and so tend to fill first. Secondly, the molten lava rising from the interior will be channeled toward the circular maria by the large zones of broken rock and rubble underlying them. The rising molten lavas will first fill the rubble zone either with a mass of minor intrusions or possibly larger coherent masses of gabbro. Subsequently, the basins themselves will fill up, mainly (see section 2.10) by accumulation of thin flows. One suggestion is that the mascons are due to the accumulation of dense iron-titanium oxides on the bottom of large lava lakes during cooling and crystallization of the lunar basalts[15]. This encounters the difficulties that there is little evidence of near-surface fractionation or sinking of such phases (see section 4.19). Possibly such a mechanism might operate where the lavas are ponded, as in the flooded craters. Such ponding might also occur during the first stages of filling of the impact basins, but there is little evidence of such processes even in such apparently favorable sites as the Taurus-Littrow Valley (Apollo 17) or at the Apollo 15 site. Indeed the best direct evidence for thin flows comes from the observations along the edge of Hadley Rille (section 2.10).

Another suggestion is that the mascons are due mainly to the transformation of the lunar basalts to the denser rock, eclogite, at the base of the circular maria. This transformation, at shallow depths and low temperatures (see Fig. 4.37) depends critically on the kinetics of the reactions[16]. Possibly deeper intrusions of gabbro in the breccia zone might transform to eclogite, but the shallow nature of the mascons indicates that the anomalies are not so deep.

One mechanism[17] for the production of the mascons proposes that the ejecta of the ringed basins blankets the surrounding highlands with a low conductivity blanket. This induces melting, and the lavas so generated move laterally to fill the fractured ringed basin. The small amount of fill in Mare Orientale is thought to be due to the excavation of the basin "late in the history of the moon"[17]. Two objections may be noted. (*a*) Old unflooded basins have been discerned on the far side, and further (*b*) the thicker crust on the far side should have caused higher rises in temperature and extensive outpouring of lavas.

The simplest explanation, that the basalt filling the ringed basins produces the shallow disk-shaped mascon, is probably correct. The filling is thin toward the edges of the basin. Thus the negative anomaly ring is a remnant of the original negative gravity anomaly caused by excavation of the ringed basin. The excess mass (800 kg/cm$^2$ in the Serenitatis basin) is equal to the density difference caused by about 20 km of mare basalt emplaced in the anorthositic highland crust.

## 6.3  LUNAR SEISMICITY

### Nature of Lunar Seismic Signals

Critical differences exist between terrestrial seismic records and the signals from the lunar seismometers (Fig. 6.2). There is a very low background noise level, well below that of earth-based seismometers. The moon is so quiet seismically that the seismometers are set at maximum sensitivity, and displacements in some frequency ranges of about 1 A unit ($10^{-8}$ cm) of the lunar surface can be measured.

The most intriguing features of the lunar seismic signals (Figs. 6.3, 6.4)

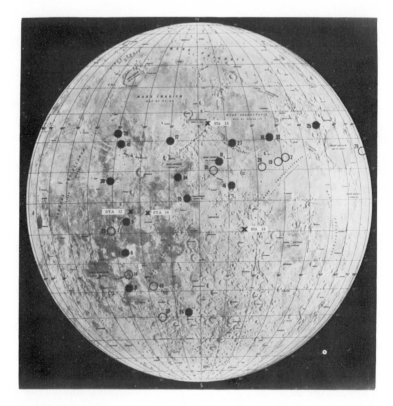

**Fig. 6.2**  Map showing the locations of the stations of the Apollo seismic network and 26 moonquake epicenters. Station numbers indicate the Apollo missions in which the stations were installed. The epicenters are the points on the surface immediately above the active zones (foci) in which moonquakes originate. Solid circles indicate foci for which the depth of the focus can be determined. Open circles correspond to cases in which data are not sufficient for determination of depth. A depth of 800 km has been assumed in these cases. The number at each epicenter is an arbitrary identification code used by the experiment team. Note that in two cases (epicenters 1 and 6, and 18 and 32), the epicenters are so closely spaced that their separation cannot be distinguished at the scale plotted. The epicenter located on the far side of the moon (6°N, 104°E) is not shown[20].

are very low attenuation[18] and a large degree of wave scattering, which are mutually exclusive in most terrestrial experience[19–21]. This scattering occurs mostly in the outer few hundred meters, which is highly heterogeneous, but significant scattering occurs to depths of 10–20 km. The scattering is attributed[22] to the brecciated nature of the upper 20–25 km. The lunar crust appears to be heterogeneous at all size ranges from micrometers to several kilometers. The effective absence of water and volatile constituents causes the seismic signals to propagate with little or no attenuation [22].

The nature of the lunar seismic signals has been reproduced by using an aluminum plate drilled with a large number of holes. The undrilled plate showed a sharp arrival and a rapid dissipation of energy. The signal in the drilled plate showed the same arrival time, but, in contrast, showed a slow buildup to maximum intensity, with much wave scattering, analogous to the lunar signals [19].

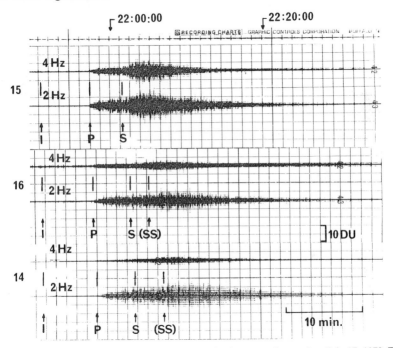

**Fig. 6.3**   Filtered short-period seismograms of seismic events detected on July 17, 1972. The signal is believed to be from a meteoroid impact on the far side of the moon. Numbers at far left indicate Apollo stations. Two traces for two different filter settings are shown for each station. The frequencies given, 4 and 2 Hz, are the center frequencies of the narrow band-pass filters used in the data playback. At these frequencies, the rise and decay times of the seismic wave-trains are sufficiently short so that the compressional- and shear-wave arrivals appear as characteristic bulges in the seismograms. $I$ indicates the estimated time of impact, $P$ the observed arrival time of the direct compressional wave, and $S$ the expected arrival time of direct shear wave (estimated to arrive at about 1.7 min before the peak of the wavetrain in the 4 Hz seismogram). Note that the characteristic shear-wave bulge, clearly visible at station 15, is missing at stations 16 and 14 when expected [20].

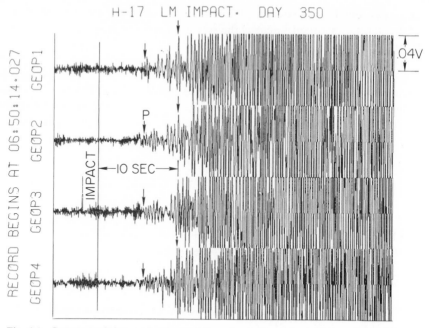

**Fig. 6.4**   Compressed time-scale record of the seismic signal received from the LM impact of the Apollo 17 mission. Arrows point to the onset of first and second arrivals. The first arrow indicates a travel time of 5.75 sec [21].

## Moonquakes

These are all less than about 2 on the Richter scale and so compare only with the smallest of terrestrial earthquakes [20, 23]. The number recorded per year is less than 3,000. The total energy release per year by moonquakes is $2 \times 10^{13}$ ergs, compared to $10^{24}$–$10^{25}$ ergs by earthquakes. The total lunar energy release is less than that of about 1/10 lb (45 g) of TNT. About 10 percent are repetitive, and many sets of nearly identical wave trains are known. This important observation means that the locations and mechanisms are fixed. Also activity occurs usually at a fixed phase of the lunar tidal cycle (Fig. 6.5).

Thirty-seven active moonquake foci have been located. These lie in two belts along great circles. The eastern belt intercepts the western at about 80° in a T-junction. The western belt lies along one of the rays of Tycho, which also, of course, follows a great circle. The moonquakes occur at depths of around 1,000 km, centered on the lithosphere-asthenosphere

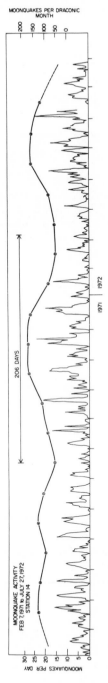

**Fig. 6.5** The number of moonquakes per day detected at Station 14 between February 7, 1971, and July 27, 1972. Peaks in activity occur at two-week intervals. A longer-term variation in moonquake activity, with a period of 206 days, is also seen in the monthly activity plot shown above the daily count. This corresponds to the period of the tidal variation introduced by solar perturbation of the lunar orbit [20].

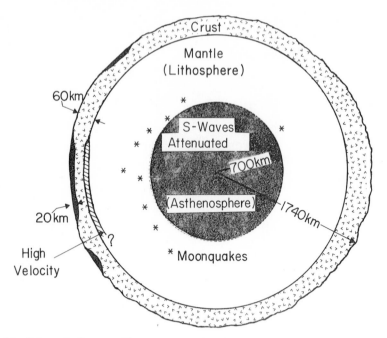

**Fig. 6.6**   Schematic diagram of lunar structure showing zone of moonquakes. The near side is to the left of the figure—maria are shown by solid shading. The possible limited extent of the high-velocity zone is indicated[25].

boundary. Fig. 6.2 shows the surface distribution and Fig. 6.6 shows the depth distribution.

### Tectonic Activity on the Moon

The moon is almost inert compared with the earth. Tidal energy, not heat energy as in the earth, is the driving force for the weak lunar seismic events. The thick lunar lithosphere is stable, and moonquake activity is concentrated at the transition region between lithosphere and asthenosphere (Fig. 6.6). There is thus a great contrast between the active, unstable thin lithosphere of the earth driven by an active thermal engine and the stable lithosphere of the moon, which is an order of magnitude thicker[23–25].

The lack of shallow seismic activity means that the moon is neither expanding nor contracting at present. Hence the outward flow of heat balances the rate of heat production. Among the early predictions of lunar seismic activity was the expectation that moonquakes would occur along the straight rilles, which so greatly resemble terrestrial grabens. The absence of this type of surface activity was only one of many surprises in store on the moon.

## 6.4   STRUCTURE OF THE LUNAR INTERIOR

The structure of the regolith, the upper 1 km, the lunar crust, the lunar lithosphere (60–1,000 km), and the asthenosphere, or "core," are treated in the following sections. The seismic data elucidating the structure of the regolith and upper kilometer or so come mainly from the Apollo 17 seismic profiling experiment[26]. For depths down to 150 km, information comes mainly from data recorded on the seismic network from the Saturn IV B booster and LM ascent stage impacts. Source to station distances range from 8.7 to 1750 km. Seismic signals from distant meteorite impacts and from moonquakes provide data for regions below 150 km[19–21, 23–25].

### Regolith Structure

The regolith has uniform properties on a moon-wide basis. The seismic *P*-wave velocities are low ($105 \pm 8$ m/sec) and uniform. The variation in thickness is small (less than one order of magnitude), as shown in Table 6.1. Although it might be expected that the highland regolith would be

**Table 6.1**   *P*-wave Velocity and Thickness of the Regolith at the Apollo Sites.

| Mission | Velocity (m/sec) | Thickness | | Geologic setting |
|---|---|---|---|---|
| | | Craters (m) | Seismic (m) | |
| 11 | — | 3–6 | — | Mare |
| 12 | 108 | 2–4 | — | Mare |
| 14 | 104 | — | 8.5 | Highlands |
| 15 | 92 | 5 | — | Mare |
| 16 | — | — | 12.2 | Highlands |
| 17 | — | 3–20 | 6.2–36.9 | Restricted mare |

Although mare basalt underlies the Apollo 17 site, the site is in a small valley surrounded by highlands and is located within a local crater field, which probably accounts for the unusual range of regolith thickness values[27].

very much thicker than that developed on the maria, in fact the final evolution of the highland landscape does not predate that of the maria surfaces by a large time interval. We know that basin-forming impacts were occurring as late as 3.9 aeons (Imbrium), while the presently visible mare basalt flooding began rather shortly thereafter. Many old regoliths must be buried beneath the great ejecta blankets of the highlands. The regolith whose properties we now measure developed on the ejecta blankets from the last basins and began to accumulate about 3.9 aeons ago. In this context, the thickness of the regolith at the Apollo 14 site at Fra Mauro is consistent with an Imbrium [27] rather than an older age [28]. The seismic data clearly reveal that the material is not "dust," but that it is composed of "rock debris."

### Lunar Sounder

This experiment, flown on the last mission [29], used radar techniques in an attempt to probe the subsurface area of the moon to a depth of 1–2 km. It is possible that this technique could enable detection of buried ejecta blankets, lava deltas, rille and wrinkle ridge structures, fine structure at ringed basin scarps, depth of regolith, and so forth. Much of the data evaluation is still in the preliminary stages, since transcription from film, on which the signals were recorded, is still in progress. The amount of subsurface scattering, critical for the method, has still to be evaluated.

### Upper 1 km (Taurus-Littrow Site)

Detailed structural interpretations became possible only on the final Apollo 17 mission to Taurus-Littrow, using the Lunar Seismic Profiling Experiment [26]. Eight explosive charges were laid by the astronauts. In addition, the impact of the LM ascent stage was only 8.7 km from the landing site. These events were recorded on a seismic array and revealed the subsurface structure at Taurus-Littrow to a depth of several kilometers. The depth of the mare basalt filling the valley is interpreted to be 1,200 m. Sampling to a depth of about 100 m has occurred at Camelot Crater. The rocks appear to be part of a flow unit. If the valley had been the site of a deep lava lake, extensive fractionation would have been expected during cooling. This does not seem to have taken place. Note that the total thickness is about half that of the exposed portion of the Skaergaard intrusion.

The upper layers [21] below the regolith have a seismic velocity of 200–300 m/sec, and there is an abrupt change to 1,000 m/sec at a depth of about 250 m. [30]. Such velocity changes are observed with depth in many terrestrial lava flows and indicate no change in rock type. At 1,200 m, the velocity changes abruptly to 4 km/sec, and this is interpreted as the base of the mare basalt valley filling. The interpretation given here is consistent with the gravity data and the geological evidence such as the observation of basaltic layers in the walls of Camelot Crater. Other views, that the maria basins are filled by dust, increasingly compacted with depth [31, 32] are refuted by these depth-velocity data. The dust-filling hypothesis predicts a smooth increase of seismic velocity with depth, not the stepwise jumps actually encountered. The interpretation here is that the upper meters are extensively fractured by small impacts and that some fracturing extends to deeper levels in the mare basalt.

## Lunar Crust

The average crustal thickness is 61 km, but there appear to be considerable differences between the near side and far side highlands [33]. The thickness of the latter is calculated by Kaula [33] at 74 km, and that of the near side highlands as 48 km. The mean density difference between maria and highlands is 0.4 g/cm$^3$. Most evidence for this is available for the eastern Oceanus Procellarum region and indicates a two-layered crust. Below about 1 km and extending downward to about 25 km, the measured velocities fit those of lunar basalt [25].

## The 25-km Discontinuity

At a depth of 25 km beneath the maria, there is an increase in the velocity of the lunar seismic compressional ($P$) waves. The velocity slowly increases to just below 6 km/sec at the 25 km depth. The velocity then sharply increases to 6.8 km/sec within a kilometer and then increases slowly to 7 km/sec at 60 km. These changes are illustrated in Fig. 6.7.

What is the significance of the abrupt velocity increase at 25 km? The sharp velocity increase at 25 km may indicate an absence of microcracks below that depth. The very slow increase in velocity from 25 to 60 km (only about 0.2 km/sec) is evidence of a uniform material; and this velocity ($\sim 7$ km/sec) is close to the intrinsic velocity of lunar samples.

If such an explanation is valid, what is the reason for the absence of cracks below 25 km? The pressure at this depth in the moon is 1.2 kbar, insufficient to close up the crevices. The sharp increase is also not consistent with the gradual boundary expected from pressure closing of the cracks. Like all natural transitions, except chemical discontinuities or

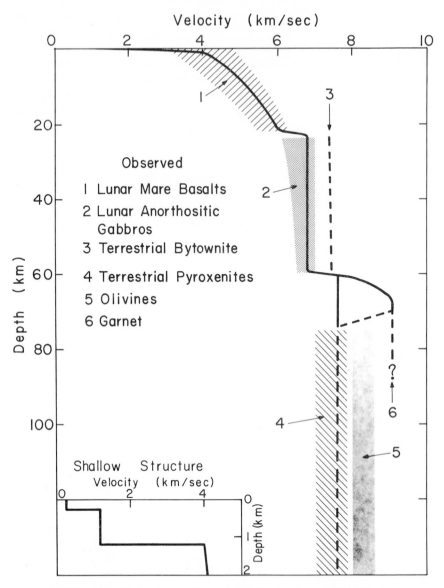

**Fig. 6.7** Comparison of the compressional velocity profile for the lunar crust and upper zones derived from seismic measurements, and the velocities of several types of lunar and terrestrial rocks. The velocity model is shown by a heavy line (or dashed heavy line where the model is uncertain). The lunar basalts for which velocities have been measured include samples from different sites. Region 2 ("anorthositic gabbro") is bounded by Apollo 16 aluminous rocks 68415 at the high-velocity bound and 62295 and 65015 at the low-velocity bound. Pyroxenites cover a wide range of composition. The garnet field is an average value for high-pressure phases of anorthite-rich rocks. Olivines cover the range 75–100 percent forsterite[25].

liquid-solid boundaries, a zone rather than a sharp boundary would be anticipated. Simmons[34] notes that two hypotheses appear equally plausible: (a) "the rocks now below 25 km have never been shock metamorphosed and the rocks now at 25 to 60 km were formed after all large impacts ceased, or (b) the rocks now below 25 km were shock metamorphosed and the shock effects have since been annealed."

## 25–60 km

From 25 to 60 km, the seismic velocity is steady at about 7 km/sec (Fig. 6.7), consistent with velocities observed in lunar anorthositic gabbros, which are typically average highland compositions. The uniform velocity argues for competent rock, without microcracks. The velocities match those of rock types 15415, 68415, and 65015 (all highland breccias) when these are corrected for microfracturing effects.

## 60–150 km

There is a velocity increase to 7.7 km/sec at 60 km. This is taken as marking the base of the crust. It is a compositional rather than a phase boundary, consistent with a change from anorthositic gabbro to an underlying pyroxene-olivine layer with density of at least 3.4 g/cm$^3$ (Fig. 6.7). There is some evidence of a higher velocity zone (9 km/sec), of limited extent, just beneath the crust, as shown in Figs. 6.6 and 6.7. The reality of this layer, which in any event would be very localized, has yet to be confirmed.

## 150–1,000 km

In the depth range of 150–1,000 km, the seismic velocities are fairly uniform (7.7–8.3 km/sec)[25]. The material is solid and rigid and stable. Moonquakes occur only at the bottom of this layer. There is no melting, and the attenuation of seismic waves is very low.

By analogy with the earth, the whole zone from 60 to 1,000 km could be called the "lithosphere." The terrestrial term "mantle," with its many chemical, mineralogical, and tectonic implications should be avoided. There is some recent evidence[35] for a minor discontinuity at about 300 km.

## 1,000–1,738 km (The "Asthenosphere")

The announcement in November, 1972, that a portion of the interior of the moon was partially molten ranks high among the many exciting discoveries about the moon. The evidence came from the impact of a large meteorite (weighing about 1 ton) on the far side of the moon in July, 1972. $P$ waves were transmitted, with slightly lower velocities through the moon, but $S$ (shear) waves, which are not transmitted through liquids, were missing (Fig. 6.3) indicating a central zone of 600–800 km radius at a depth of about 1,000 km. Either the shear waves did not propagate at all or were so highly attenuated as not to be recorded.

The transition to the melting zone is gradual, not sharp. The $P$-wave velocities[35] decrease by 0.3 km/sec, a slight drop compared with the mantle core interface in the earth, where the $P$-wave velocity drops by about 5 km/sec. Thus this zone in the moon is neither completely molten nor a phase change. The analogy is much closer to that of the "low velocity zone" in the earth's upper mantle than with the core. This has led to the rather general use of the term "lunar asthenosphere" (Fig. 6.8). The limits for an iron core, as noted earlier, set by the density and moment of inertia are about 400 km radius, much deeper than partial melting zone discussed here. An Fe-FeS core radius of 700 km is permitted by the data (section 6.1).

## 6.5   TEMPERATURES WITHIN THE MOON

### Heat Flow

The heat flow measurements[36] have had less good fortune than most other lunar surface experiments. A heat-flow probe was on board the abortive Apollo 13 mission. It was not carried on Apollo 14. The first measurements were made at the Hadley Apennines (LM) site on the mare surface, where a value of 0.74 heat flow units (HFU)[37] were measured. This was a surprisingly high result, equal to half the terrestrial average value of about 1.5 HFU. The eagerly awaited result from the highlands site at Descartes was lost due to a broken cable. Some variation with depth was encountered in one probe at the Apollo 17 site, but the heat flow at the bottom of the holes (1.3 and 2.3 m depth, respectively) was 0.67 HFU, similar to that at the Apollo 15 site. The total range in values was from 0.4 to 1.1 HFU. The variations are probably due to perturbations from subsurface boulders[38].

The equality in the average heat flows (about 0.7 HFU) at the two different sites widely separated on the moon, indicates that the high values observed are probably not local but are typical of wide areas. The average uranium content in the whole moon is 0.060 ppm if this heat flow

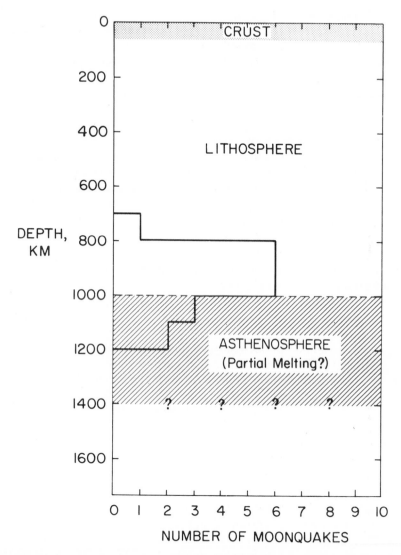

**Fig. 6.8** The asthenosphere, in which partial melting is believed to occur, may extend to the center of the moon, or it may be restricted to a thin shell at a depth of about 1,000 km. Question marks in the zone labeled "asthenosphere" indicate that present data are not sufficient to define the inward extent of this zone. A histogram of the depth distribution of moonquakes is also shown[20].

value is moon-wide. Appropriate Th and K contents, derived from Th/U and K/U ratios, are 0.16 ppm and 120 ppm, respectively. Most of the heat flow is due to the uranium and thorium contents. The element abundances for U, Th, and K provide exceedingly important geochemical constraints, as will become apparent in chapter 7.

### Electrical Conductivity

Since the conductivity of the earth[39] is not well defined after many years of effort, it is perhaps too much to expect early enlightenment from the lunar studies. Lunar electrical conductivity measurements can be made by recording the electromagnetic response of the moon to the magnetic field variations in the solar wind[41]. It is also possible to convert the electrical conductivity profiles to temperatures at depths within the moon. The basic information is obtained from the surface magnetometers and orbiting craft[41]. Conversion to a temperature profile is beset with difficulty, since the composition of the interior has to be inferred from other evidence.

The first results[41] showed a conductivity "spike" at a depth of 240 km, but other work[42] showed that a two-layer model with a boundary at 160 km depth was consistent with the same data, and the spike is not a unique or necessary feature[43]. To establish the temperature, Sonnett[41] used for calibration purposes an olivine composition containing some ferric iron. Other workers[44] pointed out the difficulties of extrapolating from laboratory data. Thus, by using olivine with low $Fe^{2+}$, a 100-fold drop in conductivity resulted. Hence the early temperature profiles[41] are much too low.

The latest values for the conductivity of the interior are shown in Fig. 6.9, from the work of Dyal and coauthors[45]. Using the assumption that the lunar interior is composed of olivine, they calculate a temperature profile with depth[45], shown in Fig. 6.10. The curve based on the geomagnetic tail data yields a temperature of 1,500°C at the critical depth of 1,000 km, where the seismic data indicate that some melt is present. There is reasonable agreement that the range of present day temperatures in the lunar interior rises steadily to about 1,000°C at 700 km depth[37]. Below this depth, the values diverge, with estimates[37] for the temperature at the center of the moon lying between 1,000°C and 1,600°C.

A very large number of thermal models for the moon have been proposed based on these data. They tend to favor an initially hot moon[37], but it is too early for a proper evaluation of the many models.

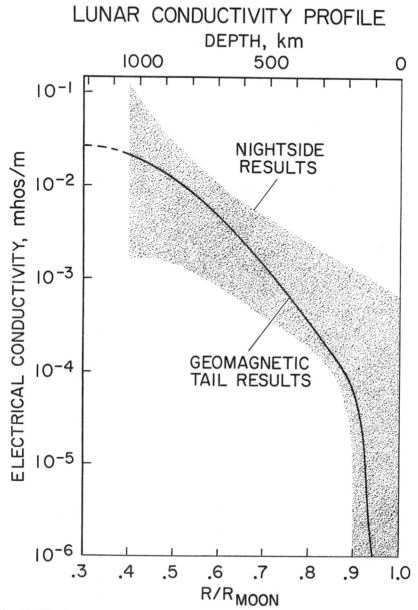

**Fig. 6.9** The lunar conductivity distribution with depth within the moon[45]. (Courtesy Palmer Dyal.)

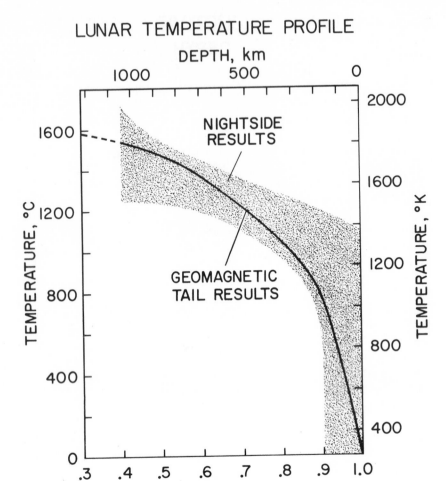

**Fig. 6.10**   The distribution of temperature with depth within the moon calculated from the conductivity data[45]. (Courtesy Palmer Dyal.)

## 6.6   LUNAR MAGNETISM

Strong planetary magnetic fields are not presently common in the solar system, with only Earth and Jupiter having fields appreciably stronger than that due to the solar wind in their vicinity. In contrast to the present magnetic field strength of the earth of 60,000 gamma[40] at the equator, the general lunar field, measured by the Explorer satellites, was vanishingly small. Accordingly, expectations of significant magnetic information were not high, and no equipment for measuring the magnetic field was carried on the Apollo 11 mission.

Among the surprises carried by the returned Apollo 11 samples was evidence of a stable natural remnant magnetism (NRM), indicative of an ancient field, now vanished. The surface magnetometer experiment[46] on Apollo 12 measured a remnant magnetic field of 38 gamma. Only 6 gamma was recorded at the Hadley-Apennine site, again on mare basalt.

The highland sites, in contrast to the maria, showed evidence of higher fields. At the Apollo 14 Fra Mauro site, values of 43 and 103 gamma were obtained at two separate locations, and 121 to 313 gamma at the Apollo 16 Descartes site. The last value was measured at North Ray crater rim and is the highest recorded on the moon. These relatively strong surface fields in the highlands affect both the implantation of outgassed ions and the accretion of solar wind particles[46].

These ground-based observations were extended by measurements made by an orbiting magnetometer aboard "subsatellites" launched from the Apollo 15 and 16 command modules[47]. The Apollo 15 system operated for 6 months. Local magnetic anomalies on the lunar surface were observed for the first time. Most of the measurements of lunar fields are made during the five days around full-moon when the moon is in the geomagnetic tail of the earth. This provides a relatively low noise environment for mapping the lunar surface magnetic fields.

Around new-moon, the moon is in the hypersonic flow of the solar wind when measurements are again possible, although these relate to the interaction of the solar wind with the moon. In between these periods, the moon passes through the turbulent "magnetosheath," an area of shocked solar wind plasma surrounding the magnetotail. These relationships are shown in Fig. 6.11.

The most important observation from the subsatellite systems was the moon-wide nature of the remnant magnetism. It also proved possible to map these magnetic fields. The most notable anomaly was found to be near, although not entirely coincident with, the crater Van der Graff. These magnetic anomalies may be related to the distribution of highlands plains-forming-type deposits like the Cayley formation[47, 49], although later fine-scale mapping does not show close correspondence between topography and field strength. Perhaps buried Cayley-type deposits are involved.

The magnetic field directions and magnitudes are variable on a kilome-

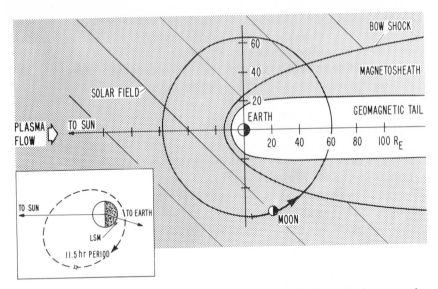

**Fig. 6.11**   Orbit of the moon projected onto the solar ecliptic plane. During a complete revolution around the earth, the moon passes through the earth's bow shock, the magnetosheath, the geomagnetic tail, and the interplanetary region dominated by solar plasma fields. The insert shows an orbit of the Explorer 35 spacecraft, also projected onto the solar ecliptic plane [48].

ter scale, as shown especially by the measurements at the Descartes site. Very strong but local fields were measured during the final few passes across the surface at low altitudes by the Apollo 16 subsatellite, just before crashing. The high values are associated with the "Cayley-type" formation crater fillings on the far side.

**Remnant Magnetism**

Magnetic data provide many potential constraints on planetary evolution and history. For example, the presence or absence of a conducting core may be inferred. Hence the report of a stable remnant magnetism (NRM) in the Apollo 11 samples excited much interest.

Two components are present in the lunar rocks. One is a "soft" component, most of which is acquired through exposure to magnetic fields during sample return from the moon. This was demonstrated by returning a demagnetized Apollo 12 basalt, 12002, with a very low "hard" component, to the moon during the Apollo 16 mission. The sample reacquired its "soft" component, indicating that this was at least in part an artifact of the trip [50].

The hard component is of lunar origin. The basalts have stable remnant magnetizations with intensities of $1–2 \times 10^{-6}$ emu/g. Some breccias have much larger intensities on the order of $1 \times 10^{-4}$ emu/g, accounting for the observed surface anomalies. This increase is correlated with the increase in total metallic iron in the breccias and to changes in grain size. The samples collected on the present surface had random magnetic orientation. Thus they were magnetized before being excavated by meteorite impact and thrown onto the lunar surface.

### Magnetic Mineralogy

Metallic iron has been identified as the dominant magnetic material in lunar samples[49] since most Curie temperatures are around 750–770°C, close to that for pure iron. This is in contrast to the earth, where the major magnetic materials are the Fe oxides within the system $FeO-TiO_2-Fe_2O_3$. Most of this iron is very fine and is attributed, because of its low nickel content, to autoreduction in glass spherules formed during impact. No magnetic effects attributable to troilite have been noted, indicating that the troilite is stoichiometric FeS.

The identification of the magnetic phase in lunar fines as metallic iron appears to have been confirmed by electron spin resonance (ESR) techniques[51], refuting earlier suggestions that hematite, magnetite, or ferric oxides with magnetite-type lattices were present[52, 53]. The magnetic mineralogy indicates that highly reducing conditions were present. The lack of $Fe^{3+}$ in ilmenite and ulvöspinel is indicated by their lack of ferrimagnetic properties. Magnetite appears to be absent, except for one possible occurrence in the Apollo 17 orange soil. Thus the magnetic data support the petrological interpretations of extreme reducing conditions.

### Magnetic Field Intensity

Only a few well-established measurements from which the intensity of the ancient magnetic field could be inferred have been carried out. These fall in the range from about 600 to 3,000 gammas[54]. These measurements are in general accord with the estimates by previous workers[53]. Some values as high as 1.6 Oersted (160,000 gammas) have been reported[55]. If correct, these high values would drastically change current thinking about the origin of the lunar field, but further confirmation is needed.

A value of 2,100 gamma for an Apollo 15 mare breccia[54] indicates that the field was still in existence at 3.3 aeons. Since the age of the breccia is younger than that of the lavas, the field may have persisted to periods less than 3.0 aeons. The establishment of the actual age of the breccia in question (15498) would be of interest.

No measurements are yet available of intensity versus time. Such measurements could help establish the origin of the field. Thus a permanent field might decay steadily with time, whereas a dynamo-generated field might, by analogy with that of the earth, show periodic fluctuations, and reversals and would run until freezing of the core. Further, we have as yet no indications of any overall magnetic field direction.

### Soils and Breccias [Magnetic Properties]

All varieties, from incoherent soils to totally recrystallized rocks are known.

(*a*) The unwelded breccias resemble the soils. Most of the iron particles are less than 150 A in diameter, and they have low thermorem-nance. The magnetic component in the soils is in the finest-grain size[56].

(*b*) The intermediate grades of breccias are dominated by single domain iron (150–300 A grain size) and possess a strong thermoremnance.

(*c*) The highly recrystallized breccias (grades 7–8) contain multidomain iron (> 300 A grain size) and do not carry a strong remnant magnetism. In this they resemble the igneous rocks from the maria, except that they tend to be magnetically inhomogeneous and contain a high content of metallic iron. Using these criteria, the anorthositic gabbro 68415 is not igneous but a strongly recrystallized breccia, a view in accord with the chemical and age characteristics of the sample. Experiments have shown that annealing at temperatures below 900°C, the fine-grained iron (100 A) typical of soils and soil breccias is produced[57]. At higher temperatures, coarser grains up to micrometer size are produced by autoreduction processes.

This correlation of iron grain size and content with metamorphic grade indicates how the breccias have both higher metallic iron contents than the maria basalts and higher thermoremnant magnetism. The 300-gamma field at Descartes could be produced by about 1 km thickness of breccia of intermediate grade with intensities of $10^{-4}$ emu/g. The implication is that this would have been heated (> 770°C) and uniformly magnetized as one unit, thus placing severe time constraints on the mode of origin of the Cayley formation.

## 6.7  ORIGIN OF THE LUNAR MAGNETIC FIELD

A strong moon-wide lunar magnetic field, with an intensity of a few thousand gammas, was present at least during the period 4.0–3.2 aeons, but has now disappeared. Thus the field was either a long-lived lunar feature or the result of many transient events.

What is the source of the field? There is considerable diversity of opinion, and the wide variety of explanations offered bear witness to the fertile imagination of *Homo sapiens.* The only consensus appears to be that the lunar rocks became magnetized as they cooled through the Curie temperature for metallic iron ($\sim 750°C$). The total lack of agreement on the nature of the field responsible may indicate that we are not asking the relevant questions. The ultimate importance of the magnetic evidence for placing constraints on lunar evolution is apparent. Even a small field will affect the solar wind and so cause changes in the regolith environment (see chapter 3).

Whether or not there was a core is of vital interest to the question of moon-wide melting, the geochemical fate of the siderophile elements, the temperature of accretion, and the subsequent thermal history. Thus, workers from many diverse disciplines await with keen interest the resolution of the magnetic problems. The most popular hypotheses are:

(*a*) The field was generated as in the earth, by a molten conducting core.

(*b*) A permanent magnetic field, now lost, was imprinted on a cold moon early in its history.

Before discussing these, some of the other suggestions are considered.

(*a*) *Earth's field.* The present magnetic field of the earth at the Roche limit (2.4 earth radii) is 4,000 gamma. If the moon had been just outside the Roche limit, the appropriate field would be available. A major difficulty lies in keeping the moon at such a close distance for more than 1 billion years. Very large tidal effects would have been present during the extrusion of the maria basalts. There seems to be no evidence of this or other features indicating such a close approach.

(*b*) *Enhanced solar wind field* [58]. It is possible that the solar wind field, at present about 10 gamma, was 100 times more intense. While such strong fields may exist in early stages of stellar evolution, it would be necessary to maintain this high value for more than 1 aeon, with a steady component along the axis of rotation of the moon. This seems unlikely.

(*c*) *Enhanced solar field* [58]. A solar field of $2 \times 10^5$ gauss would provide the necessary effect. This is about an order of magnitude higher than presently observed stellar fields. Such activity is unlikely to occur from a main sequence star and persist for 1 billion years, when all geological evidence points toward a sun similar to the present-day one at least during the period 3.5–3.0 aeons. A major difficulty with this and with all external field theories is that it is very difficult to provide a steady field in a single direction over expected cooling times.

(d) *Impact-generated fields.* Very many suggestions that the magnetic effects are in some manner connected with impact processes have been made. A review of these has been given by Fuller[55]. The large scale and number of impact events lends some credence to these theories, but experimental evidence is lacking and unlikely to be easily obtained.

(e) *Fluid core model.* This model is popular since the origin of the earth's field is due to dynamo action in the Ni-Fe conducting core. Several problems beset the direct application of such a model to the moon. Most thermal models do not allow the lunar interior to reach the melting point of iron or iron-nickel alloy. Although temperatures above 1,000°C are reached, these are not sufficient to provide the temperatures needed (1,700°C). A possible solution is that a core might be composed of an Fe-Ni-FeS eutectic mixture, with a melting temperature of about 940°C [59]. Apart from the geophysical and geochemical problems posed by a core (section 6.4), it is uncertain whether a small core would sustain a dynamo field, with widely divergent opinions expressed[55]. One problem is that the lunar interior is hot enough today (>940°C) for such a core to be molten, and hence possibly generate a magnetic field[59].

(f) *Raisin model.* In this variation, small pockets of molten iron collect during differentiation, and act as small dynamos[60, 61]. A variation of this would be the interaction of molten magma with the solar wind[62]. Again one faces the problem of maintaining such fields over long periods. They do not explain the magnetization of the breccias. Most of the maria basalts were extruded as thin flows so that accumulation of molten iron pockets or the formation of deep lava lakes (except very locally) are petrologically very unlikely.

(g) *Permanent magnet model.* For more than 300 years, the only explanation of the earth's magnetic field was that it was due to permanent magnetism. This theory eventually failed to account for rapidly varying terrestrial field changes and many other features and was discarded and effectively forgotton until recently resurrected[63]. The model depends on accretion of the moon from a sphere of dust and gas in which the solids settled. As contraction occurs, the temperature rises, and eventually the outer solid layers melt. High magnetic fields will occur in the contracting gas sphere, perhaps due to an enhanced solar field: the remnant magnetization of some meteorites may be evidence of this. A variation of this hypothesis is proposed[64] and supposes that the moon became magnetized by an early field of perhaps 20 gauss, either through close approach to the earth or because of enhanced solar wind reaction. The cold inner portion of the moon (below 780°C) is magnetized while the exterior is hot. This would most likely be at ~4.6 aeons or shortly thereafter. Subsequently, the crust cools and becomes magnetized. Next the interior heats above 780°C and erases the internal field, so that no field is now observed.

This is an ingenious suggestion, although it has some difficulties. The temperature rise in the lunar interior produces partial melting and lunar basalts at 3.7 aeons and continues to 3.16 aeons. Only after this event is the field erased, although it would seem that the internal melting causing the mare basalt flooding might erase the internal field too soon.

In summary, no clear solution to the problem is in sight. From the number and variety of the proposed solutions, it seems that we either do not have sufficient evidence, or are not addressing the appropriate questions. More data from orbital-type investigations is needed. Thus, for example, random directions of fields would rule out both the dynamo and external applied fields. Increases of field intensity with time would rule out the permanent field as would magnetic reversals.

## REFERENCES AND NOTES

1. Kaula, W. M., et al. (1974) *LS V*: 399; Gast, P. W., and Giuli, R. T. (1972) *EPSL*. 16: 299.
2. Solomon, S. C., and Toksöz, M. N. (1973) *PEPI*. 7: 15.
3. Bender, P. L., et al. (1973) *Science*. 182: 229.
4. Williams, J. G., et al. (1974) *LS V*: 845.
5. Kaula, W. M. (1969) *Science*. 166: 1581.
6. Liu, A. S., and Laing, P. A. (1971) *Science*. 173: 1017; Michael, W. H., and Blackshear, W. T. (1971) *Moon*. 3: 388.
7. Muller, P. M., and Sjogren, W. L. (1968) *Science*. 161: 680.
8. Sjogren, W. L., et al. (1972) NASA SP 289, 20-1; (1973) NASA SP 315, 24-1; NASA SP 330, 14-1; (1974) *LS V*: 712.
9. Sjogren, W. L. (1974) *Moon*. 9: 115.
10. 1 mgal is 1/1,000 of the cgs unit of gravity, the gal. The normal value of gravity for the earth is 980 gals. The accuracy of measurement of the lunar gravity field is ±5 mgals.
11. Phillips, R. J., et al. (1974) *LS V*: 596.
12. Urey, H. C., and MacDonald, J. G. F. (1971) *Phys. Astron. Moon.*, Academic Press, 213.
13. Sjogren, W. L. (1972) *Moon*. 4: 411.
14. Hartmann, W. K., and Wood, C. A. (1971) *Moon*. 3: 3.

15. O'Hara, M. J., et al. (1970) *PLC 1*: 695.
16. Ringwood, A. E., and Essene, E. (1970) *PLC 1*: 796.
17. Arkani-Hamed, J. (1973) *PLC 4*: 2673.
18. This corresponds to high values of the seismic parameter Q, which has typical values in the range 10–300 for the earth, but is an order of magnitude higher (3,000–5,000) for the moon. Values up to 5,000 are given[22] for the upper 5 km.
19. Toksöz, M. N., et al. (1973) *GSA Abstracts*, 843.
20. Latham, G., et al. (1973) *PLC 4*: 2518; (1972) NASA SP 289, 8-1; NASA SP 315, 9-1; (1973) NASA SP 330, 11-1.
21. Kovach, R. L., and Watkins, J. S. (1973) *PLC 4*: 2550.
22. Toksöz, M. N., et al. (1974) *LS V*: 801.
23. Lammlein, D., et al. (1974) *EOS*. 55: 328.
24. Press, F. (1974) *EOS*. 55: 323.
25. Toksöz, M. N., et al. (1973) *PLC 4*: 2539; Solomon, S. C., and Toksöz, M. N. (1973) *PEPI*. 7: 15.
26. Kovach, R. L., et al. (1973) NASA SP 330, 10-1.
27. Watkins, J. S., and Kovach, R. L. (1973) *PLC 4*: 2561.
28. Schonfeld, E., and Meyer, C. (1973) *PLC 4*: 125.
29. Phillips, R. J., et al. (1973) NASA SP 330, 22-1.
30. Duennebier, F. K., et al. (1974) *LS V*: 183.
31. Gold, T., and Soter, S. (1970) *Science*. 169: 1071.
32. Gangli, A. F. (1972) *Moon*. 4: 40.
33. Kaula, W. M., et al. (1974) *LS V*: 399.
34. Simmons, G., et al. (1973) *Science*. 182: 158.
35. Latham, G., et al. (1974) *LS V*: 434; Nakamura, Y., et al. (1973) *Science*. 181: 49; (1974) *Geophys. Res. Lett.*, 1: 137.
36. Langseth, M. G., et al. (1972) NASA SP 289, 11-1; (1973) NASA SP 330, 9-1. One heat flow unit (HFU) $= 10^{-6}$ cal/cm$^2$ per sec.
37. See for example Toksöz, M. N., et al. (1974) *Moon*. 9: 31; *Icarus*, 21: 389. Fricker, P. E., et al. (1974) *Moon*. 9: 211.
38. Langseth, M. G., et al. (1973) *LS IV*: 455.
39. Parker, J. (1971) *Geophys. J.* 22: 121.
40. One gamma $= 10^{-5}$ Oersted. The Oersted is the cgs unit of magnetic field strength.
41. Sonnett, C. P., et al. (1971) *Nature*. 230: 359.
42. Knuckes, A. F. (1971) *Nature*. 232: 249.
43. Dyal, P., and Parkin, C. W. (1973) *PEPI*. 7: 251.
44. Duba, A., et al. (1972) *EPSL*. 15: 301; Duba, A., and Ringwood, A. E. (1973) *EPSL*. 18: 158; Olhoeft, G. R., et al. (1974) *Moon*. 9: 79; Toksöz, M. N., and Solomon, S. C. (1973) *Moon*. 7: 251.
45. Dyal, P., et al. (1974) *LS V*: 193.
46. Dyal, P., et al. (1970) NASA SP 235, 55; (1972) NASA SP 289, 9-1; NASA SP 315, 11-1.
47. Coleman, P. J., et al. (1972) NASA SP 289, 22-1; NASA SP 315, 23-1; Russell, C. T., et al. (1973) *PLC 4*: 2833.
48. Dyal, P., et al. (1973) *PLC 4*: 2925.
49. Pearce, G. W., et al. (1973) *PLC 4*: 3045.
50. Pearce, G. W., and Strangway, D. W. (1972) NASA SP 315, 7-55.
51. Tsay, F., et al. (1973) *GCA*. 37: 1201.
52. Tsay, F., et al. (1973) *PLC 4*: 2751.

53. Nagata, T., et al. (1973) *PLC 4*: 3019.
54. Gose, W. A., et al. (1973) *Moon.* 7: 196 and personal communication.
55. Fuller, M. (1974) *Rev. Geophys. Space Phys.* 12: 23. This paper gives an excellent review of the whole field of lunar magnetism and provides appropriate skeptical comments on current theories.
56. Usselmann, T. W., and Pearce, G. W. (1974) *LS V*: 809.
57. Pearce, G. W., et al. (1973) *LS IV*: 585.
58. Nagata, T., et al. (1972) *PLC 3*: 2423.
59. Solomon, S. C., and Toksöz, M. N. (1973) *PEPI.* 7: 15.
60. Pearce, G. W., et al. (1972) *PLC 3*: 2449.
61. Murthy, V. R., and Bannerjee, S. K. (1973) *Moon.* 7: 149.
62. Nagata, T., et al. (1971) *PLC 2*: 2461.
63. Runcorn, K., and Urey, H. C. (1973) *Science.* 180: 636.
64. Strangway, D. W., et al. (1973) *LS IV*: 697.

CHAPTER 7

# The Origin and Evolution
# of the Moon

It is impossible to contemplate the spectacle of the starry universe without
wondering how it was formed: perhaps we ought to wait to look for a solution until
we have patiently assembled the elements, and until we have thereby acquired
some hope of finding a solution; but if we were so reasonable, if we were curious
without impatience, it is probable that we would never have created Science and
that we would always have been content with a trivial existence.

Poincaré (1913)

## 7.1 THE NEW MOON

The Apollo missions have revolutionized our knowledge of the moon,
and a first-order increase in understanding of lunar processes has resulted. This has rendered all previous theories obsolete, a situation that
has had many parallels in science and history[1].

Many books and papers have discussed in detail the pre-Apollo theories
on the origin of the moon[2]. Many of these hypotheses now belong, like
that of the lunar origin of tektites, to the realm of the historians of science
rather than to the domains of its active practitioners.

Many surprises awaited the lunar scientists. The clarification of many
enigmas from the rather limited set of data is a remarkable tribute to the
value of scientific inquiry and demonstrates its essentially empirical
nature. The capabilities of *Homo sapiens* for deriving truths from pure
thought seem to have been largely exhausted by the Greek philosophers
(with occasional later insights). Further advances in knowledge must rely
upon the facts produced by the rational and skeptical methods of
science[3].

Accordingly, it has seemed valuable to look at the boundary conditions imposed by the new data. These are divided into geological, age, geophysical, petrological, and geochemical constraints. Consideration of these enables resolution of the homogeneous versus heterogeneous accretion argument. Estimates of the composition of the whole moon can thus be made. Evaluation of all the available information enables a model for the geochemical evolution of the moon to be attempted.

These findings allow constraints to be placed on the hypotheses of lunar origin. Our understanding of the ultimate origin of the moon has not advanced as rapidly as our knowledge of its later evolution. A discussion of pre- and post-Apollo attempts is given, although it is concluded that data from other satellite systems, notably the inner moons of Jupiter, are probably required before definitive answers can be given. The final assessments will depend on our understanding of conditions in the early solar nebula, perhaps one of the most interesting and exciting fields of current scientific research.

## 7.2  THE BOUNDARY CONDITIONS FROM THE APOLLO MISSIONS

It is clear in retrospect that only at the close of the Apollo 17 mission was enough data accumulated for meaningful attempts at synthesis. Critical measurements became available. An example is the heat-flow result, unexpectedly high at the Apollo 15 site, lost at the 16 site, but confirmed at the Taurus-Littrow landing. The composition of the highland crust became more firmly established from the orbital data. The history of lunar events was extended back towards a beginning of 4.6 aeons with integrated contributions from several age techniques. This new knowledge, largely unsuspected before the missions, has been discussed in detail in the preceding five chapters. A brief account of the more important boundary conditions is summarized in the following sections. The reader is referred to the appropriate chapters for sources. Considering these many unexpected results, we become conscious how much further facts may lead us than thought has predicted.

### Geological Constraints

Geological constraints are discussed in detail in chapters 2 and 3. A main result is the relative stratigraphy obtained from the photogeological studies. It is probable that the intense cratering extended backwards far beyond 4.0 aeons. Impact processes produced both the large ringed basins, most of the smaller craters, and the regolith. The stratigraphic evidence shows that the lavas filling the large ringed basins came long after their excavation, so that the maria basalts cannot be the result of impact melting.

The effect of large-scale impacts on the highland crust and their role in petrogenesis of the highland rock types remain to be evaluated. The lack of evidence of young volcanic episodes is important in demonstrating that the internal heat engine shut down at about 3.0 aeons and has not been active since. Many other results, such as the extreme fluidity of the maria lavas, the detailed evolution of the regolith, and the interaction of cosmic rays and meteorites with the lunar surface, have been dealt with in the appropriate sections of chapters 2 and 3.

### Geochronological Constraints

Geochronological constraints enabled absolute dates to be attached to the relative age sequences established by the astrogeologists. Detailed discussions have been provided in chapters 3, 4, and 5. The chief and most interesting result is the great age of the lunar samples, a fact that opens a new window into early planetary evolution.

Data to be fitted into any theory include:

(a) All highland rocks are older than 3.9 aeons. Some ages extend back to 4.6 aeons and relict ages up to 4.3 aeons are common.

(b) The age of formation of the highland crust lies in the interval 4.4–4.6 aeons.

(c) The maria basalts were extruded in the interval from 3.9 to 3.2 aeons. The oldest ages overlap with the closing stages of the great basin collisions.

(d) The youngest dated basalts have ages of 3.16 aeons. The mare basalt flooding may have continued longer in western Oceanus Procellarum.

(e) The basalt Rb-Sr model ages are older than the crystallization ages, indicating that separation of Rb from Sr during formation of the magmas was not very effective. The soil model ages are perturbed by redistribution of Rb relative to Sr.

(f) The values for $^{87}Sr/^{86}Sr$ ratios are among the lowest observed and indicate a major fractionation of Rb from Sr close to 4.6 aeons.

**Geophysical Constraints**

Geophysical constraints provide most of the data about the lunar interior and are explored in detail in chapter 6. The coefficient of moment of inertia (0.395) suggests a nearly uniform density with depth. This and the low density of the whole moon (3.34 g/cm$^3$) rule out the existence of large volumes of dense phases, such as eclogite ($\rho = 3.74$ g/cm$^3$) or a large iron core, at depth. Iron cores are restricted to a radius of less than 400 km and Fe-FeS cores to less than 700 km radius. Neither the maria basalts nor the highlands anorthosites are suitable compositions for the deep interior.

The lack of major seismic discontinuities between the base of the crust at 60 km and a depth of 1,000 km suggests a rather uniform interior with gradational boundaries in mineralogy and chemical composition. The interior of the moon is divided into (a) crust (upper 60 km: 10 percent volume), (b) lithosphere (60–1,000 km: 82.4 percent volume), and (c) asthenosphere (1,000–1,738 km: 7.6 percent volume) with at least the upper portion of this zone partially liquid. The presence of orthopyroxene (with some Al and Ca) below 300 km is inferred from P-wave velocities that fit an olivine-orthopyroxene mixture better than olivine alone. The mascons are a result of the mare basalt filling of the ringed basins. Their presence indicates that the outer 100 km of the moon was solid when the maria basalts were erupted. A lower limit for the source region of the maria basalts from the experimental petrology data is about 300–400 km. Accordingly, the source of the maria basalts lies between depths of about 100 and 300 km.

Although the origins of the magnetic fields remain a mystery, fields with minimum intensities of 2,000–3,000 gamma were in existence up to about 3.0 aeons ago. These have now disappeared.

The temperature of the lunar interior is known only within rather broad limits from the conductivity data. The temperature at a depth of 1,000 km reaches the melting point of at least the lower melting point constituents at that depth. If an Fe-FeS core exists, temperatures as low as 1,000–1,100°C would suffice.

The heat-flow data place important limits on the overall lunar composition. The present results indicate that the abundance of uranium in the moon is 60 ppb. This value, about five times that observed in Type I carbonaceous chondrites, is a basic constraint. It is difficult to produce such an enrichment in a refractory residue by driving off the more volatile components. Thus it is probably necessary to appeal to initial condensation processes in the primitive Solar Nebula to provide such concentrations. The abundance of U is simply related to that of Th and K. The close positive correlations between Th and U, and the other nonvolatile elements, means that the overall lunar abundances of these elements (e.g., REE, Zr, Hf, Ba, Nb) will follow those of the heat-producing elements.

**Petrological Constraints**

The diversity of rock types in the maria and the highlands, their origins, ages, and crystallization histories are discussed in chapters 4 and 5. The highland rocks, although mostly intensely brecciated, are mixtures of only a few components. Most of the insights into these have been gained by chemical rather than petrological examination, since no primary textures have survived the bombardment.

The amount of information on the maria basalts is large. They are generated by varying degrees of partial melting in the interior. Several types of maria basalts are distinguished using major and trace element criteria; their common feature is a high Ca/Al ratio, relatively low Mg/Fe, and varying degrees of REE enrichment with Eu depletion, and varying but low contents of Ni. The maria basalts could be related by petrological schemes involving different degrees of partial melting of a common parent. Their composition suggests, however, that partial melting of slightly different mineralogies involving a combination of pyroxene, olivine, Fe-Ti phases, and plagioclase (and sulfides) has taken place. The REE abundances in maria basalts indicate that plagioclase was absent from their source regions. The basalts crystallized under highly reducing conditions.

**Geochemical Constraints**

Detailed discussions of the geochemical boundary conditions have been given in chapters 4 and 5. Among the more important observations are:

(a) Depletion of the volatile elements at or before accretion. There is no good evidence for volatile loss of elements such as sodium during extrusion of the lavas.

(b) Strong depletion of the siderophile elements in lunar rocks.

(c) Enrichment of the refractory elements both in maria and highlands rocks by 1–2 orders of magnitude over primitive abundances.

(d) Similar ratios of volatile/involatile elements (e.g., K/Zr) in both highlands and maria rocks.

(*e*) Strong positive correlations between most refractory elements.

(*f*) Large depletions or enrichment of europium relative to the other rare earths.

(*g*) Presence of three geochemically incompatible groups of elements in the lunar highland rocks.

(*h*) Very limited range of $\delta^{18}O$ values.

(*i*) Lateral variations in composition in the highlands.

(*j*) No correlation between orbital chemistry and occurrences of plains-forming units.

(*k*) No evidence of water, organic matter, or life forms in any returned samples.

(*l*) The major and trace element compositions are distinct from those of most terrestrial rocks and meteorites.

These selections of important new constraints are necessarily incomplete. Others would emphasize different points, and many facts have had to be glossed over in the interests of brevity. The reader should consult the appropriate chapters for full details.

## 7.3  HOMOGENEOUS VERSUS HETEROGENEOUS ACCRETION

Although the place and the mechanics of origin of the moon remain elusive, the Apollo data provide restrictions on the chemistry of the accreting material. From the earliest visual observations, the highlands were considered chemically distinct from the maria. Since the moon's surface was heterogeneous to superficial inspection, possibly this reflected an initial heterogeneity. As mapping progressed, it became clear that the highlands were older than the darker maria. Were they a more primitive layer, or did they represent an early lunar crust[4]?

When the composition of the lunar crust was revealed, further difficulties arose. It was clear that the surficial concentrations of the heat-producing elements could not persist at depth. An alumina-rich crust, high in refractory elements, provided many petrological, geochemical, and thermal difficulties for theories of origin. Such element fractionations were more readily imagined to take place in the nebula, and the late accretion of such a chemically distinct layer was proposed. This was the *Heterogeneous Accretion Model* [5–7]. The alternative model, the *Homogeneous Accretion Model* [8–11] proposes that the moon was accreted homogeneously and that the chemically distinct crust was produced by early melting and differentiation.

The heterogeneous accretion model had some attractive features. It was clear from the earliest studies that depletion of volatile elements had occurred at or before the accretion of the moon. Thus, if such element fractionation was occurring, plausible models involving selective accretion could be constructed. One immediate difficulty was that the most refractory elements had to be accreted last, the reverse of a condensation sequence. Solutions to this problem were not beyond the scope of human ingenuity.

Subsequent studies have shown that a number of chemical problems beset the heterogeneous accretion model [10, 11]:

(a) The ratios of volatile to involatile elements (e.g., K/Zr) are similar in both maria and highland samples [12]. The constancy of these ratios, discussed in chapters 4 and 5, is not predicted by the model. The highland samples should show strong depletions in the volatile elements relative to the maria samples.

(b) The abundances of the nonvolatile elements in the highland crust are related to ionic charge and radius. There is no correlation with volatility. These observations have been interpreted as evidence for fractionation based on crystal-liquid equilibria, and hence imply large-scale melting in the outer layers of the moon.

(c) The enrichment of large cations, rare earths, and large high valency cations in the lunar crust parallels their enrichment in the earth's crust [11]. It is the consensus that the latter is derived from the interior by differentiation, not from an accreted layer of differing composition.

(d) Accretion of the most refractory material at the final stages of planetary formation is a difficult problem, although it can be predicted from the precipitation hypothesis of lunar origin [7].

These general difficulties have made the heterogeneous accretion model unattractive and it has been abandoned by some of its previous adherents [13]. Attention has been redirected to the homogeneous accretion model. An important consequence of this theory is that very efficient large-scale element fractionation is required to account both for the high near-surface concentrations of refractory elements (e.g., Th, U, REE, Zr, Ba) and for the Ca-Al rich crust. This is because the observed concentrations in lunar samples commonly represent enrichments by two orders of magnitude over any estimate of primordial solar nebula abundances. Thus the difficulties lie chiefly in providing an adequate initial heat source to produce melting of a large portion of the whole of the moon and in allowing a suitably rapid rate of cooling. These problems appear less severe, and more capable of solution to a geochemical reviewer than do the chemical objections to heterogeneous accretion. Although variations on this latter theme may appear, the geochemical arguments for homogeneous accretion or homogenization after accretion appear decisive.

## 7.4  THE OVERALL COMPOSITION OF THE MOON

If the assumption that the moon was accreted homogeneously is accepted, it then becomes possible to arrive at the bulk composition of the moon. Several independent constraints are available. All these refer to the *involatile* elements. However, once the abundances for these elements have been established, it is possible, for example, to derive values for volatile elements such as K from K/La, K/Zr, or K/Ba ratios.

(a) The heat-flow data provide a critical compositional constraint. The heat flow ($\sim 0.7$ HFU) indicates a total lunar abundance[14] of uranium of about $60 \pm 15$ ppb. The abundance of U in CCI is variable but generally estimated[15] at about 12 ppb. On this basis the moon is enriched at least 5 times over the CCI abundances.

(b) The orbital gamma-ray value[16] for Th averages about 1.5 ppm. If the 60-km-thick highland crust (10 percent of the moon) has this value, then $4 \times$ CCI levels are required just to provide for the crustal concentrations. In addition there must have been some Th (with U and K) in the lunar interior to provide radioactive heating during the period 3.8–3.2 aeons in order to produce the maria basalts.

(c) The highland trace element abundances (Table 5.15) set further limits. If the concentration levels are representative of the 60-km-thick crust and not some thinner surficial zone, then 3–4 $\times$ CCI abundances are required to provide enough Ba and light REE for the crustal abundances alone. Maria basalts, derived from deeper levels by partial melting after the highland crust was formed, contain also high levels of Ba, U, Th, REE, Zr, Hf, Nb, and so on (relative to CCI abundances), increasing the abundance problem. These problems are illustrated in Table 7.1. A total lunar composition for the involatile elements of $5 \times$ CCI abundances is assumed (column 1). The amount of each element in the highland crust, as a percentage of the total lunar composition, is shown in column 3. Thus, for example, 63 percent of the barium in the whole moon now resides in the highland crust.

The abundances in the upper 60–300 km of the moon are given in column 4, based on the assumptions that none of these lithophile elements will be retained in the deep interior.

**Table 7.1**    Trace Element Abundances in the Total Moon, in the Highlands (0–60 km), and in the Region 60–300 km.

| Element | Total moon (ppm) | Average highlands (ppm) | Percent in highlands (%) | Residual concentration in upper 60–300 km (ppm) |
|---------|------------------|--------------------------|---------------------------|-------------------------------------------------|
| Ba | 17.5 | 110 | 63 | 18.7 |
| Sr | 43 | 200 | 47 | 67 |
| Th | 0.23 | 1.5 | 65 | 0.23 |
| U | 0.06 | 0.4 | 67 | 0.057 |
| Zr | 30 | 105 | 35 | 60 |
| Hf | 0.67 | 2.3 | 34 | 1.20 |
| Nb | 2.2 | 7.5 | 34 | 3.84 |
| La | 1.1 | 8.8 | 80 | 0.60 |
| Ce | 3.10 | 21.6 | 70 | 2.67 |
| Pr | 0.44 | 3.06 | 70 | 0.39 |
| Nd | 2.10 | 12.4 | 59 | 2.46 |
| Sm | 0.75 | 3.26 | 43 | 1.23 |
| Eu | 0.27 | 1.70 | 63 | 2.94 |
| Gd | 1.10 | 3.86 | 35 | 2.07 |
| Tb | 0.18 | 0.59 | 33 | 0.30 |
| Dy | 1.15 | 3.87 | 34 | 2.23 |
| Ho | 0.27 | 0.89 | 34 | 0.54 |
| Er | 0.75 | 2.51 | 34 | 0.72 |
| Tm | 0.11 | 0.37 | 34 | 0.21 |
| Yb | 0.73 | 2.25 | 31 | 1.50 |
| Lu | 0.11 | 0.35 | 32 | 0.22 |
| ΣREE | 12 | 66 | 55 | 13.5 |
| Y | 7.5 | 22.4 | 30 | 15.5 |
| (K) | 100 | 600 | 60 | 120 |
| (Rb) | 0.29 | 1.7 | 59 | 0.36 |
| (Cs) | 0.013 | 0.07 | 55 | 0.018 |

It is assumed that none of these elements are present in the zone 300–1,000 km. The composition of the zone 1,000–1,738 km (7.6 percent) is assumed to be the same as the bulk moon.

(d) The uniform inter-element ratios in lunar samples (e.g., K/La, K/Ba, K/Th, K/Zr) set limits for the lunar abundance of K. Assuming $5 \times CCI$ for the *involatile* elements, the K concentration is 100 ppm. On this basis, about 60 percent of the K (and associated Rb and Cs) are in the highland crust (Table 7.1).

In summary, some limits can be set. The lower limit of $4 \times CCI$ appears well established by the element abundance levels. The heat-flow values set upper limits of perhaps $7 \times CCI$. An overall lunar average for the involatile elements of about $5 \times CCI$ appears reasonable and is adopted here.

The major element abundances in the moon may then be estimated as follows. The refractory elements Ca, Al, and Ti are taken as $5 \times CCI$. The iron content is set at 10.5 percent FeO to accommodate density and magnetic requirements[17]. The Si/Mg ratio in chondrites is used to obtain Si and Mg concentrations.

These estimates for total lunar composition are given in column 1 of Table 7.2. They are based essentially on an empirical approach, using the heat-flow constraints, the composition of the highlands, the inter-elemental ratios, and so on. Several other estimates of the major and trace element of the moon have been made[18–21]. It is of interest to compare these with those made here, since they are based on different premises.

Ganapathy and Anders[18] have proposed an alternative composition based on the assumption that the moon was formed from the solar nebula by the same processes that produced the meteorites. These basic processes are:

($a$) condensation of the elements from a solar gas;
($b$) fractionation of the early condensates and of metal from silicate and partial melting of the condensates.

The conclusion is that at least six components are present. The resulting proportions of these in the moon (and other planets) may be estimated from key inter-elemental ratios (e.g., K/U, Tl/U, FeO/MnO) and from the absolute abundances of U (obtainable from heat-flow data) and Fe (estimated from density and magnetic data).

The resulting composition is given in column 2 of Table 7.2. It is very close to that derived here from a somewhat different approach. Whether this agreement is fortuitous or whether both methods yield a valid answer to the problem, remains to be established. Within these limitations, it is encouraging that a measure of agreement on the total lunar composition is being reached.

Another approach has been used by Wänke et al.[19], who used volatile/involatile element ratios (e.g., K/La) to calculate the proportions of high and low temperature components in the moon. The high temperature constituents were identified with the compositions of the refractory portions of the Allende meteorite, and the low temperature component with that of Type I carbonaceous chondrites (CCI).

A somewhat similar approach has been used by Anderson[20]. Among

**Table 7.2**  The Composition of the Moon.

| Element | | 1 | 2 | Element | | 1 | 2 | Element | | 1 | 2 | Oxide | 1 |
|---|---|---|---|---|---|---|---|---|---|---|---|---|---|
| H | | — | 1.6 | Zn | | — | 15.8 | Pr | | 0.44 | 0.40 | SiO$_2$ | 44.0 |
| Li | | — | 6.5 | Ga | | — | 0.52 | Nd | | 2.1 | 2.1 | TiO$_2$ | 0.3 |
| Be | ppb | — | 140 | Ge | | — | 1.29 | Sm | | 0.75 | 0.65 | Al$_2$O$_3$ | 8.2 |
| B | ppb | — | 16 | As | | — | 0.84 | Eu | | 0.27 | 0.25 | FeO | 10.5 |
| C | | — | 7.2 | Se | | — | 1.04 | Gd | | 1.10 | 0.89 | MgO | 31.0 |
| N | | — | 0.19 | Br | ppb | — | 4.6 | Tb | | 0.18 | 0.17 | CaO | 6.0 |
| O | % | — | 41.9 | Rb | | 0.29 | 0.30 | Dy | | 1.15 | 1.11 | | |
| F | | — | 27 | Sr | | 43 | 45 | Ho | | 0.27 | 0.25 | | |
| Na | | — | 810 | Y | | 7.5 | 8.1 | Er | | 0.75 | 0.72 | | |
| Mg | % | 18.7 | 18.5 | Zr | | 30 | 49 | Tm | | 0.11 | 0.11 | | |
| Al | % | 4.3 | 4.35 | Nb | | 2.2 | 2.47 | Yb | | 0.73 | 0.71 | | |
| Si | % | 20.6 | 20.0 | Mo | | — | 7.3 | Lu | | 0.11 | 0.12 | | |
| P | | — | 504 | Ru | | — | 3.7 | Hf | | 0.67 | 0.71 | | |
| S | % | — | 0.31 | Rh | | — | 0.78 | Ta | ppb | — | 72 | | |
| Cl | | — | 0.86 | Pd | | — | 0.23 | W | | — | 0.56 | | |
| K | | 100 | 96 | Ag | ppb | — | 7.5 | Re | ppb | — | 190 | | |
| Ca | % | 4.3 | 5.49 | Cd | ppb | — | 0.70 | Os | | — | 2.7 | | |
| Sc | | 20 | 30 | In | ppb | — | 0.092 | Ir | | — | 2.6 | | |
| Ti | | 1,800 | 2,520 | Sn | | — | 0.066 | Pt | | — | 5.2 | | |
| V | | 48 | 250 | Sb | ppb | — | 6.5 | Au | ppb | — | 0.067 | | |
| Cr | | 1,330 | 1,120 | Te | | — | 0.16 | Hg | ppb | — | 0.34 | | |
| Mn | | 1,000 | 300 | I | ppb | — | 0.59 | Tl | ppb | 0.5 | 0.17 | | |
| Fe | % | 8.2 | 8.52 | Cs | ppb | 13 | 30 | $^{204}$Pb | ppb | — | 0.067 | | |
| Co | | — | 220 | Ba | | 17.5 | 12.5 | Bi | ppb | — | 0.13 | | |
| Ni | % | — | 0.48 | La | | 1.1 | 1.17 | Th | ppb | 230 | 210 | | |
| Cu | | — | 5.3 | Ce | | 3.1 | 3.1 | U | ppb | 60 | 59 | | |

All data in parts per million except where indicated as parts per billion or percent.
1. Taylor (this work).   2. Ganapathy and Anders [18].

other problems, the high abundance of elements such as iridium in the Allende inclusions provides a high siderophile element component. The resulting lunar compositions are also very high in Ca and Al. The major element constituents would allow the formation of dense phases, such as garnet, in the lunar interior, in conflict with the density and moment of inertia constraints. Another serious restriction on the use of Allende-type white inclusions as major lunar constituents comes from the large differences between the lunar and the Allende oxygen isotope ratios[21]. (See also section 7.11.)

## 7.5  RARE EARTH PATTERNS IN THE LUNAR INTERIOR

It is a reasonable assumption that the total REE patterns in the moon will be parallel to those of chondrites, although the overall concentration levels are several times those in the primitive Type I carbonaceous chondrites. Given the assumption of a homogeneously accreted moon, in which the highland crust developed by differentiation, then the interior should display a pattern complementary to that of the crust.

This is not a trivial consequence, on account of the great enrichment of rare earth elements in the crust. Estimates that 70–80 percent of the total moon abundances of the light REE are in the highland crust (10 percent of the whole moon) (Table 7.1) are not unreasonable. In contrast, the volume of the maria basalts is so small (0.5 percent of total lunar volume) that they may be neglected in these calculations.

Both crustal and interior residual patterns are shown in Fig. 7.1. These are based on a total lunar abundance of $5 \times CCI$ for the rare earths. The patterns shown are not sensitive to the overall abundances. On this basis crustal abundances are enriched about 10–20 times those of chondrites. It is probable that most of the REE and associated elements in the lunar interior are in the upper 300 km (as indicated in Fig. 7.1). Within this zone the REE abundances are probably higher in the shallower parts.

The resemblance of the residual REE pattern to that found in the maria basalts is notable. Eu is depleted. There is a progressive depletion of the light REE (La-Sm), similar to that observed in many maria basalts, particularly the high-Ti varieties. This pattern is complementary to that of plagioclase and resembles that of clinopyroxenes. Accordingly, the REE abundance patterns in the interior would be consistent with prior removal of a plagioclase component from the source region of maria basalts, explaining the europium depletion observed in the basalts. The subtler features such as depletion of the light REE (La-Sm), a common feature

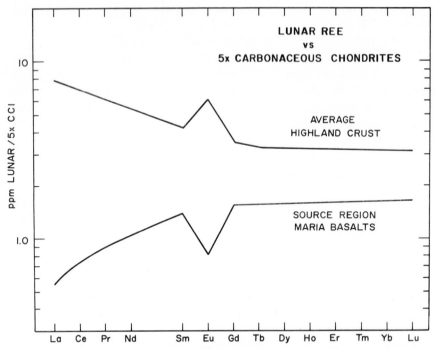

**Fig. 7.1**   REE patterns relative to $5 \times CCI$ abundances, taken as representing the whole moon composition. Note the positive Eu anomaly in the highland crust. All the remaining REE in the moon are assumed concentrated in the upper 60- to 300-km zone (33.4 percent) except for the deep interior (1,000–1,738 km: 7.6 percent), which is assumed to contain unfractionated material. Data from Table 7.1.

are consistent with a clinopyroxene source. These conclusions come from a simple differentiation model, following melting and homogeneous accretion, without recourse to more exotic mechanisms[22].

## 7.6   GEOCHEMICAL EVOLUTION OF THE MOON

Many scenarios are possible. In this section, an attempt is made to reconcile the geochemical information with the geophysical constraints, derive the composition of the deep lunar interior, and correlate the overall composition with the sequence of geological events, beginning with a homogeneously accreted moon, which underwent partial or total melting, due to accretional heating. Early heating and melting of large parts of the moon is compatible with the later thermal history of the moon[23]. Total melting of the moon can be achieved if short accretional times on the order of 100–1,000 years are considered[24].

Three alternative models may account for the deep lunar interior (asthenosphere, below 1,000 km):

(*a*) An immiscible Fe-FeS liquid sinks to form a core effectively removing most siderophile and chalcophile elements[25]. The core radius is restricted to less than 700 km by the coefficient of moment of inertia. Enough sulfur (~0.5 percent) is retained in the whole moon to form FeS. The partially liquid zone suggested by the seismic evidence below 1,000 km, is interpreted as due to dispersed Fe-FeS in an olivine-orthopyroxene matrix. The magnetic field appearing in remanently magnetized rocks results from a core dynamo mechanism. An important feature of this model[25] is that temperature at the 1,000-km discontinuity may be as low as 1,000–1,100°C.

(*b*) The initial melting did not extend below 1,000 km. The central part of the moon is formed of primitive unfractionated material, now in a partially molten state from heating due to trapped initial K, U, and Th. The seismic data are satisfied by 0.5–1 percent partial melting. This model precludes core formation, since sinking Fe-FeS will drive these incompatible elements upwards. In this model, the remanent magnetism of lunar rocks is caused by external magnetic fields[26].

(*c*) The molten zone is a relict of early melting.

The choice between these models for the lunar interior depends critically on the amount of the early siderophile and chalcophile element depletion. If the siderophile elements were accreted, even in the amounts corresponding to the supposed low bulk Fe content of the moon, a lunar core is required to remove them in a very efficient manner. If these elements were depleted before accretion[27], then this reason for postulating a core disappears. It is assumed in the following discussion that a core did not form and that an inner zone some 700 km thick (7.6 percent volume) was not melted initially (Model *b*).

After accretional melting of 90 percent of the moon, the first silicate phase to crystallize from the primitive molten moon was Mg-rich olivine. The early precipitation of olivine removes $Co^{2+}$, $Cr^{2+}$, and $Ni^{2+}$. If the oxygen fugacity is close to or below the Fe-FeO buffer, much of the nickel will be in the metallic state. However, since the extreme reduction observed in maria basalts may be a near-surface phenomenon developed during crystallization[28] much nickel in the moon may be present as $Ni^{2+}$.

The surface of the moon cooled rapidly forming a "frozen crust," although this was continually broken up by the declining meteoritic bombardment. This frozen surface layer, analogous to the chilled margins of terrestrial intrusions, retained high concentrations of Mg, Cr, and so on, in near-surface regions. Thus its composition is probably representative of the melt composition during the early stages of crystallization of the lower interior. This chilled early lunar crust was later incorporated into the overall highland composition and contributed the Mg and Cr "primitive" component in the crust. This material is now thoroughly mixed in the highland crustal material, although the 4.6-billion-year-old dunite[29] may have been derived from such an early primitive crust.

As crystallization proceeded in the deep lunar interior, the Si/Mg ratio changed and orthopyroxene precipitated. This had a similar effect on the composition of the residual melt as olivine except for Si/Mg ratios. Most cations except Mg, Fe, Ni, Co, and $Cr^{2+}$ were excluded from the olivine and orthopyroxene lattice sites and migrated upwards, concentrating in the still voluminous residual melt. These include Ca and Al. The high $Cr^{3+}$ abundances in most accessible lunar materials indicate that separation of clinopyroxene, if any, was minor, and olivine and orthopyroxene were probably the major components.

The density and seismic properties, and the Si/Mg ratio in the deep lunar interior are satisfied by 75–80 percent olivine ($\sim Fo_{85}$) and 20–25 percent orthopyroxene ($\sim En_{85}$). The composition of the lower part of the moon (300–1000 km) (assuming 2.2 percent $Al_2O_3$ and 2.5 percent CaO in the orthopyroxene) is given in Table 7.3, column 2. The model requires, however, that even the lower parts of the moon are compositionally and mineralogically zoned. Orthopyroxene with some $Al_2O_3$ and CaO content is present at shallower depths together with olivine, whereas Mg-rich olivine is present in deeper parts.

Increasing crystallization of Mg-rich olivine, later accompanied by orthopyroxene at depth, leads to an increasing concentration of refractory elements (Ca-Al) trapped between the already crystallized lower (Ol-Opx) lunar interior and the chilled surface layer. The composition of this zone (upper 300 km of the moon) is given in Table 7.3, column 3. When the concentration of Al reaches 12–17 percent $Al_2O_3$, An-rich plagioclase precipitates, and concentrates or remains suspended beneath the frozen surface, whereas the Mg-Fe phases continue to crystallize and sink[30]. The Ca-Al rich region (plagioclase) incorporates $Sr^{2+}$ and $Eu^{2+}$, but most other elements are unable to enter the $Ca^{2+}$ sites in significant amounts.

**Table 7.3**  Major Element Compositions of Various Zones in the Moon.

|                  | 1    | 2    | 3    | 4    |
|------------------|------|------|------|------|
| $SiO_2$          | 44.0 | 44.3 | 44.9 | 43.3 |
| $TiO_2$          | 0.3  | —    | 0.56 | 0.7  |
| $Al_2O_3$        | 8.2  | 0.6  | 24.6 | 14.4 |
| FeO              | 10.5 | 9.9  | 6.6  | 12.6 |
| MgO              | 31.0 | 44.7 | 8.6  | 17.7 |
| CaO              | 6.0  | 0.7  | 14.2 | 11.3 |
| Volume %         | 100  | 49   | 10   | 33.4 |

The composition of the asthenosphere (1,000–1,738 km; 7.6 percent volume) is assumed to be undifferentiated and equivalent to that of the whole moon.

1. Whole moon composition.
2. Composition of 300- to 1,000-km zone.
3. Average highland crust (upper 60 km).
4. Composition of 60- to 300-km zone of moon (source region of maria basalts).

Experimental petrology provides constraints on the $Al_2O_3$ content of melts in precipitating plagioclase together with Fe-Mg silicates (olivine and pyroxene). Values above 12 percent $Al_2O_3$ are necessary[31]. The absence of plagioclase in the source region of maria basalts explains the high Ca/Al ratios, negative Eu anomalies, and the low content of Al in maria basalts[32]. The source region of maria basalts is zoned in respect of Ca-Al and also Mg/Fe and consequently in mineralogy.

The high Al maria basalts come from plagioclase-bearing regions shallower than other maria basalts[33]. The model suggests that the content of plagioclase decreases from the base of crust (60 km) downwards, whereas the contents of Fe-Mg silicate increases. These silicates become more Mg-rich with depth. Pockets or zones rich in Fe-Ti oxides and FeS in shallower regions account for the high Ti and S contents of the Apollo 11 and 17 basalts[34]. Small zones of FeS provide a convenient place to trap lead in a uranium and thorium-free environment[35].

The source region of basalts such as 15555 (Great Scott) and the green glass may represent a lower boundary of plagioclase precipitation. It is assumed that plagioclase separation commenced when a large part (~40 percent) of the moon was still molten, i.e., during formation of source region of maria basalts, above a depth of 300 km. The composition of the region from the base of the crust at 60 km to a depth of 300 km, which encompasses the source region of the maria basalts, is given in Table 7.3, column 4. (For the composition of the highland crust, see Table 7.3, column 3.)

As crystallization of the future source region of the maria basalts and the crust proceeds, elements unable to enter the Ca-Al sites in plagioclase (above) or the Mg-Fe sites (below) are trapped between. In this trapped or residual zone, all the remaining elements concentrate. These include K, Ba, Rb, Cs, REE, Th, U, Zr, and Nb. It is a geochemical characteristic of great importance that the principal lunar mineral phases do not readily accommodate the refractory trace elements. The evidence of high concentrations of these elements near the surface of the moon is a dramatic consequence of this crystal chemical fact. The behavior of ions in entering crystal lattice sites in lunar minerals should be simpler than in terrestrial geochemistry, because of the nearly total absence of water and other volatiles.

Following the primordial fractionation, a chemically zoned moon is produced, with residual phases enriched below the chilled margin and plagioclase crust and above the source region and maria basalts (Fig. 7.2). This crustal zonation established at about 4.5 aeons is changed very quickly. The declining stages of the meteoritic bombardment pulverize the chilled zone, and larger impacts mix in the underlying anorthosite. The high concentration of the heat-producing elements K, U, and Th (and Zr, Hf, REE, etc.) trapped beneath the plagioclase zone provides the high-element abundances for the Fra Mauro or KREEP basalts. Possibly this zone did not solidify, but the liquids from it invaded the crust, where impact mixing of the primitive surface layer, the Ca-Al plagioclase-rich layer, and the liquids beneath produced the parent material for the anorthositic gabbro (highland basalt) and the Fra Mauro basalts. The mixing and overturning continues to 3.9 aeons, culminating in the production of the ringed basins and the cessation of the intense highland cratering.

Partial melting next occurs in successively deeper layers as the smaller amounts of the heat-producing elements induce partial melting and a succession of "maria-type" basalts are erupted. The general progressive deepening with time of the source region of the maria basalts is attributed here to the decrease in K, U, and Th with depth. The higher near-surface concentrations of these heat-producing elements result in early melting and removal of the heat sources (since K, U, and Th are concentrated in the melt). The lesser amounts of K, U, and Th at depth generate a

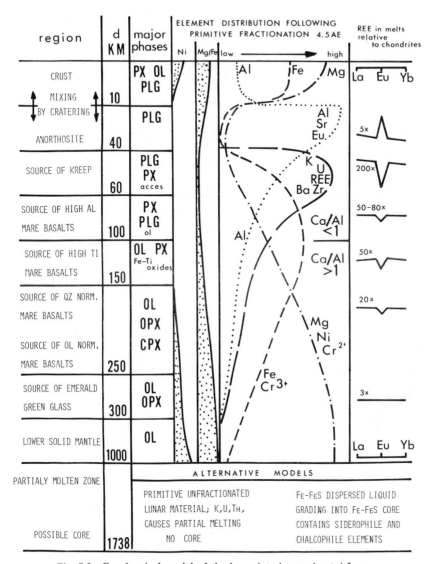

**Fig. 7.2**   Geochemical model of the lunar interior at about 4.5 aeons.

smaller amount of heat, and it takes longer for melting temperatures to be reached.

The high-Al maria basalts formed, in this model, at shallow depths beneath the crust. This emplacement overlaps with the later stages of the bombardment and predates the Imbrium collision in part, as shown by their presence in Fra Mauro breccias. Some of the high-Al maria basalts were emplaced later (~3.4 aeons), suggesting that partial melting in shallower zones were not limited to early periods of maria formation (e.g., Luna 16 rocks).

Following these, the Ti-rich Apollo 11 and 17 basalts were extruded during the period 3.8–3.6 aeons from a zone where Fe-Ti oxides and FeS accumulated. They contain about 1 ppm Ni. Later (3.4–3.2 aeons) the Apollo 12 and 15 quartz- and olivine-normative basalts were extruded. These contain higher contents of nickel, indicating extensive partial melting involving olivine, and many show evidence of near-surface fractionation. A negative Eu anomaly is characteristic of all maria basalts and contrasts with the deepest material erupted, the Apollo 15 emerald green glass with 180 ppm Ni and primitive REE patterns, low total REE (3–5 times chondrites), and a small Eu anomaly[36]. This material is the least fractionated lunar material that has been sampled.

The thickness of the crust above this zone, as well as the residual high melting point material and the lack of heat sources due to the upward movement of K, U, and Th, causes cessation of lunar vulcanism at 3.2 aeons. For the past 3 billion years the moon has been relatively inactive, and the major process has been the slow meteorite bombardment of the surface, producing occasional young ray craters such as Copernicus, Kepler, and Tycho.

## 7.7  LUNAR ORIGINS

The data from the Apollo missions allow us to construct realistic models of lunar evolutionary history. The details may alter, and the model discussed in the previous section is only one of several possibilities. Nevertheless, five years after the first sample return, it is fair to claim that we have an excellent understanding of lunar history. The models are in as good or possibly better condition than earth models, although this is partly a consequence of the simpler lunar history and the smaller size of the body.

The ultimate origin of the moon is another question. Much information and many constraints have been obtained from the Apollo missions, but the problem is one of broader significance, embracing the origin of other planets and of the solar system itself. The answer depends on a much larger set of data than can be obtained by surface sampling. Critical parameters include conditions in the early solar nebula during condensation and accretion.

Progress, much of it inspired by lunar and meteoritic studies, is rapidly being made in this fascinating but dimly perceived field. Many additional data are required from the other planets and satellites before definitive answers can be given, but the identification of the basic and relevant questions is much clearer than before the manned lunar missions.

The classical hypotheses of lunar origin fell into three groups:

(*a*) Formation along with the earth as a double planetary system.
(*b*) Fission from the earth.
(*c*) Capture by the earth of a body formed elsewhere in the solar system.

These theories have enjoyed varying fortunes, but none survived unscathed from their encounter with the Apollo data. It was immediately realized from the earliest results that a new set of chemical constraints had appeared to reinforce the formidable dynamical and density problems posed by the existence of the earth's unique satellite.

Several attempts have been made to integrate this new information with the classical theories. The most difficult feat to accomplish is to deplete both the volatile and the siderophile elements in the moon relative to primitive solar nebula abundances. Opinions have been about equally divided between modified versions of the fission and the capture theories. Very recently, versions that embrace elements of both these explanations have appeared. In this quest, different workers have attached varying degrees of significance to the new data. These aspects are explored in the following sections.

## 7.8   THE DOUBLE PLANET HYPOTHESIS

The accretion or condensation of the moon as a sister planet to the earth has been the least popular of the three explanations. It suffers from two basic defects, in its simplest form. If the formation of the moon had occurred close to the earth, its orbit would be expected to lie at that time in the equatorial plane; if formed farther away, the orbit should be in the plane of the ecliptic. Goldreich[37] showed that, regardless of the original orbit, the moon should now lie in the ecliptic plane. The present inclination of the lunar orbit to the plane of the ecliptic is 5°09'.

The theory also fails to explain the low density of the moon compared with the earth. If both bodies condensed from the same portion of the solar nebula at the same time, then there is no *a priori* reason to expect that one body will be 1.6 times denser than the other. To overcome this difficulty in the hypothesis, some form of chemical fractionation was introduced. Thus, if metal and silicate fractions were present, the metal phase could be accreted preferentially into the earth. However, we have seen that the composition of the lunar interior is not the same as that of the terrestrial mantle, so that some additional selective fractionation of silicates is needed to account for these chemical differences. It is clear from the Apollo data that revision of this hypothesis is necessary to account for both the density and the chemical differences between earth and moon. The twin difficulties of density and orbital inclination have not encouraged such revision, although elements of the hypothesis appear in modifications of the fission theory.

## 7.9  FISSION HYPOTHESIS

The principal attraction of the early forms of the fission hypothesis was that it provided a solution to the density difference between the earth and the moon. The density of the moon could be made to match that of the uncompressed density of the upper mantle of the earth. It was a necessary requirement of the theory that the core-mantle separation occurred before or during fission. The original suggestion was due to George Darwin[38], who proposed that tidal forces separated the moon from the earth. There are many dynamical objections to the hypothesis, and these have been pointed out repeatedly[39–42]. The total angular momentum of the present or former earth-moon systems appears inadequate[17], while the inclination of the lunar orbit appears as an insuperable objection[17, 40, 41]. Nevertheless, some recent workers have disputed the conclusion that the moon was never in the equatorial plane of the earth[43].

A number of workers continue to espouse the theory[43–46] since it leads to interesting geochemical consequences. In addition to solving the density dilemma, it provides an apparent solution to the siderophile element depletion, by placing "the moon's nickel in the earth's core." Certainly there are considerable difficulties in storing the siderophile elements within the moon, if they were ever accreted[47].

The argument depends chiefly on the nickel content. Nickel is more siderophile than iron and preferentially enters a metal phase. If the moon had accreted its cosmic component of nickel, then most of the volume of the lunar core would be required to contain it, since the density and moment of inertia constraints restrict a metal core to a radius of less than 400 km[48].

There are some basic geochemical objections to the fission hypothesis.

Although the formation of the earth's core is expected to deplete the mantle in siderophile elements, the upper regions of the earth contain moderately high amounts of elements such as nickel, indicating that equilibrium was not fully attained. In general, the lunar rocks (excluding the meteoritic component added from impact events) are much more strongly depleted in siderophile elements than are terrestrial analogues. These differences have been noted throughout this book, in particular in chapter 4 in which terrestrial and lunar basalts are compared. If the lunar interior and the mantle of the earth share a common origin, it is reasonable to suppose that lavas extruded on the moon would closely resemble those familiar on the earth. The many distinctions observed are strong evidence that the lunar interior is not similar to the mantle of the earth[49, 50]. This is a formidable objection to the fission hypothesis.

The prospect that differing early geochemical differentiation processes might have masked such similarities does not provide much comfort. If, as is judged likely, the anorthositic lunar highland crust is derived from differentiation of a homogeneously accreted moon, then it must have arisen from a different source material to that which produced the granodioritic upper crust of the earth. O'Keefe[47] adduces support for the fission hypothesis from a supposed lunar origin of tektites. These strongly resemble the composition of terrestrial upper crustal materials, and so, if derived from lunar sources, would be compatible with an intimate connection between the earth and the moon in former ages. The decisive evidence, summarized in section 3.7, against a lunar origin for tektites removes this claim from serious consideration.

Further constraints arise from the isotopic data. Large-scale fractionations of Rb from Sr and Pb from U and Th took place very close to 4.6 aeons. Hence fission has to be accompanied by some form of chemical fractionation, removing one of the most attractive features of the model. In summary, the fission hypotheses satisfy neither the geochemical nor the dynamical constraints.

### The Precipitation Hypothesis

A modification of the fission theory, referred to as the precipitation hypothesis[51], removes several difficulties associated with fission. It combines elements of both the double planet and fission theories.

This model proposes that the moon was formed by accretion from a ring of planetesimals which formed around the earth following condensation of the planet[51, 52]. This ring of planetesimals arises in the following manner, as a consequence of the final stages of accretion. It is assumed that the earth began to condense from cold solar nebula material, equivalent in composition to the Type I carbonaceous chondrites. This accretion took place in a short period of time. As the radius of the growing earth increases, so does the gravitational energy of infall. By making suitable assumptions about the time of accretion, the surface temperature of the earth can approach 2,000°C in the final stages, when all incoming material is vaporized. The primitive earth develops a massive atmosphere, mainly of hydrogen and carbon monoxide, resulting from the reduction of iron from oxide to metal, but containing perhaps 10–20 percent of volatilized silicates. These condense and form a "sediment ring" around the earth. The gases and the more volatile components are driven away mainly by early intense solar radiation leaving behind the refractory components, from which a metallic phase may have already been separated. Thus, material depleted in the volatile and siderophile elements and enriched in the refractory elements is left. Opik[52] has discussed the condensation of the moon from such a sediment ring. As the moon increases in size, larger objects are swept up due to the increasing gravitational attraction. The heavy cratering of the uplands may represent this stage. Finally, the large (50–100 km) objects are captured and produce the giant ringed basins by impact. Thus the moon is formed.

This model possesses an instinctive appeal to geochemists. There are close links with the O'Keefe fission theory[46], but it avoids some of the difficulties with the disposal of the siderophile elements. The dynamical difficulties remain. One feature of the model was its ability to provide a late addition of more refractory material[53], although this modification has been abandoned[13]. More recently, accretion of refractory phases to explain the Eu anomaly has been proposed[54] in terms of this model[55]. It is not clear that such material would survive the large-scale melting processes required by a homogeneous accretion model. Whether selective accretion would occur depends on several factors, but sorting due to size and mass is more likely to occur than more subtle effects based on compositional differences among silicates.

## 7.10  CAPTURE HYPOTHESES

The capture hypotheses possess the considerable disadvantage of removing the origin of the moon from any association, except the accident of capture, with the earth. Such theories are disagreeable to geochemists and geophysicists. Most of the new evidence and constraints arise from their work, and it is aesthetically unsatisfying to relegate these processes to a remote and unspecified part of the solar system.

Nevertheless, it has appeared to those impressed by the dynamical problems posed by the lunar orbit to be the only viable hypothesis. An early argument that the moon might be a primitive object (since the density was not far removed from that of carbonaceous chondrites) did not survive the initial examination of the lunar samples. Thus the capture theory was immediately faced with the necessity of providing for large-scale chemical fractionation in the primitive solar nebula.

The theory has long been advocated by Urey[56–57], concerned with the density problem and unable to accept the fission theories. The theoretical basis for the theory has been provided by Gerstenkorn[40], MacDonald[41], Goldreich[37], and Kaula[42]. More recently, it has been strongly advocated by Singer[58] and Alfvén and Arrhenius[59].

The philosophical basis for the theory turns on the uniqueness of the earth-moon system. Many moon-sized objects exist[57]. Seven of 32 principal satellites are comparable in size[60]. The density of the moon is not unique. At least two of the Jovian satellites, Io and Europa, have about the same mass and density as the moon. Thus moon-type objects formed elsewhere. Five of the lunar-sized satellites are in equatorial orbits, but both the moon and Triton (N-1) occupy nonequatorial orbits. In all, 12 of the 32 satellites are in nonequatorial orbits, with six having retrograde motion. Such statistics have provided comfort to the proponents of the view that both the formation of moon-sized objects, and their capture, was a common occurrence during the formation of the solar system.

Although the present earth-moon system is unique[61], it has been argued that this was not always so[62]. The present-day mass ratio for other satellites does not allow for loss of gases or ices at an early stage of the solar nebula. Whether this objection is valid depends critically on the time of accretion relative to condensation. In this connection, the absence of moon-type Venusian[61] and Martian satellites[63] points to special or unique conditions in the earth-moon system.

Before any of the questions related to capture can be sensibly attacked, the answer to a more fundamental problem is required. *Is the moon unique chemically?* The lack of knowledge of the chemistry of other satellite systems remains a serious limitation.

An analogous situation existed before the chemistry of the moon was revealed to us by the Apollo missions, and all prelanding theories have had to be revised. The compositions of the closest relatives of the moon,

Io and Europa, are of vital importance to this problem. If they are of similar composition, then theories that fractionate the elements in the primitive solar nebula on the basis of volatility and siderophile character will gain in credibility. Attempts to secure such information should be accorded high priority. Unmanned orbital missions, if equipped with XRF and gamma-ray analytical facilities, might answer many of these questions[64].

The capture of a large satellite includes the possibility that it would sweep up any smaller earth-orbiting objects, thus providing a mechanism for producing the large ringed basin collisions. Thus, it is critical to establish the ages of these events. Arguably, a peak or spike in the ages would favor the capture hypothesis. If the collisions occupy a longer time scale, this evidence becomes less decisive. Such an engaging solution encounters the problem that appropriate swarms of small satellites do not exist around Venus at present. The problem of providing an early flux of large objects is not, however, confined to the moon. Both Mars and Mercury (Fig. 7.3) show the effects of a similar bombardment.

The Apollo data have shown that the moon was not a sample of the primitive solar nebula, as once hoped. Although the attraction of the capture hypothesis has disappeared, it remains a strong contender. We shall have to search further afield for samples representative of the primitive solar nebula. Possibly sampling of comets by space probes would provide this.

### Disintegrative Capture

More complex theories were evolved as the large number of constraints imposed by the Apollo data became apparent. Two recent proposals that have many features in common are concerned with integrating the chemical and dynamical constraints[65, 66]. Recognizing the inherent dynamic difficulties in capturing a moon-sized object[42], they attempt to account for these, and for the depletion of the volatile and siderophile elements by a disintegrative capture mechanism.

The view is taken that "half a loaf is better than a whole one"[66], and the scenario runs as follows: During the condensation of the solar nebula many bodies form. Selective condensation depletes the volatile elements. Melting and fractionation produce metal cores and silicate mantles in these planetesimals. A number of these approach the earth on parabolic orbits. Those approaching within the Roche limit[67] will disintegrate. Wood[66] estimates that most (80–90 percent) of the bodies coming

**Fig. 7.3**  The cratered surface of Mercury. The largest crater seen is 200 km in diameter. Larger basin-type structures are known. Note the similarity to the lunar highlands. (Mariner 10 photomosaic P. 14470.)

within the Roche limit would escape impacting the earth. A debris ring accumulates in earth orbit. Because of the dynamical constraints, this would consist preferentially of the silicate portions of the moonlets, which accrete to form the moon. The more massive metallic core material either escapes[66, 68] or is accreted to the earth[65].

These ingenious hypotheses neatly solve both the dynamical and geochemical problems. However, the conditions again appear to emphasize the unique nature of the earth-moon system. Do such mechanisms account for the formation of Io, Europa, and Triton and the absence of a satellite associated with Venus? Answers to such questions, as noted earlier, depend on further exploration of the satellites.

## 7.11   THE SOLAR NEBULA [69]

The composition of the moon shows that it has probably accreted from homogeneous material, enriched in the refractory elements by about 5 times the chondritic (CCI) abundances and depleted both in volatile and siderophile elements. What were the conditions that permitted a body of this composition to form? Basic questions hinge upon the nature of the early solar nebula and of condensation processes within it. Those students interested in the statistics of such situations might reflect that the earth makes up 3 parts per million, the moon 37 parts per billion, and the meteorites one part per billion of the solar system.

Was the solar nebula isotopically homogeneous? The capture hypothesis for the origin of the moon implies that it was formed elsewhere in the solar system. Thus, it might provide us with samples from a region far removed from where the earth or the meteorites formed. In any event, it gives another source of information on the homogeneity or otherwise of the solar nebula.

The possibility is always present that a late injection of $r$-process nuclides (produced from a nearby supernova) may have occurred shortly before or during condensation of the solar system. Such a cause has been suggested as a triggering mechanism to initiate condensation [70]. The galaxy has been in existence for at least 13 aeons. The origin of the element concentrations in the nebula are the result of a combination of "initial" element abundances (mainly hydrogen and some helium) and heavier elements formed subsequently by element synthesis processes in stars and supernova. The heavy elements, derived from a variety of nucleosynthetic processes, are mixed back into the interstellar medium, as stars give off mass or explode in supernova events. The net result is a steady increase of the heavy element content of the interstellar dust, with perhaps local enrichment from supernova explosions of those elements produced in an intense neutron flux (rapid or $r$-process); these include gold, uranium, and thorium [71]. There is mounting evidence for the production of very short-lived $r$-process nuclides just before condensation. Most of the evidence comes from anomalies in rare gas nuclides [72], which indicate the former presence of $^{129}I$ ($t_{\frac{1}{2}}$: 16 million years), $^{244}Pu$ ($t_{\frac{1}{2}}$: 83 million years), and possibly $^{248}Cm$ ($t_{\frac{1}{2}}$: 0.5 million years).

Most investigations of stable isotope abundances in lunar samples have shown that they are identical to those in terrestrial and meteoritic samples [73], but this argument for a well-mixed solar nebula is subject to increasing doubt. Thus it has been suggested that the interpretation that the differing isochron ages for some meteorites are not true age differences but are a result of isotopic abundance variations in differing parts of the solar nebula[74]. It has been established both by lead[75] and strontium[76] techniques that the crystallization ages of some basaltic achondrites differ by 10–30 million years[75, 76]. Cameron[74] suggests that a late spike of $r$-process nuclides, incompletely mixed, would account for these apparent age differences.

Further suggestive data come from the oxygen isotopic data. An excess of $^{16}O$ has recently been found in the white inclusions of the Allende meteorite[21, 77]. This is interpreted as due to the addition of small amounts of a primitive $^{16}O$ component that was not homogenized.

If these suggestions are correct, then they are a new constraint in our understanding of early nebula history. The implications for lunar origin are considerable. The lead and strontium data may provide the key to mixing models of the nebula, rather than providing detailed early chronologies.

The role and importance of the refractory white inclusions in the Allende meteorite are still obscure. The composition of these objects have been much employed in lunar models[20, 80]. The great enrichment in the lunar samples of the refractory elements has encouraged their derivation from such apparently high temperature condensates. Thus Anderson[20, 78] forms the entire moon from such material. In order to account for the anomalous density and composition of the moon, it is postulated to have accreted outside the median plane of the nebula, adding a third dimension to theories of lunar formation.

Two principal difficulties, as noted earlier, beset such attempts to apply simple condensation models. The high temperature condensates are enriched in the refractory siderophile elements such as Re, Os, and Ir. To dispose of these, it is necessary to accrete iron (at a lower temperature!) so that they may be removed by a core. A second incompatible situation arises from the oxygen isotope data. A substantial amount of low temperature condensate must be added (with a high component of volatile elements), to satisfy the lunar $^{18}O$ values[20, 77, 79, 80]. Thus, simple condensation models do not account for lunar composition[81].

The ultimate answer to the question of lunar origin is still to be sought, a prospect that should encourage both imagination and scientific resourcefulness.

The stimulation produced by the lunar data has caused much interest in the state of the early solar nebula. We are at a most preliminary stage in the investigation. A resurgence of interest in meteorite data and a new understanding of the significance of meteorite chemistry has arisen. The gathering of data from other planets and satellites is in progress, or planned, or within the reach of a motivated society. The scientist interested in the origin and development of the solar system, one of the fundamental questions, can look forward to exciting and interesting times ahead.

## REFERENCES AND NOTES

1. The reader may select analogies to suit his fancy. An example in science is the use of X-rays to study crystal structure, which outdated the previous work on external crystal morphology. An analogous historical event, dating from the same period, was the construction of the Dreadnought, an event that rendered obsolete the capital ships of the world's navies.
2. See, for example, Baldwin, R. B. (1963) *The Measure of the Moon*, Chicago; Kopal, Z., and Mikhailov, Z. K. (1962) *The Moon*, Academic Press.
3. Those readers who question this verdict might reflect that theory usually lags behind experiment. Thus current astrophysical theories failed to predict the existence of quasars.
4. In contrast to the moon, the first data from Venus indicate that the surface values for K (4 percent), U (2.2 ppm) and Th (6.5 ppm) are close to those of terrestrial granites. Vinogradov, A. P., et al. (1973) *Geochimiya*, p. 3.
5. Gast, P. W., et al. (1970) *PLC 1*: 1161; Gast, P. W., and McConnell, R. K. (1972) *LS III*: 289.
6. Gast, P. W. (1972) *Moon*. 5: 121.
7. Ringwood, A. E. (1972) *LS III*: 651.
8. Smith, J. V., et al. (1970) *PLC 1*: 897.
9. Philpotts, J. A., et al. (1972) *PLC 3*: 1293.
10. Taylor, S. R. (1973) *Nature*. 245: 203.
11. Brett, R. (1973) *GCA*. 37: 2697.
12. Duncan, A. R., et al. (1973) *PLC 4*: 1097.
13. Ringwood, A. E. (1974) *GCA*. 38: 983.
14. Toksöz, M. N., et al. (1973) *PLC 4*: 2529.
15. Mason, B. H. (1970) *Elemental Abundances in Meteorites*, Gordon and Breach.
16. Trombka, J. I., et al. (1973) *PLC 4*: 2847.
17. Parkin, C. W., et al. (1973) *PLC 4*: 2947.
18. Ganapathy, R., and Anders, E. (1974) *LS V*: 254.
19. Wänke, H., et al. (1973) *PLC 4*: 1461; (1974) *LS V*: 820.
20. Anderson, D. L. (1973) *EPSL*. 18: 301.
21. Clayton, R. N., et al. (1973) *PLC 4*: 1540.
22. Taylor, S. R., and Jakeš, P. (1974) *PLC 5*.
23. Toksöz, M. N., *et al.* (1973) *PLC 4*: 2529.
24. Mizutani, H., et al. (1973) *Moon*. 4: 476.
25. Brett, R. (1973) *GCA*. 37: 165.
26. Strangway, D. W., and Sharpe, H. A. (1974) *LS V*: 755.
27. See section 5.10 on Cr/Ni ratios.

28. Sato, M., et al. (1973) *PLC 4*: 1061.
29. Albee, A. L., et al. (1974) *LS V*: 3.
30. Wood, J. A. (1972) *Icarus*. 16: 229, 462; (1973) *Meteoritics*. 8: 467.
31. Walker, D., et al. (1973) *EPSL*. 20: 325; Hays, J. F., and Walker, D. (1974) *PLC 5*. In press.
32. Schnetzler, C. C., et al. (1972) *Science*. 175: 426.
33. Reid, A. M., and Jakeš, P. (1974) *LS V*: 627.
34. LSPET (1973) *Science*. 182: 659.
35. Nunes, P. D., and Tatsumoto, M. (1973) *Science*. 182: 916.
36. See section 4.3 on emerald green glass.
37. Goldreich, P. (1966) *Rev. Geophys*. 4: 411. For an extensive discussion of the dynamics of the earth-moon system, see Kopal, Z. (1969) *The Moon*, Reidel.
38. Darwin, G. H. (1879) *Phil. Trans. Roy. Soc*. 170: 447; (1880) Ibid., 171: 713. In its popular form, the Pacific Ocean basin was the scar remaining from a Velikovsky-type catastrophe. For a rational account of the geological basis for many such myths, see Vitaliano, D. B. (1974) *Legends of the Earth*, Indiana University Press.
39. Jefferies, H. (1929) *The Earth*, Cambridge University Press.
40. Gerstenkorn, H. (1955) *Z. Astrophys*. 36: 245.
41. MacDonald, G. J. F. (1964) *Rev. Geophys*. 2: 467.
42. Kaula, W. M. (1971) *Rev. Geophys. Space Phys*. 9: 217.
43. O'Keefe, J. A. (1972) *Irish Astron. J*. 10: 241; Rubincam, D. D. (1974) *EOS*. 55: 331.
44. Wise, D. U. (1963) *JGR*. 68: 1547.
45. Wise, D. U. (1969) *JGR*. 74: 6034.
46. O'Keefe, J. A. (1969) *JGR*. 74: 2758; (1970) *JGR*. 75: 6565; (1972) *Naturwiss*. 59: 45.
47. O'Keefe, J. A. (1974) *Moon*. 9: 219.
48. See section 6.1.
49. Binder, A. B. (1974, *LS V*: 63) does not consider the decisive trace element data.
50. See section 4.13 especially.
51. Ringwood, A. E. (1970) *EPSL*. 8: 131.
52. Opik, E. J. (1955) *Irish Astron. J*. 3: 245; (1961) *Astron. J*. 66: 60.
53. Ringwood, A. E. (1972) *LS III*: 651.
54. Ringwood, A. E. (1974) *LS V*: 636.
55. See section 4.7.
56. Urey, H. C. (1959) *JGR*. 64: 1721.
57. Urey, H. C., and MacDonald, G. J. F. (1971) in *Physics and Astronomy of the Moon* (Z. Kopal, editor), Academic Press; Urey, H. C. (1972) *Moon*. 3: 383.
58. Singer, F. (1970) *EOS*. 51: 637; (1972) *Moon*. 5: 206.
59. Alfvén, H., and Arrhenius, G. (1972) *Moon*. 5: 211. See also Alfvén, H. (1964) *The Origin of the Moon*, Oxford University Press.
60. These are, in order of mass: Ganymede (J-3), Titan (J-6), Callisto (J-4), Triton (N-1), moon (E-1), Io (J-1), and Europa (J-2).
61. The mass of the secondary to that of the primary is 1/81 compared with typical values of $10^{-4}$ in other satellite systems. A moon-type satellite of Venus, for example, would be slightly larger than Europa, the second moon of Jupiter.
62. Ringwood, A. E. (1972) *PEPI*. 6: 366.
63. Both the small Martian satellites, Phobos and Deimos, are in equatorial orbits, although the consensus is that they are captured objects from the asteroidal belt. Before the Mariner photography was available, Singer[58] proposed that they were natural

satellites of Mars on account of this orbital regularity. The satellites in nonequatorial orbits are numbers 6–12 of Jupiter, Iapetus (S.8) and Phoebe (S.9) (Saturn), and both the Neptunian satellites (Triton and Nereid). The first five Jovian satellites, seven of the 10 Saturnian satellites and all five of the satellites of Uranus occupy equatorial orbits. Six satellites (J. 8, 9, 11, 12, Phoebe and Triton) have retrograde orbits.

64. See sections 5.8, 5.9, and 5.10.

65. Smith, J. V. (1974) *LS V*: 718.

66. Wood, J. A., and Mitler, H. E. (1974) *LS V*: 851.

67. Although this is usually given as 2.5 earth radii, Smith[65] points out that the distance at which a body will disintegrate as a result of the gravitational attraction varies from 2.2 earth radii for liquid iron bodies to 3 for silicates.

68. Opik, E. J. (1972) *Irish Astron. J.* 10: 190.

69. The term "solar nebula," rather than alternatives such as "source plasma," has been retained throughout this book, although it has been thought to possess "an 18th century image"[59]. This reviewer has no objection to the use of terms reminiscent of the Ages of Reason and Enlightenment. The present decline in the popularity of rational thought, best illustrated by the tendency to embrace the egocentric absurdities of astrology, can only be deplored.

70. A recent review of nucleosynthesis has been given by J. W. Truran (1973, *Space Sci. Rev.* 15: 23). These questions relate back to the ultimate origin of the universe. This author confesses to a philosophical preference for "steady state" rather than "big bang"-type theories. The latter seem inherently too localized in time and space. Note that the 3°K background radiation, frequently claimed as definitive proof of a primordial fireball, may be due to the rotation of interstellar silicate grains (Wesson, P. S., 1974, *Space Sci. Rev.* 15: 469).

71. A recent review of cosmochronology is given by D. N. Schramm (1973, *Space Sci. Rev.* 15: 51).

72. Alexander, E. C., et al. (1971) *Science.* 172: 837; Rao, M. N., and Gopalan, K. (1973) *Nature.* 245: 304.

73. See, for example, Barnes, I. L., et al. (1972) *PLC 3*: 1465; (1973) *PLC 4*: 1197; (1974) *LS V*: 38.

74. Cameron, A. G. W. (1973) *Nature.* 246: 30.

75. Tatsumoto, M., et al. (1973) *Science.* 180: 1279.

76. Papanastassiou, D. A., and Wasserburg, G. J. (1969) *EPSL.* 5: 361.

77. Clayton, R. N., et al. (1973) *Science.* 182: 485.

78. See, for example, Anderson, D. L. (1972) *Nature.* 239: 263.

79. Grossman, L., and Larimer, J. W. (1974) *Rev. Geophys. Space Phys.* 12: 71.

80. Grossman, L., et al. (1974) *LS V*: 298.

81. Accretion and condensation processes in the solar nebula are extensively discussed in the following papers: Grossman, L. (1972), *GCA.* 36: 597; Cameron, A. G. W. (1973) *Icarus.* 18: 407; Cameron, A. G. W., and Pine, M. R. (1973) *Icarus.* 18: 377. See also reference 79.

EPILOGUE

# On the Usefulness of Manned Space Flight

The manned missions were clearly a scientific success, as is evident from the voluminous literature summarized here. Could the same expenditure, or less, on unmanned missions, have accomplished as much and led to the present state of knowledge of the moon? Most scientists who have studied the moon would say no. Professional views are of course always open to charges of special pleading or bias[1]. In this reviewer's opinion at least, there are many facets of lunar exploration and establishment of "ground truth" that could only have been accomplished by the astronauts. The obvious ability to collect documented and oriented rock samples, which are vital for so many studies, is one such. The diverse interpretations from photogeologic studies[2] of the nature of much of the highlands are a salutary reminder of the difficulties inherent in remote sensing, even though these interpretations were made late in the missions. The very success of the operations and the advances in knowledge gained tend to make us forget the earlier obscurity. Thus, a summary[3] of lunar geology in 1967, two years before the first Apollo mission, lamented that "no conclusions can be drawn other than that the interpretation of the existing experimental data leads to many ambiguities."

Of many possible examples, one illustration of the difference between manned and unmanned sample return must suffice. The state of the art of unmanned sample return at the time of the Apollo landings is shown by the Luna 16 and 20 missions. These returned 100 and 30 g of soil, respectively. We have seen that the lunar surface materials are an exceedingly complex mixture, difficult to unscramble without pieces of the original components; witness the difficulties in deciphering the

337

chemistry of the highlands samples. But a particular trap awaited the interpretation of the soils. The model ages for all soils fell close to the magic age of 4.6 aeons, the expected age of the moon, and of the formation of the solar system. Thus, the immediate interpretation would have been to compress all lunar events into a short interval. A supercatastrophic sequence of events, encompassing accretion, ringed basin excavation, and mare flooding would have become an acceptable point of view. Contrary views, perhaps coming from the stratigraphic studies of the astrogeologists, would have been hampered by the scarcity of samples. Younger basaltic rock fragments, if recovered, could have been dismissed as late minor volcanic episodes, unconnected with the major mare filling events. Perhaps a decade, perhaps more of patient work would have been needed to get the story straight and to uncover the long sequence of lunar events, which extended over one and a half billion years. The very small amounts of samples available would have greatly restricted the number of investigators, and the burgeoning of lunar science would not have taken place.

Now, with hindsight, we know exactly how to deal with a small unmanned lunar sample return, as was demonstrated on the Luna 16 and 20 material. The experience, expertise, and techniques acquired from the Apollo studies paid off in a spectacular fashion and are of sufficient tribute to the skills developed by the large group of principal investigators.

Other planetary surfaces appear to have had an analogous history. This is illustrated by the surface of Mercury (Fig. 7.3). The resemblance between this surface, that of the Martian uplands, and of the lunar highlands, is striking. We can now contemplate an unmanned sample return from Mars, Mercury, or other similar bodies with some confidence in our ability to ask the correct scientific questions. This is the immediate legacy of the manned Apollo missions.

Other planets and satellites, however, will have their store of surprises and unanticipated problems, if the investigations of the moon are a guide. Our satellite is, after all, within easy reach of telescopic observation, but the resolution of many problems had to await the visits by the astronauts. These reasons, coupled with the overriding human wish that we will always want to go and see, will ensure the continuance of manned space flight [4].

# REFERENCES AND NOTES

1. The opinions quoted by Mitroff, I. (1974) in *The Subjective Side of Science* (Elsevier) lend some credence to this.
2. See section 2.8.
3. Cook, J. J. (1967) A summary of lunar geology. USGS Interagency Report NASA-95.
4. The triumphs of the space age should not blind us to the reality that no evolutionary development has occurred since the appearance of Cromagnon man. We face the exploration of the solar system with intellects possibly inferior to those of the cave painters. Fortunately the complexity of space missions will always ensure that the best characteristics of the human species will be called upon. Such endeavors offer the hope of diverting our aggressive instincts into productive directions and may ensure our survival.

# APPENDIX I

# *Reference Abbreviations*

*AJS*: American Journal of Science

Apollo 15: The Apollo 15 Lunar Samples, Lunar Science Institute, Houston, Texas (1972)

*Bull GSA*: Bulletin of the Geological Society of America

*EOS*: EOS, Transactions of the American Geophysical Union

*EPSL*: Earth and Planetary Science Letters

*GCA*: Geochimica et Cosmochimica Acta

*JGR*: Journal of Geophysical Research

*LS III*: Lunar Science III (Lunar Science Institute)

*LS IV*: Lunar Science IV (Lunar Science Institute)

*LS V*: Lunar Science V (Lunar Science Institute) See Extended Abstracts of Lunar Science Conferences.

NASA SP: National Aeronautics and Space Administration Special Publication Series

*PEPI*: Physics of Earth and Planetary Interiors

*PLC 1*: Proceedings Apollo 11 Lunar Science Conference, Geochim. Cosmochim. Acta Suppl. 1.

*PLC 2*: Proceedings 2nd Lunar Science Conference, Geochim. Cosmochim. Acta Suppl. 2.

*PLC 3*: Proceedings 3rd Lunar Science Conference, Geochim. Cosmochim. Acta Suppl. 3.

*PLC 4*: Proceedings 4th Lunar Science Conference, Geochim. Cosmochim. Acta, Suppl. 4.

*PLC 5*: Proceedings 5th Lunar Science Conference, Geochim. Cosmochim. Acta, Suppl. 5.

USGS: United States Geological Survey

## APPENDIX II

# Primary Data Sources

(A) Lunar Sample Preliminary Examination Team (LSPET) Reports
Apollo 11, *Science.* 165: 211 (Sept. 19, 1969).
Apollo 12, *Science.* 167: 1325 (March 6, 1970).
Apollo 14, *Science.* 173: 681 (August 20, 1971).
Apollo 15, *Science.* 175: 363 (Jan. 28, 1972).
Apollo 16, *Science.* 179: 23 (Jan. 5, 1973).
Apollo 17, *Science.* 182: 659 (Nov. 16, 1973).

(B) Lunar Science Conference Proceedings
Apollo 11 Lunar Science Conference, Houston, Texas, 1970. Proceedings. A. A. Levinson, editor. *Geochimica et Cosmochimica Acta, Supplement 1.* Pergamon Press, Elmsford, N.Y.

2nd Lunar Science Conference, Houston, Texas, 1971. Proceedings. A. A. Levinson, editor. *Geochimica et Cosmochimica Acta, Supplement 2.* MIT Press, Cambridge, Mass.

3rd Lunar Science Conference, Houston, Texas, 1972. Proceedings. Editors: v. 1—Elbert A. King, Jr., v.2—Dieter Heymann, v. 3—David R. Criswell. *Geochimica et Cosmochimica Acta, Supplement 3.* MIT Press, Cambridge, Mass.

4th Lunar Science Conference, Houston, Texas, 1973. Proceedings. Wulf A. Gose, editor. *Geochimica et Cosmochimica Acta, Supplement 4.* Pergamon Press, Elmsford, N.Y.

5th Lunar Science Conference, Houston, Texas, 1974. Proceedings. Wulf. A. Gose, editor. *Geochimica et Cosmochimica Acta, Supplement 5.* Pergamon Press, Elmsford, N.Y.

(C) Extended Abstracts of Lunar Science Conferences have been published by the Lunar Science Institute, Houston, Texas for the 3rd, 4th, and 5th Lunar Science Conferences.

1. *Lunar Science III*, Carolyn Watkins, editor. 1972.
2. *Lunar Science IV*, J. W. Chamberlain and Carolyn Watkins, editors. 1973.
3. *Lunar Science V*, 1974.

These are referred to in the references as *LS III*, *LS IV*, and *LS V*, respectively.

4. In addition, an extended set of abstracts deals with the Apollo 15 samples:

The Apollo 15 Samples, J. W. Chamberlain and Carolyn Watkins, editors. 1972. This is cited as "Apollo 15" in the references.

(D) Preliminary Science Reports: Superintendent of Documents, U.S. Government Printing Office, Washington, D.C. 20402. Surveyor Program Results, NASA SP 184 (1969).
Apollo 11 NASA SP 214 (1969) 209 pp.
Apollo 12 NASA SP 235 (1970) 235 pp.
Apollo 14 NASA SP 272 (1971) 313 pp.
Apollo 15 NASA SP 289 (1972) 502 pp.
Apollo 16 NASA SP 315 (1972) 636 pp.
Apollo 17 NASA SP 330 (1973) 710 pp.

(E) USGS Apollo Geology Team Reports.
Apollo 11 geologic setting is included in PET article, *Science.* 165: 1211 (Sept. 19, 1969).
Apollo 12 geologic setting contained in PET article, *Science.* 167: 1325 (March 6, 1970).
Apollo 14, *Science.* 173: 716 (Aug. 20, 1971).
Apollo 15, *Science.* 175: 407 (Jan. 28, 1972).
Apollo 16, *Science.* 179: 62 (Jan. 5, 1973).
Apollo 17, *Science.* 182: 672 (Nov. 16, 1973).

(F) Lunar Sample Information Catalogs. NASA Manned Spacecraft Center, Houston, Texas.
Apollo 11 Aug. 31, 1969 (No identifying number).
Apollo 12 MSC-S-243 (June, 1970).
Apollo 14 TM X-58062 (Sept., 1971).
Apollo 15 MSC-03209 (Nov., 1971).
Apollo 16 MSC-03210 (July, 1972).
Apollo 17 MSC-03211 (April, 1973).

(G) Lunar Sample Data Bank.
A computer compilation of all lunar analytical data is maintained by

the lunar sample curator's office. Requests for information about this compilation should be sent to

*Data System, Code TL4*
*Nasa-Johnson Space Center*
*Houston, Tx 77058*

(H) Lunar Orbiter Photographs.
   *Lunar Orbiter* Photographic Atlas of the Moon, by D. E. Bowker and J. K. Hughes. NASA SP-206 (1971).
   Atlas and Gazeteer of the *Near Side of the Moon*, by G. L. Gutschewski, D. C. Kinsler and E. Whitaker. NASA SP-241 (1971).

# Glossary

Because of the wide-ranging nature of lunar science, it is to be expected that readers of this book may be unfamiliar with one or more of the fields covered. For such a reason this glossary has been added. It is intended as a dictionary-type aid, to preserve continuity and understanding through unfamiliar territory.

Glossaries possess both the advantages and disadvantages of dictionaries. They should preserve the virtue of simplicity and are not intended for the serious student or specialist, who is at best likely to become displeased by the definitions adopted. The latter reader is referred to the subject index, the references and notes and to the text itself for enlightenment.

*Accessory Mineral*—A term applied to a mineral occurring in small amounts in a rock.

*Accretion*—A term applied to the growth of planets from smaller fragments or dust.

*Achondrite*—Stony meteorite lacking chondrules.

*Aeon*—One billion years (=$10^9$ years).

*Agglutinate*—A common particle type in lunar soils, agglutinates consist of comminuted rock, mineral and glass fragments bonded together with glass.

*Albedo*—The percentage of the incoming radiation that is reflected by a natural surface.

*Alkali Element*—A general term applied to the univalent metals Li, Na, K, Rb and Cs.

*Alkane hydrocarbon*—Hydrocarbon saturated with hydrogen atoms.

*ALSEP*—Apollo lunar surface experiments package.

*Amino acid*—Organic compound comprising both acid and basic functional groups; the unit constituents of proteins.

*An*—Abbreviation for anorthite.

*Angstrom (A)*—A unit of length, $10^{-8}$ cm; commonly used in crystallography and mineralogy.

*Anion*—A negatively charged ion (for example, $O^{-2}$, $F^{-1}$).

*Anorthite (An)*—$CaAl_2 Si_2 O_8$, the most calcium-rich member of the plagioclase (feldspar) series of minerals.

*Anorthosite*—An igneous rock made up almost entirely of plagioclase feldspar.

*Aphyric*—Not having distinct crystals.

*Aromatic Hydrocarbon*—Hydrocarbons unsaturated in hydrogen comprising benzene, $C_6 H_6$, and related compounds.

*Atmophilic*—Denotes elements that tend to reside, permanently or as transients, within an atmosphere.

*Atmosphere*—Unit of pressure (= 1.013 bars).

*Bar*—The international unit of pressure (one bar = 0.987 atmosphere).

*Basalt*—A fine-grained, dark colored igneous rock composed primarily of plagioclase (feldspar) and pyroxene; usually other minerals such as olivine, ilmenite, etc. are present.

*Basaltic achondrite*—Calcium-rich stony meteorites, lacking chondrules and nickel-iron, showing some similarities to terrestrial and lunar basalts; eucrites and howardites are types of basaltic achondrites.

*Base surge*—A debris cloud near the ground surface that moves radially from a chemical, nuclear, volcanic or meteorite impact explosion center.

*Biolipids*—Organic compounds from living matter, soluble in organic solvents.

*Bow shock*—A shock wave in front of a body.

*Breccia*—A rock consisting of angular, coarse fragments embedded in a fine-grained matrix.

*Carbide*—A compound of an element, with carbon.

*Carbonaceous chrondrites*–The most primitive stony-meteorites, in which the abundances of the non-volatile elements are thought to approximate most closely to those of the primordial solar nebula.

*Carbonaceous material*–Substance predominantly composed of carbon, with complex molecular structure involving hydrogen, oxygen, nitrogen, and related elements.

*Cation*–A positively charged ion (for example, $Na^{+4}$, $Ti^{+4}$).

*Chalcophile element*–An element which enters sulfide minerals preferentially. See page 202, ref. 56.

*Chondrite*–The most abundant class of stony meteorite characterized by the presence of chondrules.

*Chondrule*–Small, rounded body in meteorites (generally less than 1 mm. in diameter), commonly composed of olivine and/or orthopyroxene.

*Clast*–A discrete particle or fragment of rock or mineral; commonly included in a larger rock.

*Clinopyroxene*–Minerals of the pyroxene group, such as augite and pigeonite, which crystallize in the monoclinic system.

*CM*–Command module.

*Coordination number*–The number of anions (usually oxygen) which surround a cation in crystalline solids.

*Cosmic element abundances*–The abundances of the chemical elements in the solar nebula before formation of the sun, planets and meteorites.

*Cosmochemistry*–The study of the abundance and distribution of elements in the universe.

*CSM*–Command and service module.

*Cumulate*–A plutonic igneous rock composed chiefly of crystals accumulated by sinking or floating from a magma.

*Curie temperature*–The temperature in a ferromagnetic material above which the material becomes substantially nonmagnetic.

*Divalent*–An element with a double charge (e.g. $Ca^{+2}$).

*Dunite*–A peridotite that consists almost entirely of olivine and that contains accessory chromite and pyroxene.

*Eclogite*–A dense rock consisting of garnet and pyroxene, similar in chemical composition to basalt.

*Ejecta*—Materials ejected from the crater by a volcanic or meteorite impact explosion.

*Electron volt (eV)*—The energy acquired by a particle carrying unit electronic charge moving through a potential difference of one volt.
KeV - one thousand eV.
MeV - one million eV.
BeV - one billion eV.

*Epicenter*—The point on a planetary surface directly above the focus of an earthquake.

*Eucrite*—A meteorite composed essentially of feldspar and augite.

*Euhedral*—Well-formed crystals exhibiting crystal faces.

*EVA*—Extravehicular activity.

*Exsolution-unmixing*—The separation of some mineral-pair solutions during slow cooling.

*Exposure age*—Period of time during which a sample has been at or near the lunar surface, assessed on the basis of cosmogenic rare gas contents, particle track densities, short-lived radioisotopes, or agglutinate contents in the case of soil samples.

*Extrusive*—An igneous rock solidifying on the surface.

*Ferromagnetic*—Possessing magnetic properties similar to those of iron (paramagnetic substances with a magnetic permeability much greater than one).

*Fines*—Lunar material arbitrarily defined as less than 1 cm in diameter; synonymous with "soils".

*Fractional crystallization*—Formation and separation of mineral phases of varying composition during crystallization of a silicate melt or magma, resulting in a continuous change of composition of the magma.

*Fractionation*—The separation of chemical elements from an initially homogeneous state into different phases or systems.

*Gabbro*—A coarse-grained, dark igneous rock made up chiefly of plagioclase (usually labradorite) and pyroxene. Other minerals often present include olivine, apatite, ilmenite, etc. A coarse grained equivalent of basalt.

*Gardening*—The process of turning over the lunar soil or regolith by meteorite bombardment.

*Gas chromatography*—Process for analyzing and separating components of a gaseous or volatile liquid mixture, based on transit times through a packed bed of powder.

*Geochemistry*—The study of the abundance, distribution and migration of chemical elements.

*Granite*—An igneous rock composed chiefly of quartz and alkali feldspar.

*Granular*—A rock texture in which the mineral grains are nearly equidimensional.

*Groundmass*—The fine-grained rock material between larger mineral grains; used interchangeably with matrix.

*Half-life*—The time interval during which a number of atoms of a radioactive nuclide decay to one half of that number.

*Howardite*—A type of basaltic achondrite (qv).

*Hydrocarbon*—Compound consisting solely of carbon and hydrogen.

*Igneous*—Applied to rocks or processes involving the solidification of hot, molten material.

*Impact melting*—The process by which country rock is melted by the impact of meteorite or comet.

*Intersertal*—A term used to describe the texture of igneous rocks in which a base or mesostasis of glass and small crystals fills the interstices between unoriented feldspar laths.

*Involatile element*—See refractory element. See page 202, ref. 59.

*Ionic radius*—The effective radius of ionized atoms in crystalline solids; ionic radii commonly lie between 0.4-1.5 Angstrom units.

*Isochron*—A line on a diagram passing through plots of samples with the same age but differing isotope ratios.

*Isotopes*—Atoms of a specific element which differ in number of neutrons in the nucleus; this results in different atomic weight, and very slightly differing chemical properties (for example, $U^{235}$ and $U^{238}$).

*Iron meteorite*—A class of meteorite composed chiefly of iron or iron-nickel.

*Isostatic*—Subjected to equal pressure from all sides.

*Kilobar (Kb or Kbar).*—1000 bars.

*KREEP*—Potassium, rare-Earth elements, and phosphorus.

*LAC*—Lunar Aeronautical Chart.

*Lamellae*—Thin plates or layers of one mineral in another mineral.

*Lattice site*—The position occupied by an atom in a crystalline solid.

*Lava*—Fluid rock which emanates from the interior of the Earth (or moon) from volcanoes, etc.; upon solidification forms an extrusive igneous rock (see magma).

*Layered igneous intrusion*—A body of plutonic igneous rock which has formed layers of different minerals during solidification; it is divisible into a succession of extensive sheets lying one above the other.

*Leucocratic*—A term used to describe light-coloured rock, especially igneous rocks that contain between 0 and 30 percent dark minerals.

*LIL*—Large Ion Lithophile elements. Those lithophite elements (e.g. K, Rb, Ba, REE, U, Th) which have ionic radii larger than common lunar rock-forming elements, and which usually behave as trace elements in lunar rocks and in meteorites.

*Liquidus*—The line or surface in a phase diagram above which the system is completely liquid.

*Lithophile element*—An element tending to concentrate in oxygen-containing compounds, particularly silicates. See page 202, ref. 56.

*LM*—Lunar module.

*Low oceanic tholeiite*—See oceanic tholeiite.

*LRL*—Lunar Receiving Laboratory, NASA Lyndon B. Johnson Space Center.

*LRV*—Lunar roving vehicle (Rover).

*LSAPT*—Lunar Sample Analysis Planning Team.

*LSI*—Lunar Science Institute.

*LSM*—Lunar surface magnetometer.

*LSPET*—Lunar Sample Preliminary Examination Team.

*LSRP*—Lunar Sample Review Panel.

*Lunatic asylum*—The lunar laboratory at the California Institute of Technology.

*Magma*—The term applied to molten rock in the interior of a planet.

*Magmatic differentiation*—The production of rocks of differing chemical composition during cooling and crystallization of a silicate melt or magma by processes such as removal of early formed mineral phases.

*Magnetosheath*—The transition region between the magnetopause and the solar-wind shock wave.

*Magnetosphere*—The region of the atmosphere where the geomagnetic field plays an important role; the magnetosphere extends to the boundary between the atmosphere and interplanetary plasma.

*Magnetotail*—A portion of the magnetic field of the Earth that is pulled back to form a tail by solar plasma.

*Mantle*—The solid region of the Earth extending from the base of the crust (10-60 km depth) to the top of the core (2900 km depth); principal constituents are iron, magnesium, silicon and oxygen, occurring as mineral phases of increasing density with depth.

*Mare*—(Pl. Maria). A term used to describe those dark, generally flat areas of the moon formerly thought to be seas.

*Mascon*—Regions of excess mass concentrations per unit area, identified by positive gravity anomalies, on the lunar surface.

*Maskelynite*—Feldspar converted to glass by shock effects due to meteorite impact.

*Matrix*—The fine-grained material in which larger mineral or rock fragments are embedded; often used interchangeably with groundmass.

*Metamorphic*—A term used to describe rocks that have recrystallized in a solid state as a result of drastic changes in temperature, pressure, and chemical environment.

*Meteorite*—A metallic or stony (silicate) body that has fallen on Earth or the moon from outer space.

*Methane*—The simplest hydrocarbon, $CH^4$.

*Mesostasis*—The interstitial, generally fine-grained material, between larger mineral grains in a rock, may be used synonymously with matrix and groundmass.

*Microcrater (Zap Pit)*—Crater produced by impact of interplanetary particles generally having masses less than $10^{-3}$ g.

*Micromoon*—An informal unit of mass sometimes used to describe the size of lunar mascons. 1 micromoon = $10^{-6}$ lunar masses = $7.355 \times 10^{16}$ kg.

*NASA*—National Aeronautics and Space Administration.

*Noble gases*—The rare gases, helium, neon, argon, krypton, xenon and radon.

*Norite*—A type of gabbro in which orthopyroxene is dominant over clinopyroxene.

*Nucleon*—Sub-atomic nuclear particles (mainly protons and neutrons).

*Nuclides*—Atoms characterized by the number of protons (Z) and neutrons (N). The mass number (A) = N + Z; isotopes are nuclides with same number of protons (Z) but differing numbers of neutrons (N); isobars have same mass number (A) but different numbers of protons (Z) and neutrons (N).

*Oceanic tholeiite*—Basaltic rock characterized by very low concentrations or potassium and related elements; probably the most common lava erupted at the mid-ocean ridges.

*Oersted*— The cgs unit of magnetic intensity.

*Ophitic*—A rock texture which is composed of elongated feldspar crystals embedded in pryoxene or olivine.

*ORNL*—Oak Ridge National Laboratory.

*Orthopyroxene*—An orthorhombic member of the pyroxene mineral group.

*Peridotite*—An igneous rock characterized by pyroxene and olivine (but no feldspar).

*Petrography*—The science concerned with the systematic description and classification of rocks.

*Petrology*—The science of rocks, includes identification, chemical composition, classification origin, etc.

*Phenocryst*—A large, early formed crystal in igneous rocks, surrounded by a fine-grained groundmass.

*Photosphere*—An outer layer of the sun, about 350 km thick, which is the source of most solar radiation.

*Plagioclase*—A sub-group (or series) of the feldspar group of minerals.

*PI*—Principal Investigator.

*Plumose*—A radiating arrangement of crystals.

*Plutonic*—A term applied to igneous rocks which have crystallized at depth, usually with coarsely crystalline texture.

*Poikilitic*—A rock texture in which one mineral, commonly anhedral, encloses numerous other much smaller crystals, commonly euhedral.

*Poikiloblastic*—A metamorphic texture in which large crystals form in the solid state during recrystallization, to enclose preexisting smaller crystals.

*Poise, cgs*—Unit of viscosity (= 1 dyne sec/cm$^2$).

*Porphyritic*—Having larger crystals set in a finer groundmass.

*PPB*—Parts per billion — 1 ppb = 0.001 ppm.

*PPM*—Parts per million — 1 ppm = 0.0001%.

*Pyrolysis*—Heating under controlled conditions such as an inert atmosphere to prevent oxidation.

*Pyroxene*—A closely-related group of minerals which includes augite, pigeonite, etc.

*Radiogenic lead*—Lead isotopes formed by radioactive decay of uranium and thorium ($Pb^{206}$ from $U^{238}$; $Pb^{207}$ from $U^{235}$; $Pb^{208}$ from $Th^{232}$).

*Rare-earth (RE or REE)*—A collective term for elements with atomic number 57-71, which includes La, Ce, etc.

*Rare gases*—The noble gases, helium, neon, argon, krypton, xenon, and radon.

*Refractory (involatile) element*—See page 202, ref. 59.

*Regolith*—Loose surface material, composed of rock fragments and soil, which overlies consolidated bedrock.

*Residual liquid*—The material remaining after most of a magma has crystallized; it is sometimes characterized by an abundance of volatile constituents.

*r-process nuclides*—Those nuclides produced under conditions of intense neutron flux in supernovae explosions.

*SEM*—Scanning electron microscope.

*SIDE*—Suprathermal ion detector experiment.

*Silicate*—A mineral (or compound) whose crystal structure contains $SiO_4$, tetrahedra.

*SM*—Service module.

*Soil*—Fine-grained lunar material arbitrarily defined as less than 1 cm in diameter.

*Soil breccia*—Polymict breccia composed of cemented or sintered lunar soil.

*Solar nebula*—The primitive disk shaped cloud of dust and gas from which all bodies in the solar system originated.

*Solar wind*—The stream of charged particles (mainly ionized hydrogen) moving outward from the sun with velocities in the range 300-500 km/sec. See page 117, ref. 111.

*Solid solution*—Substitution of one element (or compound) for another element (or compound) in a mineral.

*Solidus*—The line or surface in a phase diagram below which the system is completely solid.

*Spinel-group*—General term for several minerals (e.g. chromite) with chemical, physical and structural properties similar to spinel; general formula is $AB_2O_4$.

*Stony Meteorite*—A class of meteorite composed chiefly of silicate minerals suc
as pyroxene, olivine, etc.

*Suntan*—Period of time during which a sample has resided on the lunar surface
without shielding; determined from solar flare-induced particle tracks.

*Tektites*—Small glassy objects of wide geographic distribution formed by splashing of melted terrestrial country rock during meteorite asteroid or
cometary impacts.

*Terminator*—The line separating illuminated and dark portions of a celestial
body.

*Texture*—The arrangement, shape and size of grains composing a rock.

*Trace element*—An element found in very low (trace) amounts; generally less
than 0.1%.

*Transponder*—A combined receiver and transmitter which transmits signals auto-
matically when triggered.

*Vesicle (Vesicular)*—Bubble-shaped, smooth-walled cavity, usually produced by
expansion of vapor (gas) in a magma.

*Volatile element*—An element volatile at temperatures below $1300°C$. See page
202, ref. 59.

*Vug (Vuggy)*—Small, irregular shaped, rough-walled cavity in a rock.

# Author Index

Abell, P. I., 119
Adler, I., 114, 241, 272, 274
Ahrens, L. H., 204
Albee, A. L., 201, 272, 273, 274, 335
Aldrin, E. E., 6
Alexander, E. C., 336
Alfvén, H., 329, 335
Anaxagoras, 1
Anders, E., 116, 169, 170, 172, 203, 258, 260, 261, 262, 274, 315, 334
Anderson, A. T., 119
Anderson, D. L., 315, 334, 336
Apollo Soil Survey, 231, 233, 234, 238, 273
Appleman, D. E., 272
Arkani-Hamed, J., 304
Armstrong, N. A., 6
Arnold, J., 117, 241, 274
Arrhenius, G., 115, 117, 329, 335
Ashworth, D. G., 116

Bailey, N. G., 54
Baldwin, R. B., 2, 10, 27, 29, 30, 32, 35, 37, 41, 52, 53, 54, 84, 116, 201, 334
Bannerjee, S. K., 305
Bansal, E. B., 273
Barber, D. J., 117
Barghoorn, E. S., 118
Barnes, I. L., 336
Battacharya, S. K., 117
Bauer, H., 118

Beals, C. S., 53
Begemann, F., 117
Behrmann, C., 105
Bence, A. E., 201, 205, 272
Bender, P. L., 3, 303
Bendini, S. A., 9
Bhandari, N., 115, 117
Bieberstein, M. von, 53
Biemann, K., 119
Biggar, G. M., 202, 205
Binder, A. B., 335
Bingham, J. W., 52
Birck, J. L., 204
Bjorkholm, P. J., 118
Bogard, D. D., 103, 104, 118
Boyce, J. M., 54
Breen, J., 114
Brett, R., 201, 203, 334
Brown, G. M., 201, 202, 272
Brownlee, D. E., 116
Bryan, W. B., 51, 54
Burns, R. G., 201

Cameron, A. G. W., 333, 336
Carrier, W. D., 115
Carter, I. D., 119
Cassini, G. D., 1
Cattermole, P. J., 10
Chang, S., 118
Chao, E. C. T., 54, 272

355

# Subject Index